STATISTICS

APPLIED TO

EDUCATION AND PSYCHOLOGY

By

CLARENCE T. GRAY

PROFESSOR OF EDUCATIONAL PSYCHOLOGY
UNIVERSITY OF TEXAS

DAVID F. VOTAW

PROFESSOR OF EDUCATION
SOUTHWEST TEXAS STATE TEACHERS COLLEGE

THE RONALD PRESS COMPANY
NEW YORK

PREFACE

This book has been prepared to meet the need for statistical techniques on the part of the classroom teacher, the school principal, the student of psychology or education, and the educational research worker. It is also intended to aid the teacher or student in the interpretation of educational literature as found in books and journals.

Statistical procedure has made possible much of the educational progress of the past two or three decades. Whereas educational problems were dealt with formerly largely on the basis of experience, opinion, and logic, they are dealt with today on the basis of objective data. This change in methods of studying educational problems has resulted in a new type of educational literature with new terms and new patterns of thought requiring new types of training on the part of students if they are to read this literature with understanding.

For the most part, the teaching experiences of the authors have furnished the materials of the book. These experiences include that of the classroom teacher, that of the school principal, and that of the college and university instructor in psychology and statistics. To this background has been added the experience of one of the authors in the development and standardization of tests. With few exceptions, only problems actually originating in the classrooms of teachers, in the offices of principals, and in the laboratories of educational investigators have been used for illustrative materials and for exercises to be solved.

No special training in mathematics is needed for the successful use of the text. The student should possess the ability to execute ordinary arithmetical processes, to substitute values for symbols in formulas, and to solve simple equations. Full details are given in the arithmetical solutions of illustrative problems in order to relieve the student of the burden of devising procedures.

Formulas are given usually without proof. The student's confidence in the adequacy of formulas is sought through discussion and through empirical treatments. The *Tables to Facilitate Calculations* which are included in the book make it unnecessary for tabular aids to be supplied.

In the preparation of this volume the authors have borne in mind the fact that students are strongly tempted to devote all of their time to the learning of techniques with a consequent loss of opportunity to make applications and interpretations. To overcome this tendency, practical applications and practical interpretations are coupled throughout with techniques. Some applications and interpretations have been included which are not generally found in textbooks on statistics. A few of these departures are as follows: use of a zone instead of a point on a scale to indicate normality; conversion of distribution of measures observed under one series of conditions to an equivalent distribution observed under a different series of conditions; application of regression lines to such practical school problems as age-grade data, scholarship-attendance data, and activity-participation-scholarship data; and the application of principles of ranking to practical school contest situations.

The writers have attempted to treat only those topics which are usually involved in texts for a first course in educational statistics. If two semesters are to be allotted to such a course, few if any omissions need be made. If the course is only one semester in duration, the authors recommend that Chapter 10 and certain topics in Chapters 8 and 9, together with their corresponding exercises, be omitted, depending upon the time available and upon the interest of the students. Perhaps in no case should the material in Chapters 1 to 7 be omitted or condensed. Frequent challenges for students of exceptional ability are provided in the exercises and problems at the end of each chapter.

The numerous illustrations and problems from the field of tests and measurements make the book suitable for use as a basic text for a course in tests and measurements or for a course which combines statistics with tests and measurements. If the text is to be so used, supplementary material usually found in printed tests and their manuals, including descriptions of processes of developing tests, explanations of purposes and uses of tests, directions for administering tests, and other similar material, along with practice in administering and scoring tests, would be required.

The authors acknowledge their indebtedness to their students in statistics and psychology for solving and checking many of the exercises and problems; to Mr. W. I. Woodson for his aid in adjusting the exercises and problems to college classes; to Dr. J. Murray Lee for his experimental use and valuable criticism of the exercises and problems; and to numerous other colleagues who have given encouragement in this undertaking.

C. T. GRAY
D. F. VOTAW

August, 1939.

CONTENTS

CONTENTS

TABLES

CHARTS

STATISTICS

APPLIED TO

EDUCATION AND PSYCHOLOGY

CHAPTER 1

MAKING DATA MEANINGFUL

One of the chief problems of STATISTICS is to make data meaningful for the student or for the reader. Many data in which the student of psychology or of education is interested, in their raw form as they exist in school registers, in test sheets, or in superintendents' reports, have little meaning. Statistics undertakes to make such material meaningful. The purpose of this chapter is to set forth a series of devices by which raw data are often made understandable. These methods are largely in the nature of rearrangements. They are usually based on counting, and so involve only the simplest computations. However they are all important and should be carefully considered by the student.

Materials of Statistics.—Statistical processes, as used in Educational Psychology, usually deal with measures of some type. The term *measure* is a general term applying either to methods of measurement or to records of measurements. For example, records of height are often used as measures of growth; weight records are considered as measures of another phase of growth; scores on an intelligence test are often thought of as measures of certain phases of mental development; chronological age involves measures of time; school grades are taken as measures of rate of school progress; and school marks are used as measures of achievement. The word *measure* in the general sense as here used, refers to the actual recorded inches of height, pounds of weight, scores on a test, years of age, marks on a subject, and so on. A distinction between the trait or quality being measured, the actual measuring of the trait, and the records of these measures should be kept clearly in mind. A few traits or qualities with possible forms of measures are listed below to illustrate the distinction:

Trait or Quality	Examples of Measures Used
Growth of skeleton...................	62″, 59½″, 61″ (heights)
Growth of total tissue..................	112 lb., 116 lb. (weights)
Knowledge of arithmetic...............	43, 37, 41 (scores)
Time................................	8 yrs., 7½ yrs., 9 yrs. (ages)
School achievement....................	B, A, C (subject marks)

No attempt to define statistics will be made here, but from time to time throughout this book efforts to describe statistics will be made. Most, if not all, mathematical processes, however simple, which reorganize data, which make comparisons by means of them, which determine how reliable measurements are, or which perform other similar processes, are statistical in nature. For the present we may be content to say that in dealing with records of measurements already referred to, any process, however simple, which succeeds in bringing order out of chaos is a statistical process. For example, if twenty-one children have taken a test in spelling, and have made the following scores listed in the same order as the alphabetical arrangement of the children's names, the scores are practically without meaning: 16, 20, 27, 23, 34, 22, 25, 22, 14, 23, 31, 17, 11, 23, 29, 24, 27, 23, 17, 25, 22. The simple process of rearranging these scores in some regular order (either ascending or descending) presents a clearer picture of the group of scores and affords a better means of understanding any individual score. Note the improvement in the picture of the group of scores which comes from such orderly rearrangement: 34, 31, 29, 27, 27, 25, 25, 24, 23, 23, 23, 23, 22, 22, 22, 20, 17, 17, 16, 14, 11.

Ranking.—A second method which can be used to give meaning to these data is called ranking, and may be illustrated at this point of procedure. According to this method, the highest score is assigned rank 1, the second highest score is assigned rank 2, and so on. This method of assigning the highest rank to the highest number is arbitrary, but it is deemed advisable because of the fact that people generally think of rank 1 as referring to the best or highest.

There are as many ranking positions as there are scores or other measures in the group being considered. The rank of 1 means there is none better; the rank of 4 means there are three better; the rank of N means there are N − 1 better. If two or more individuals have equal scores, their rank must be equal. They will share equally the average of the ranking positions of their scores.

By following these rules the spelling scores mentioned above can be ranked as follows:

TABLE I. SIMPLE RANKING

Score	Rank	Score	Rank
34	1	23	10.5
31	2	22	14
29	3	22	14
27	4.5	22	14
27	4.5	20	16
25	6.5	17	17.5
25	6.5	17	17.5
24	8	16	19
23	10.5	14	20
23	10.5	11	21
23	10.5		

When this process is carried out, mere mention of an individual's rank locates him.

Composite Ranking.—Ranking scores or other measures which have been obtained by some objective method is a simple procedure. However, when subjective (opinion) methods are used to determine rank it is a very common practice to employ several judges, each of whom records his ranking separately.

TABLE II. COMPOSITE RANKING

	Contestants							
	A	B	C	D	E	F	G	H
Judges:								
No. 1..............	3½	7	1	8	2	3½	6	5
No. 2..............	5	5	3	8	1	2	7	5
No. 3..............	4	6	3	8	1½	1½	5	7
Total of ranks........	12½	18	7	24	4½	7	18	17
Composite rank........	4	6½	2½	8	1	2½	6½	5

From these reports a composite ranking can be determined. The procedure is often used in determining awards in contests, in evaluating samples of handwriting, and in many similar school problems. For a simple illustration let us consider a declamatory

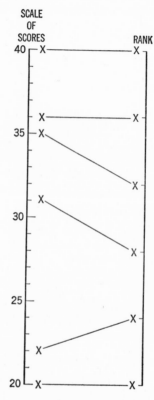

Figure 1. Change in Spacing Caused by Ranking

contest in which eight contestants were entered. The composite opinion of three judges was used to determine awards with results as shown in Table II.

The total rank is obtained by adding the separate ranks, and the composite rank is found by assigning rank 1 to the lowest total, rank 2 to the second lowest total and so on.

E is winner of first award while C and F must either divide second award equally or "toss" for it. If the awards were money and both a second and third prize were being offered, C and F might each receive half of the sum of second and third awards.

While ranking is very useful because of its simplicity and variety of applications, it may be objected to when exact evaluation is required. One objection arises from the fact that the process of ranking will arbitrarily space scores equally on the scale.

In Figure 1 compare the actual positions of the scores 40, 36, 35, 31, 22, and 20 on the scale of scores with the equally spaced positions they are forced by ranking to assume. It is apparent that the ranks which seem to be equidistant are not so in reality, and hence certain calculations based on them may lead into difficulties.

Classification by Tabulation.—A junk yard into which automobile parts have been thrown promiscuously presents a picture of extreme disorder, but if the parts are rearranged by placing all of one kind in a pile and all of another kind in a second pile, and so on, the yard finally assumes orderliness. Such an arrangement might lend itself to making a chart or diagram, by means of which any type of part could be found quickly.

Psychological or educational data are often found in forms which are unwieldy and disorganized. By setting up a series of class intervals in the form of a table, and by placing each measure in the class interval to which it belongs, the space required for recording the data may be materially reduced and a summarizing view of the total mass of data is made easy.

An example will make this clear. Fifteen children took a spelling test of ten words and made the following scores: 6, 6, 9, 3, 5, 6, 4, 6, 5, 7, 6, 5, 4, 6, 7. To set up the class interval for tabulating the scores it is necessary to note the highest score and the lowest score involved. These are 9 and 3, so the scale must be made to include these two extremes. Using a class interval of 1, the following tabulation makes the data much more meaningful:

Class Intervals	Tallies	Frequency
9	1	1
8		
7	11	2
6	₶₶₶ 1	6
5	111	3
4	11	2
3	1	1
		N = 15

Although no actual score of 8 occurred, the interval 8 must be included to avoid distortion of the distribution of scores.

A second example may be taken from the transcript of a senior high school student who established the following record of semester marks during his three years of attendance: B, C, A, C, C, B, B, C, A, C, C, B, D, C, C, A, C, C, B, D, C, B, B, C. In this case, the class intervals are indicated by letters instead of by quantitative terms. Table III shows the form which this tabulation takes.

TABLE III. DISTRIBUTION OF ACHIEVEMENT MARKS

Class Intervals	Tallies	Frequency
A	111	3
B	₶₶₶ 11	7
C	₶₶₶ ₶₶₶ 11	12
D	11	2
		N = 24

Number and Size of Class Intervals.—A class of twenty-five children made the following scores in a vocabulary test: 27, 31, 28, 40, 34, 43, 39, 36, 22, 25, 43, 30, 20, 34, 42, 22, 35, 52, 36, 31, 48, 45, 32, 39, 37. Considering the range of these scores, it is easy to see that it is neither necessary nor wise to use class intervals of one under all circumstances. Thirty-three class intervals would be required to include all of the vocabulary scores above. That is too many. A better plan is to throw the scores together in intervals of five, as seen in Table IV.

TABLE IV   DISTRIBUTION OF VOCABULARY SCORES

Class Intervals	Tallies	Frequency
50–54	1	1
45–49	11	2
40–44	JHH	4
35–39	JHH 1	6
30–34	1111 1	6
25–29	111	3
20–24	111	3
		N = 25

In using the larger class interval we have sacrificed a certain degree of exactness because from the tabulation it is impossible to tell the exact score made by each child, but economy of space and labor justifies the sacrifice.

Fixing the size of the class intervals must be a compromise usually between two extremes. For example, in the data of the vocabulary test one could use as many as thirty-three class intervals or as few as one. If only one interval were used, the table would become

Class Interval	Frequency
20–52	25

and little meaning would attach to such a form. No definite rule can be offered for determining the most appropriate number of intervals into which a given group of data should be classified. Indeed, it is possible in some cases that different intervals could be used with equally satisfactory results. Ordinarily fewer than five or six intervals or more than eighteen or twenty should be avoided.

How to Designate Class Intervals.—Intervals may be any size from a small fraction to many thousands. For convenience in dealing with, for clearness in thinking of, and for correctness in applying certain computation techniques to data in tabulated form, it is very important that certain forms for the designation of intervals be understood. Some of these forms are as follows:

1. The midpoint only of the class intervals may be used to designate the class interval. For example, note the results in Table V.

TABLE V. MIDPOINTS USED TO DESIGNATE INTERVALS

Intervals of Three	f	Intervals of Five	f
27	2	35	1
24	4	30	3
21	6	25	7
18	9	20	12
15	8	15	9
..	..	..	..
..	..	..	..
..	..	..	..
Etc.	..	Etc.	..

The eight measures above in the interval indicated by 15 may be 14's, 15's, or 16's.

The nine measures above in the interval indicated by 15 may be 13's, 14's, 15's, 16's, or 17's.

When this plan of designating class intervals is used, the midpoints should be multiples of the size of the interval.

For the actual work of tabulation it is usually not advisable to indicate intervals by their midpoints unless relatively small intervals are being used. Quick detection of the interval in which a measure belongs is difficult when this plan is used with large intervals. The result will be many misplaced measures.

2. The lowest and highest measures included in the interval, sometimes called the tabulation limits, may be used to designate each interval. This plan is often used. The plan of expressing an interval by merely indicating the lowest and the highest scores or other measures that may be included in the interval provides not only a simple guide by which to tally the measures, but it provides other advantages later in computations to be made from the table.

Discrete and Continuous Traits.—The problem of dealing with measures of discrete traits as distinguished from measures of continuous traits is unnecessarily confusing to beginners in statistical work. In dealing with such data as class sizes, for example, one would have classes of 20, or 21, or 22 children, and so on. One could not have a class of 20.43 children. The characteristic being measured is discrete. The class interval used to tabulate such data (if class intervals of 3 are used) would be

21–23
18–20
15–17
Etc.

The midpoints of the class intervals are 22, 19, 16, and so on. Nevertheless, the scale may be considered continuous with 20.5, 17.5, and so on, as the respective points of separation between intervals.

However, in dealing with measures of growth, time, achievement, and similar traits, it must be remembered that the traits which are being measured are continuous. As a boy grows taller he passes through every point on the scale of height; as a boy grows older he passes through every point on the scale of time; and as a boy gains more experience he passes through every point on the scale of achievement. Such traits should be regarded as continuous, which in fact they are, but *the measures ordinarily reported for such traits are discrete (discontinuous).* Data are merely records of the amount of some trait. A trait may be continuous, but quantitative records (data) of it as a trait should generally be thought of as discrete. There are possible exceptions to this statement, seldom arising in educational problems, however, in cases of indirect measurement. When data of this type are being tabulated, intervals of five, let us say, may be designated as 90–94.99 and regarded as containing all measures from 90 to 94.9999+ inclusive. Here 90 is properly considered the point on the scale at which the interval begins and 92.5 the point on the scale which marks the midpoint of the interval.

Even in dealing with data of the type described above, this form of interval may be avoided by following certain rules in making the measurements. For example, in measuring intelligence (a quotient obtained by dividing mental age by chronological age) suppose we adopt the following rules:

1. When the quotient contains any fraction except .5 use the nearest integer to express the quotient.
2. When the quotient contains a fraction of exactly .5 use the nearest even integer to express it until half the quotients are computed, and thereafter use the nearest odd integer.

Thus a systematic error is avoided when the intelligence quotients are tabulated in intervals designated as 90–94 with 92 the midpoint, instead of intervals designated as 90–94.99 + with 92.5 the midpoint.

In general the intervals employed for tabulating a given set of data should be adjusted in size and limits so that the repeated occurrence of measures at points of separation between intervals will be avoided.

Various examples which illustrate different aspects of the problem of tabulation will now be cited.

Example 1. The heights (continuous trait) of a large number of boys have been recorded to the nearest half inch—54, 53.5, 52.5, 52.5, 50.5. One convenient plan of tabulation for such measures is as follows:

Scale of Heights	f
54.0	1
53.5	1
53.0	
52.5	2
52.0	
51.5	
51.0	
50.5	1

In this case the midpoint of the class interval indicated as 52 is actually 52 inches, the midpoint of the class interval indicated as 52.5 is actually 52.5 inches, and the point on the scale which separates the two class intervals is 52.25.

Example 2. If in measuring the height of boys the measurer had regarded a boy as 50.5 inches if he reached 50.5 inches but did not reach 51 inches, and had regarded a boy as 51 inches if he reached 51 inches but did not reach 51.5 inches, then 50.75

inches would be the midpoint of the lower interval and 51.25 would be the midpoint of the next interval, and so on.

Example 3. An achievement test in spelling has been given to a class. The test is of such a nature that all scores must be integers (23, 36, 28, 41, etc.). The table should be made as follows:

Scores	*f*
40–44	
35–39	
30–34	
25–29	
Etc.	

In this table, 42, 37, 32, 27, and so on are the midpoints of the intervals, for these values represent the true points of balance of the successive intervals.

A class interval, say 35–39, from the preceding table may be shown graphically as follows:

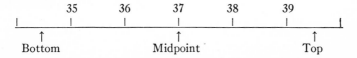

| | 35 | 36 | 37 | 38 | 39 | |
| Bottom | | | Midpoint | | | Top |

Example 4. An achievement test was given to a group of children. The test had ten divisions, and a child's total (average) score was one tenth of the sum of scores made on the separate divisions. Therefore, the scores appeared as 74.9, 68.0, 57.3, etc. In this case the tabulation should be as follows:

Scores	*f*
75.0–79.9	
70.0–74.9	
65.0–69.9	
..	
..	
..	
Etc.	

In this situation the midpoint of the top class interval is 72.45, and so on. (Note that these midpoints are found by taking half the sum of the lowest and highest scores which can be placed in the respective intervals.)

Example 5. Another achievement test was administered to a group of children. There being nine divisions in the tests, total (average) scores appeared as $63\frac{4}{9}$, 48, $52\frac{5}{9}$, $57\frac{6}{9}$, etc. In this case scorers may well have been directed to round off the scores to the nearest integer. Since, by chance, fractions of $\frac{1}{9}$ and $\frac{8}{9}$ will occur with equal frequency, as will fractions of $\frac{2}{9}$ and $\frac{7}{9}$, $\frac{3}{9}$ and $\frac{6}{9}$, and $\frac{4}{9}$ and $\frac{5}{9}$, the true midpoints of intervals will not be disturbed by this rounding process.

The tabulation may then be indicated as follows:

Scores	*f*
60–64	
55–59	
50–54	
..	
..	
..	
Etc.	

The midpoints of the intervals are 62, 57, 52, etc.

In Examples 2, 3, 4, and 5, the figures used for indicating intervals are often called tabulation limits. Distinction between tabulation limits and the true limits of the interval on the scale should be kept clear. There can be no space between intervals. Only a point separates them and a succession of them constitutes the scale. The illustration of Example 3 above shows that while 35 and 39 are the tabulation limits, 34.5 and 39.5 are the true interval limits on the scale.

These examples and discussions indicate the need for a clear understanding of the nature of data which are to be classified in intervals.

Percentage Frequencies.—It is often desirable to express the frequencies of measures falling into the various class intervals in terms of percentages of the total number of measures instead of in terms of actual numbers. The two main advantages of using percentage frequencies are (1) to provide accurate knowledge of the weight of an interval in terms of its relation to N of the distribution, and (2) to provide means of comparing a distribution with one or more other distributions.

The need for percentage frequencies as a means of making comparisons may be seen readily from the following example:

The sixth grades of School A and School B were administered an achievement test with results as shown in Table VI.

TABLE VI. DISTRIBUTION OF TEST SCORES FOR SCHOOL A
AND SCHOOL B

Class Intervals	f School A	f School B
75–79		11
70–74	18	29
65–69	22	42
60–64	34	58
55–59	46	76
50–54	87	105
45–49	63	84
40–44	44	65
35–39	20	43
30–34	16	17
25–29		10
Totals	350	540

Since the totals for the two schools are different, no number from the frequency column of School A is comparable with the

TABLE VII. PERCENTAGE FREQUENCIES USED FOR COMPARISON

Class Intervals	School A	School B
75–79		2.0
70–74	5.1	5.4
65–69	6.3	7.8
60–64	9.7	10.7
55–59	13.1	14.1
50–54	24.9	19.4
45–49	18.0	15.6
40–44	12.6	12.0
35–39	5.7	8.0
30–34	4.6	3.1
25–29		1.9
Totals	100.0	100.0

companion number from the frequency column of School B. Comparisons are possible only after these numbers have been changed to percentages as shown in Table VII.

The frequencies expressed in terms of percentages are now comparable, of course.

Cumulative Frequencies.—Frequently the interpretation of data in a table may be simplified by indicating for each interval

TABLE VIII.   DISTRIBUTION OF HIGH SCHOOL SENIORS' SCORES ON A MENTAL-ABILITY TEST

Scale of Scores	f	Cum. f* to Tops of Intervals	Cum. f† to Midpoints of Intervals
69–71	1	400	399.5
66–68	2	399	398
63–65	9	397	392.5
60–62	15	388	380.5
57–59	12	373	367
54–56	31	361	345.5
51–53	37	330	311.5
48–50	34	293	276
45–47	36	259	241
42–44	63	223	191.5
39–41	48	160	136
36–38	34	112	95
33–35	31	78	62.5
30–32	29	47	32.5
27–29	9	18	13.5
24–26	6	9	6
21–23		3	3
18–20	1	3	2.5
15–17	2	2	1
	400		

* The top of an interval is actually the point on the scale which separates the interval from the interval immediately above. For the interval designated as 15–17 this point is 17.5, for interval 18–20 the point is 20.5, etc.

† The midpoint of an interval is assumed to separate the measures in the interval into two equal parts. The midpoint of interval 15–17 is exactly 16.

the total of measures up to it. The summations may be made either to the points separating the successive intervals, or to the midpoints of the successive intervals. Either method may be employed, depending upon the use to which the distribution is to be put, but it is not necessary to make both computations. Both computations are shown in Table VIII.

Portraying the Frequency Table by Use of Graphs.—Often a clearer view of a distribution of data may be secured by reporting it in graphic form. There are four common methods of making such graphs. They are the frequency-rectangles graph, the histogram, the frequency polygon, and the frequency curve. Using a distribution of thirty-one arithmetic reasoning scores (all scores being integers) as seen in Table IX, the frequency rectangle may now be illustrated.

TABLE IX.   ARITHMETIC REASONING SCORES

Scores	f
35–39	3
30–34	6
25–29	11
20–24	7
15–19	4
	N = 31

Figure 2 shows frequency rectangles formulated from the data in Table IX. This graph may be converted into a histogram by simply omitting all the vertical lines which serve as common boundaries for the rectangles. The results will then appear as in Figure 3.

To show these data in the form of a frequency polygon or a frequency curve one important difference should be noted. In order to close up the graph at the two extremes, one should start at the midpoint of the interval next below 15–19, and finish at the midpoint next above 35–39. The fact that the frequencies in each of these two intervals is zero brings the graph down to the base line at both ends, as seen in Figure 4.

It is unnecessary to illustrate the frequency curve here since with one exception it is made in exactly the same manner as the frequency polygon shown in Figure 4. Instead of drawing straight lines to connect the points, thus producing angles at each point, a smooth curve is drawn to pass through all points

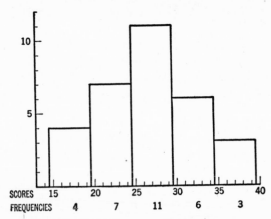

Figure 2. Frequency Rectangles

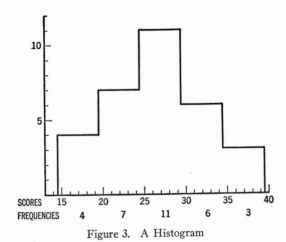

Figure 3. A Histogram

thus eliminating all angles. In all of these graphs the area inclosed is the same as the N of the distribution of Table IX on page 17.

In the construction of all of these graphs the reader's attention should be directed to the fact that, in measuring the height for each interval, we begin at a point on the base (scale of scores) which represents the true midpoint of the interval—12, 17, 22, etc. Arbitrarily shifting the graph on the base a

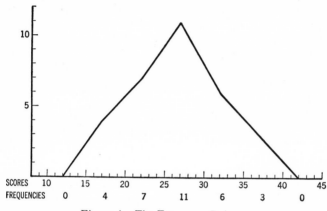

Figure 4. The Frequency Polygon

half unit to the right, which is done so often, will slightly distort the true picture of the original data.

Construction of graphs such as those shown in Figures 2, 3, and 4 is satisfactory for viewing the characteristic of a single distribution of data. However, when the graphs of two or more distributions are to be superimposed upon the same base for comparison, percentage frequencies must be used instead of actual frequencies unless, of course, the N's of the distributions are equal. We seldom find equality of N's in data encountered in natural situations.

For example, if we desire to make a graphic comparison of test data from School A and School B we find it impracticable to do so from Table VI. Yet the percentage frequencies of Table VII serve our purpose satisfactorily.

Since the N of a distribution is the same as the area inclosed by its graph, the use of percentage frequencies arbitrarily changes the N of each distribution to 100 and thus forces the two graphs to have the same area.

This type of graph, as shown in Figure 5, may be used to show the overlapping of a series of distributions—such for example, as distributions of ages for a series of grades, distribution of scores for a series of grades, etc.

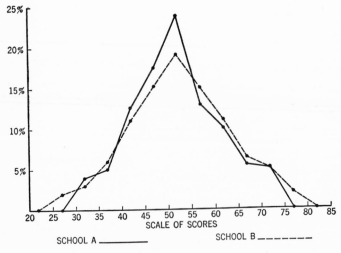

Figure 5.   Graphic Comparison of Test Data from School A and School B

Another very important use of the frequency polygon or frequency curve is found in the work of converting a distribution from one form of interval classification to another. To illustrate this use, let us suppose that two research workers, A and B, have made investigations of the heights of boys. A took his heights in units of half inches and expressed them to the nearest half inch. In other words, A recorded a boy's height as 59½ inches if the actual height came within a quarter inch under 59½ inches or within a quarter inch over 59½ inches, and so on. On the other hand, B took his heights in units of whole inches and expressed them in terms of the whole number of inches next below the actual height. In other words, B recorded a boy's height as 59 inches if the actual height came to 59 inches or higher so long as it fell short of 60 inches.

The two tabulations are reproduced in Table X.

TABLE X. TWO DISTRIBUTIONS OF HEIGHTS OF BOYS

	A's Data Scale of Heights	f		B's Data Scale of Heights	f
	65	2		65	12
Over height	64½	4		64	40
	64	5	28 or	63	72
	63½	7	23.33%	62	124
	63	10		61	108
				60	80
	62½	14		59	64
	62	18		58	44
Normal height	61½	15	68 or	57	16
	61	12	56.67%		N = 560
	60½	9			
	60	8			
	59½	6			
Under height	59	4	24 or		
	58½	4	20.00%		
	58	2			
	N = 120				

These two distributions of data are not comparable as they stand, but they may be made approximately comparable by converting the form of either distribution to the form of the other.

Let us suppose that A wishes to change the form of B's table so as to make B's data comparable, interval by interval, with A's. Also for the particular group of boys with which A is dealing, over-height, normal-height, and under-height classifications have been made. A wishes to know how the percentages of these three classifications compare with B's percentages. Figure 6 shows how such comparisons may be approximated.

Since each year on the scale is represented by four units of the graph paper, and the ordinates are one fourth as great as B's frequencies, the number of squares in each interval is the same as the frequency for that interval. Then the frequencies for

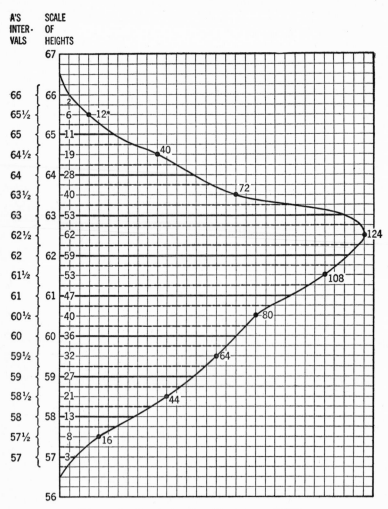

Figure 6. Graph for Changing Form of Table

* B's frequencies are shown in the figures at right of graph. The column of figures inside the graph is B's data converted to A's form of tabulation.

B's data as they would appear in a table with A's intervals can be made by actual count of the squares. B's distribution can now be seen in Table XI.

TABLE XI. DISTRIBUTION OF HEIGHTS CONVERTED TO NEW FORM OF TABULATION

	Scale of Heights	f	
	66	2	
	65½	6	
Over	65	11	159 or
height	64½	19	28.40%
	64	28	
	63½	40	
	63	53	
	62½	62	
	62	59	261 or
Normal	61½	53	46.60%
height	61	47	
	60½	40	
	60	36	
	59½	32	
	59	27	
Under	58½	21	140 or
height	58	13	25.00%
	57½	8	
	57	3	

$$N = 560$$

In making the count of squares in the strips two squares wide, there is no need to attempt accuracy greater than that expressed by integers. Also, after making the count it may develop that the sum of the converted frequencies will not total exactly the sum expected (N of the original distribution). When this happens the necessary slight adjustments should be made in the frequencies of some of the intervals to insure the correct total. If the sum is too small, as it most likely will be by a few measures, the shortage should be made up by throwing necessary extra measures into the two or three heaviest intervals. Because of the turn of the graph at its highest point, one is most likely to undercount in that vicinity.

Although the process described here may seem to lack exactness, it remains the only process applicable to the salvaging of data in some instances. Although it provides only approximate comparisons, its use is justified often in saving valuable data.

Exercises and Problems

1. Rearrange the following scores in descending order of size:
   33, 37, 45, 33, 37, 25, 54, 55, 49, 34, 35, 27, 46, 54.

2. Rearrange the following scores in ascending order of size:
   17, 13, 10, 15, 11, 10, 8, 15, 12, 15, 17, 10, 11, 8, 15, 7.

3. Rank the individuals within each group below with respect to the trait indicated:

Heights of Ten Boys		Intelligence of Ten Girls	
Inches	Rank	I.Q.'s	Rank
48		84	
63		102	
45		126	
47		112	
48		102	
64		98	
65		126	
49		107	
63		102	
48		87	

4. In an amateur contest participated in by seven contestants three judges turned in rankings which are recorded below. If the prizes offered were first $50, second $30, third $20, and fourth $10, which contestants should receive prizes and how much should each receive?

			Contestants				
Judges:	A	B	C	D	E	F	G
No. 1......6		1	5	4	2½	7	2½
No. 2......5		2½	6	4	1	7	2½
No. 3......5		1½	7	3	1½	6	4

5. Each of three judges rated three performers in a vocal contest. A scale ranging from 0 to 100 was used with the following results:

Contestants

Judges:	A	B	C
No. 1.........85		71	70
No. 2.........85		65	84
No. 3.........87		90	83
Totals.........257		226	237
Order of awards.. 1st		3rd	2nd

If these judges had been required to rank the contestants, what difference, if any, would have resulted in the order of awards?

6. A class of twenty-five children engaged in a spelling exercise. The numbers listed below indicate the number of words spelled correctly by the members of the class. Tabulate the results in intervals of one unit each:

14, 17, 13, 15, 13, 16, 11, 16, 13, 14, 17, 13, 12, 15, 14,
12, 14, 13, 14, 12, 15, 14, 15, 13, 14.

7. (a) Below are listed the ages of twenty-seven children in one division of a first grade. The ages were taken to the nearest half years. Tabulate in intervals of one-half unit each:

6½, 6, 7½, 6½, 6½, 7, 6, 6½, 5½, 7, 7, 6½, 8, 6, 8½, 7½,
7, 7½, 7, 5½, 7, 5½, 6½, 6, 7, 8, 7½.

(b) What is the midpoint of interval 6½? What point on the scale of ages separates interval 6½ from interval 7?

8. (a) At mid-semester a group of high school English students had accumulated points (two objective tests plus points for reading books) as indicated below. Each number represents the total points for a student. Tabulate in intervals of five units each:

31, 35, 50, 27, 62, 45, 31, 25, 55, 35, 26, 40, 46, 41, 24,
32, 56, 41, 24, 50, 52, 64, 36, 32, 33, 46, 36, 37, 27, 42,
42, 33, 28, 37, 33, 43, 37, 54, 58, 49, 38, 39, 38, 24, 34,
43, 39, 34, 29, 39.

(b) What is the midpoint of the interval designated by 35-39?

(c) What point on the scale separates this interval from the one designated by 40–44?

9. The twenty-six marks listed below represent the record of a senior high school student. Reorganize the record in tabular form.

B, C, C, A, C, B, D, B, A, D, B, F, B, C, C, D,
A, C, B, A, F, C, D, B, B, A.

10. (a) The ages given below were taken from a census roll of a state which requires that ages be recorded as of September 1 each year and which requires that the age on last birthday be counted the official age. Use intervals of one year each to tabulate:

9, 7, 10, 7, 8, 8, 7, 8, 9, 8, 9, 7, 8, 8, 10, 7, 6, 9, 8, 7, 8.

(b) On September 1, what is the true midpoint of interval designated by 8?

(c) What are the upper and lower limits of this interval?

11. (a) Tabulate in intervals of five units each the following scores which were made on an achievement test of ten divisions:

50.2, 57.4, 43.7, 48.1, 53.0, 41.9, 44.9, 37.3, 46.6, 49.5,
63.8, 54.0, 56.8, 47.2, 48.9, 38.5, 47.0, 41.8, 58.7, 53.3,
63.6, 42.6.

(b) How many different scores could be placed in one interval?

(c) What is the midpoint of interval 45.0–49.9?

(d) What point on the scale separates this interval from the next higher interval?

(e) What point on the scale separates it from the next lower interval?

12. (a) The scores below are from an achievement test of nine divisions. Round off each score to the nearest integer and tabulate in intervals of five units each:

42 3/9, 51 2/9, 35 6/9, 43 7/9, 45, 48 8/9, 58, 53 5/9,
44 4/9, 32 7/9, 48 1/9, 53 2/9, 47 5/9, 35 3/9, 56 4/9,
40, 53 7/9, 47 3/9, 38 2/9, 41 1/9, 46 5/9.

(b) What is the midpoint of interval 45–49?

13. The two distributions below show the marks at midyear for two departments of a certain high school. Make a graphic com-

parison of the two distributions by changing them to percentage frequencies and then graphing them upon a common base. (Segments of the base representing the five marks should be equal.)

Marks	Frequencies Math	H. E.
A	54	54
B	83	65
C	96	57
D	54	14
F	33	0
	320	190

Using scratch paper experiment with histograms and frequency polygons before deciding on the most appropriate form of graph to use.

14. To the frequency table which you made in Exercise 8 add a column showing cumulative frequencies to tops of intervals. Also add another column showing cumulative frequencies to midpoints of intervals.

15. Age-grade data for the eighth grade collected by the State Department of Education in a certain state from cities of 5,000 to 10,000 population are shown in the table below. In this table an age is defined by the age at last birthday as of September 1 of the present school year. Thus all children listed as twelve had reached their twelfth birthdays by September 1, but had not reached their thirteenth birthdays. It is desired to change the form of this tabulation to intervals of half years wherein ages have been taken to the nearest half year as of September 1. The change is necessary in order to compare the age-grade data of this state

Ages	$f*$
17	3
16	7
15	13
14	19
13	15
12	4
	61

* Frequencies are here rounded to nearest 100.

with similar data of another state which used the half-year intervals. After converting to the new form, change frequencies to percentages.

Considering the eighteen months' span of 13, 13½, and 14 normal age for the eighth grade find the percentages of overageness, normal ageness, and underageness.

CHAPTER 2

THE ARITHMETIC MEAN

The preceding chapter has indicated certain methods by which so-called raw data can be made to have added meaning. In a way, these methods call only for the substitution of one plan of grouping for another plan of grouping. However, when groups are large, there are usually many intervals, so that the help which rearrangement or regrouping gives the student in interpreting the data is not sufficient.

The present chapter sets forth some methods by which simplification can be carried further. Certain of these devices call for the substitution of a single measure for an entire group. While it is possible for any measure in the group to represent the group, yet the form taken by the data, say in Table VIII, indicates that there is a weighting near the center, or that there is a tendency for the scores to cluster about the center. This tendency is found in many of the data studied by students of psychology and education. Under such conditions, if a measure can be found which will give an indication of this clustering, it may be used as a representative measure for the whole group.

A measure such as has just been indicated is often called a measure of central tendency.

Definition of Central Tendency.—A measure of central tendency is a point on the scale of measures, or one of the measures of the distribution, or a segment of the scale of measures which indicates the tendency of the data to group themselves about a point or position which can be designated as the center.

Uses of Central Tendency.—The three most important uses of a measure of central tendency are (1) to describe a group of measures by use of a single measure, (2) to provide a basic point of reference for considering individual measures of a group, and (3) to make possible the comparison of one group of data with another group of data of similar nature.

The term average is often applied to all measures of central tendency. Elementary statistics usually makes use of five such measures. These five measures are often spoken of as types of averages. This chapter is concerned with one of these averages —the arithmetic mean. Later chapters will deal with others. In its simplest form, the mean, sometimes called the common average, is the quotient derived by dividing the sum of a group of measures by the number of measures. Since other processes are frequently used for greater convenience in finding the arithmetic mean, clearer concepts may result in thinking of the mean as always implying a process of adding the individual measures and dividing their sum by N.

Computing the Mean from Unclassified Data.—If the mean of 14, 12, and 10 is required, one may actually add the three measures for a total of 36, divide by 3, and arrive at the result of 12. However, realizing that the mean always involves the concept of center, and that a center always involves the concept of balance, the student may note the following relations:

10	12	14
−2	0	+2

∧

In this way it is clear that 12 is the mean and that the deviation of each measure from this central point is such that a perfect balance is maintained.

The twenty measures given below may be used to indicate other important points in the calculation of the mean. Scores indicating the number of words spelled correctly by each of twenty children are as follows: 7, 9, 8, 8, 11, 9, 10, 8, 6, 9, 5, 7, 9, 12, 10, 7, 5, 8, 6, 11. To find the mean, the total of these scores, 165, is divided by 20. This gives a quotient of 8.25, the mean. It should be noted here that no child could actually spell 8.25 words correctly.

The value 8.25 merely represents a point on the scale of scores (the scale may be considered continuous, even though the measures are discrete) on each side of which there is a balance, rather than as a score which represents the reactions of children.

The value of 8.25 for this series could have been arrived at in a slightly different manner by assuming 8 to be the average, as follows:

X: 7, 9, 8, 8, 11, 9, 10, 8, 6, 9, 5, 7, 9, 12, 10, 7, 5, 8, 6, 11
x': −1, +1, 0, 0, +3, +1, +2, 0, −2, +1, −3, −1, +1, +4, +2, −1, −3, 0, −2, +3

The x' indicates the deviation of each measure from the assumed average, 8. The algebraic sum of the x''s is +5, indicating that our assumed average was too small. When +5 is divided by 20, a correction of +.25 is provided, which added to 8 gives us the mean of 8.25.

The Mean Computed from Tabulated Data.—It may be seen readily that the process of finding the mean as it has been illustrated is cumbersome and tedious. Errors of addition are likely to occur in dealing with a long series. If the arithmetic mean can be found for the above measures after they have been tabulated, several advantages (some of these to be pointed out later) will result. In a previous chapter, the statistical necessity for tabulation of data has been shown, so that most investigations begin with tabulation. The derivation of the mean must, then, follow tabulation. Illustrations of this procedure follow.

Let it be required to find the mean of the twenty scores already used from a tabulated form, as seen in Table XII.

TABLE XII. SPELLING SCORES OF A FIFTH-GRADE CLASS

Scores	f
12	1
11	2
10	2
9	4
8	4
7	3
6	2
5	2
	20

From Table XII the arithmetic mean may be computed by multiplying each score value by the frequency of its occurrence, by totaling the products, and by dividing by twenty. The computation is as follows:

Computation A

Scores	f	Scores $\times f$
12	1	12
11	2	22
10	2	20
9	4	36
8	4	32
7	3	21
6	2	12
5	2	10
	20	165

$$165/20 = 8.25$$

While the processes of Computation A just used reduce somewhat the computations necessary in finding the mean, further shortening of the addition work may be accomplished by taking a convenient assumed mean (say at 8) and finding the necessary correction, as shown in Computation B which follows:

Computation B

Scores	f	d	fd
12	1	+4	+4
11	2	+3	+6
10	2	+2	+4
9	4	+1	+4
8	4	0	
7	3	−1	−3
6	2	−2	−4
5	2	−3	−6
	20		+5

$$+5/20 = +.25$$

Assumed Mean $=$ 8.00
Correction $= +.25$

Mean $=$ 8.25

To place the deviations properly and conveniently, one should place the 0 deviation opposite the assumed mean (8 in this case), and insert the other deviations upward and downward from the 0.

This table shows that there is one score of twelve which stands four units above the assumed mean, making a total of plus four units of deviation. Also there are two scores of eleven, each of which deviates three units above the assumed mean, making a total of plus six units of deviation for all elevens, and so on. In fact, all of the x' 's (deviations) for this original series of raw scores previously given may be found grouped in the fd column of this table.

The process may be reduced to the formula

$$M = A.M. + \frac{\Sigma fd}{N} \qquad (1)$$

(Σ is read *summation* or *the sum of*. In this formula the algebraic sum is required.)

The use of 8 for the assumed mean is not necessary to a correct solution. Any other score could be used, for example 10 as shown below:

Computation C

Scores	f	d	fd
12	1	$+2$	$+2$
11	2	$+1$	$+2$
10	2	0	
9	4	-1	-4
8	4	-2	-8
7	3	-3	-9
6	2	-4	-8
5	2	-5	-10
	20		-35

$$M = 10 + \frac{-35}{20}$$
$$= 10 - 1.75$$
$$= 8.25$$

The same result as before is reached by using ten as the assumed mean. As a matter of fact there is no essential difference between Computations A, B, and C. In Computation A the assumed mean was zero.

So far as mathematical principles are concerned there are no restrictions on the value to be taken for the assumed mean in solving this problem. One could take $+1000$ for the assumed mean or one could take -1000. In either case the application of the correction will yield the correct mean. Neither is it necessary to use an integer for the assumed mean. To illustrate this fact let us use an assumed mean of 7.75 in solving for the mean of the data in Table XII.

Computation D

Scores	f	d	fd
12	1	$+4.25$	$+4.25$
11	2	$+3.25$	$+6.50$
10	2	$+2.25$	$+4.50$
9	4	$+1.25$	$+5.00$
8	4	$+\ .25$	$+1.00$
7	3	$-\ .75$	-2.25
6	2	-1.75	-3.50
5	2	-2.75	-5.50
	20		$+10.00$

$$M = 7.75 + \frac{+10.00}{20}$$
$$= 7.75 + .50$$
$$= 8.25$$

Of course, the use of such unusual values for the assumed mean is not the part of wisdom. Economy of labor dictates that if possible the assumed mean should be taken at the midpoint of the interval in which the true mean lies. Use of the value of the midpoint of an interval permits the assignment of zero deviation to that interval. Thus a minimum of labor will be involved in the computation.

Computation of Mean When Measures of Different Values are Grouped in Intervals.—The preceding computations all gave the same result, 8.25, regardless of the process used. The reason for this is that all measures in a given interval were exactly alike in value or were thought of as coming at the same point in the interval. However, as was shown in Chapter 1, it is often more convenient to set up intervals large enough to include a small range of measures differing slightly in value. For example, the thirty-one scores in arithmetic reasoning tabulated in Table IX actually totaled 825, and therefore had a mean of 26.61. The mean computed from the table, however, gives a slightly different result, as may be seen from the computation below:

Computation E

Scores	f	$d*$	fd
35–39	3	10	30
30–34	6	5	30
25–29	11	0	
20–24	7	−5	−35
15–19	4	−10	−40
	31		−15

$$M = 27 + \frac{-15}{31}$$
$$= 27 - .48$$
$$= 26.52$$

* The deviations here are expressed in terms of scale units. The midpoint of interval 30–34 is five units above the assumed mean, the midpoint of interval 35–39 is ten units above the assumed mean, and so on.

The plan of expressing deviations in terms of units on the scale is not advisable in general. It was used in Computation E to show the connection with previous computations. A better plan is to express deviations in terms of intervals, to find the

Computation F

Scores	f	d	fd
35–39	3	+2	6
30–34	6	+1	6
25–29	11	0	
20–24	7	−1	−7
15–19	4	−2	−8
	31		−3 (intervals)

$$M = 27 + \frac{-3}{31} \times 5$$
$$= 27 - .0968 \times 5$$
$$= 26.52$$

correction in terms of intervals, and to convert to terms of units. Instead of saying the midpoint of interval 30–34 deviates *five units* above the assumed mean, we say it deviates *one interval* above the assumed mean. These suggestions are illustrated in Computation F on page 35.

The formula may be expressed

$$M = A.M. + \frac{\Sigma fd}{N} \times h \qquad (2)$$

(*h* is the width of the interval)

Of course, one can multiply Σfd by h before dividing by N, but it is usually considered better to form the habit of finding the value of $\frac{\Sigma fd}{N}$ independently of other computations for the reasons that later we shall deal with a computation (standard deviation) that requires the use of this quotient.

Errors of Assumption.—A moment's consideration will reveal the reason for the failure of the different computations for the mean to agree. In the table it is assumed the measures are so arranged that the center of weight of the measures in an interval is at the midpoint of the interval. For example, there are five different ways by which such arrangement could be made for the three measures in interval 35–39 above. They are 35, 37, 39; 36, 37, 38; 35, 38, 38; 36, 36, 39; 37, 37, 37. Now, we do not know that the three measures included in the interval represent any of these five groups. If the three measures were 35, 35, 39, their average would be 36⅓, a value below the 37 which they are assumed to average. Such errors are called errors of assumption. They fall into two distinct classes.

The first class of such errors is illustrated in Figure 7. If a group of measures falls into a truly normal distribution, the true centers of gravity of intervals in the upper half of the distribution will be below their midpoints. In the lower half of the distribution, the true centers of gravity of intervals will be above their midpoints. According to the assumption, intervals in the two divisions of the distribution pair off by relative position, one of each pair having an error in one direction (+), and the other having the same error in the other direction (−). The result is perfect compensation.

There is perfect compensation of errors shown in Figure 7 in so far as computation of means is involved, but we shall see later that these same errors become systematic and cumulative in certain other computations.

Intervals	Scale of Measures	f	Midpoint of Interval	True Ave. of Measures in Interval	Difference	Compensating Errors (Dif. ×f)
	29	1				
27–29	28	11	28	27.78	−.22	−1.32
	27	111				
	26	111				
24–26	25	1111	25	24.83	−.17	−2.04
	24	11111				
	23	111111				
21–23	22	11111111	22	22.00	.00	.00
	21	111111				
	20	11111				
18–20	19	1111	19	19.17	+.17	+2.04
	18	111				
	17	111				
15–17	16	11	16	16.22	+.22	+1.32
	15	1				
					Total	.00

Figure 7. Illustrating Perfect Compensation for Errors of Assumption in a Symmetrical Frequency Distribution

The second class of errors of assumption may be referred to as the "hit-or-miss" type. In actual practice we seldom encounter data which represent a true normal distribution. In other words, none of the intervals may have the true center of weight at the point expected, but since these errors are as likely to go in one direction as the other, their algebraic sum tends to approach zero. In this case the result may not be perfect compensation, however.

So long as only compensating errors of assumption are made, no violence is done to principles of computation. However,

great care should be exercised to avoid *systematic errors* of
assumption. In tabulating data, one should keep in mind that
measures can be expressed quantitatively only in discrete form,
regardless of whether the trait being measured is continuous or
discrete. One should express intervals in keeping with the purpose which they are to serve; viz., to define the measures to be
included within each interval. (As stated in Chapter 1, this is
done by indicating an interval in terms of the lowest measure
and the highest measure which may be placed in the interval.)

For illustration, let us take scores in arithmetic reasoning
made by thirteen pupils in a timed test. The score of each pupil
represents the number of his correct answers. The scores are:
27, 20, 24, 12, 22, 29, 19, 33, 21, 15, 25, 31, 23.

Let it be required to find the mean of these scores. In
Table XIII the scores are classified and the mean is computed.

TABLE XIII. ARITHMETIC REASONING SCORES FOR SMALL CLASS

Scale of Scores	f	d	fd
30–34	2	+2	+4
25–29	3	+1	+3
20–24	5	0	
15–19	2	−1	−2
10–14	1	−2	−2
	13		+3

$$M = 22 + \frac{+3}{13} \times 5$$
$$= 22 + 1.154$$
$$= 23.154$$

It should be noted that the highest class interval was designated by 30–34, and not 30–34.99. Since all of the scores are
integers, no reason exists for the use of fractions in expressing
the intervals.

A check on the accuracy of the solution above may be made
by determining the common average of the thirteen scores.
Their total is 301, which divided by thirteen equals 23.154. In
the table the assumption was made that the measures in each
interval were symmetrically distributed about its center (an

assumption which is actually true in this case). The centers of gravity of the successive intervals, therefore, are 32, 27, 22, 17, and 12.

Some may argue that the treatment of the scores in intervals of 20–24.99, and so on, with 22.5 the midpoint or assumed mean, is justified by the circumstances that each child did more on the test than his integral score indicates. These fractional excesses would range from a mere beginning on an extra problem to a point barely short of completing an extra problem. Those who make such contentions would be compelled for the sake of consistency to regard each of the above scores one-half point higher when comparing it with the mean computed by their method. They seldom do this, however, choosing rather to use one definition of a score on the one occasion and a different definition on the other occasion.

Of course the assumption that the midpoints of the intervals are 32.5, 27.5, 22.5, 17.5, and 12.5, instead of their correct values in this case would introduce a systematic error of .5 which will persist to the end of the computation and be present in the final answer. A simple rule to avoid systematic errors is to treat the scale as continuous, but to determine the limits of intervals and to locate their centers on the *basis of the nature of the data and the method of their observation.*

If, for example, heights have been recorded in terms of half inches, all within a quarter inch above or below being put in the same class, there can be no question about the center of gravity of each interval. To record the heights thus observed would require intervals such as here illustrated:

Scale of Heights	f
54	1
53½	2
53	2
52½	4
52	3
51½	2
51	1
	15

Here the mean computed from an assumed mean of 52½ by setting the zero deviation opposite that interval will be a correct reference point for the exact height of any of the fifteen individuals.

Methods of avoiding the systematic error may be illustrated further by the examples which follow:

Example 1. A general achievement test consisting of ten divisions was given twenty-six pupils. Each pupil's score, therefore, is the average of the ten divisions and will require the use of one decimal place to express. The scores will appear as 74.9, 68.0, 57.3, etc. Expressing the intervals to indicate merely the lowest score and the highest score that can be included, the tabulation appears as follows:

TABLE XIV. GENERAL ACHIEVEMENT SCORES

Scale of Scores	f	d	fd
75.0–79.9	4	+2	+8
70.0–74.9	6	+1	+6
65.0–69.9	8	0	
60.0–64.9	5	−1	−5
55.0–59.9	3	−2	−6
	26		+3

$$M = 67.45 + \frac{+3}{26} \times 5$$
$$= 67.45 + .58$$
$$= 68.03$$

Using the mechanical method suggested in Chapter 1 for finding the midpoint $\left(\dfrac{65.0 + 69.9}{2} \right)$ of an interval, the midpoint of interval 65.0–69.9 is found to be 67.45. This is the correct value to be used for the assumed mean.

Example 2. The ages of thirty children have been recorded on September 1 by whole years expressed in terms of their last birthdays. The mean of their ages is required from the following tabulation:

TABLE XV.   AGES OF PUPILS

Ages	f	d	fd
14	3	+2	+6
13	6	+1	+6
12	10	0	
11	7	−1	−7
10	4	−2	−8
	30		−3

$$M = 12.50 + \frac{-3}{30} \times 1$$
$$= 12.50 - .10$$
$$= 12.40$$

The manner of observing the data of Table XV should make it clear that 12.5 years is the true center of the interval indicated as 12 in the age column.

At this point in the discussion of the mean, we may summarize by saying that the observer and recorder of data is obliged to accompany his data with exact statements of the nature of the data and of the manner in which they were observed and recorded. Such information is necessary to proper tabulation, computation, and interpretation.

Combining the Means of Two or More Distributions.—The rigorously algebraic definition of the mean permits the computation of the mean of a total distribution when the means of its several parts are known. This fact is often of great convenience to school officials. Suppose, for example, that an intelligence test has been given to the three grades of a junior high school. Six tabulations of the scores have been made—one for each sex in each grade. The means for each of the six tabulations have been determined and recorded as follows:

TABLE XVI.   MEANS OF SCORES ON AN INTELLIGENCE TEST

	Gr. 7		Gr. 8		Gr. 9	
	Boys	Girls	Boys	Girls	Boys	Girls
N	82	96	78	90	66	83
M	24.84	25.31	27.08	28.52	30.42	32.14

The principal now wishes to know the mean for all boys, the mean for all girls, and the mean for his entire building. Without going to the trouble of making further tabulations of scores it is possible to get the information required from the facts shown in Table XVI by use of the formula

$$M_T = \frac{N_1M_1 + N_2M_2 + \ldots + N_nM_n}{N_1 + N_2 + \ldots + N_n} \tag{3}$$

Substituting the necessary values to find the mean for all boys we have

$$M_B = \frac{82 \times 24.84 + 78 \times 27.08 + 66 \times 30.42}{82 + 78 + 66}$$

$$= \frac{6156.84}{226} \text{ or } 27.24$$

In similar manner the mean for all girls may be found. The mean for the entire school may then be found by applying Formula (3) to the means found for the two sexes, or by applying it to the six separate sets of facts shown in Table XVI.

A slight modification of Formula (3) will permit the determination of the mean of one subdivision of a total distribution where the mean of the total and the means of all other subdivisions are known.

In Formula (3) suppose that M_1 is the only unknown element. Then solve the equation for M_1 as follows

$$N_1M_1 + N_2M_2 + \ldots + N_nM_n = M_T (N_1 + N_2 + \ldots + N_n)$$

$$M_1 = \frac{N_TM_T - N_2M_2 - \ldots - N_nM_n}{N_1} \tag{4}$$

To illustrate the use of Formula (4) let us suppose that the grade-point mean has been computed for a senior high school on the basis of $A=4$, $B=3$, $C=2$, $D=1$, and $F=0$. The mean for all high school students (458 in all) is 2.67. The mean for the 211 boys has been found to be 2.56. What is the mean for the girls? Applying Formula (4) we have

$$M_G = \frac{458 \times 2.67 - 211 \times 2.56}{247}$$

$$= \frac{682.70}{247} \text{ or } 2.76$$

It should be observed here that the mean of the whole cannot be found by taking the average of the means of its parts unless, of course, the number of cases is the same for all parts.

Exercises and Problems

1. The scores below were made by a class in high school English.

> 32, 27, 35, 25, 18, 30, 39, 28, 29, 32, 37, 21, 41, 38, 30,
> 30, 31, 36, 35, 23, 23, 29, 25, 20, 26, 20, 34, 25, 27, 38,
> 29, 19.

(a) Find the common average by dividing the sum of the scores by N (thirty-two).

(b) Tabulate the scores in intervals of one and find the mean. Do you get the same result as in (a)? Why?

(c) Tabulate the scores in intervals of two and compute the mean. (Use an assumed mean of 28.50 which is the midpoint of one interval.) Do you get the same result as in (a)? If not, explain why.

(d) Tabulate the scores in intervals of three and compute the mean twice—once using 28 as the assumed mean and once using 31, the midpoint of the next higher interval, as the assumed mean.

2. The measures tabulated below are scores from a seventh-grade test on social studies. The scores were all integers.

Scale of Scores	f
70–74	3
65–69	7
60–64	10
55–59	13
50–54	9
45–49	6
40–44	4
	52

(a) Find the mean using the midpoint of interval 55–59 as the assumed mean.

(b) Compute the mean using 32 as the assumed mean. Do you get the same result as in (a)?

(c) You are challenged to try a computation of the mean using 56 as the assumed mean. In this case is it correct to set zero deviation opposite interval 55–59? If the thirteen measures of the interval are assumed to be symmetrically arranged in the interval, at what point on the scale does their average weight rest? This point is how many units, or what fractional part of an interval, above your assumed mean? You must get the same mean as in (a) or (b).

3. The table below is a distribution of intelligence quotients for a junior high school. Each I.Q. (mental age ÷ chronological age) was expressed to the nearest integer.

Scale of I.Q.'s	f
140–149	2
130–139	1
120–129	20
110–119	46
100–109	50
90– 99	44
80– 89	34
70– 79	19
60– 69	9
50– 59	5
	230

Find the mean I.Q.

4. The heights of twenty boys were taken to the nearest half inch as here recorded.

63½, 65, 64½, 66, 65½, 62, 66½, 68, 65, 69½, 66, 63, 69, 68½, 65, 62½, 67, 60½, 63½, 68.

Tabulate these heights in intervals of 1½ inches. These intervals will be

69 –70
67½–68½
66 –67
64½–65½
Etc.

Find the mean height of the twenty boys.

5. On September 1, the opening day of school, Miss Smith requested each child in her room to write on a slip of paper his age on his last birthday. She collected the slips and tabulated the numbers on them as follows:

Ages	*f*
14	3
13	8
12	14
11	7
10	2
	34

(a) Find the mean age of Miss Smith's children on the opening day of school.

(b) Find the mean age of the same thirty-four children nine months later on the closing day of school.

6. (a) In theory what is the maximum limit of difference which could exist between the common average of a series of measures and the mean of the scores computed from a tabulation of them?

(b) In actual practice what is the greatest difference that could arise between these two results for the data of Exercise 2?

(c) Explain fully (by use of companion intervals above and below the mean) why this difference gravitates towards zero.

7. If exactly ten were added to each of the scores of Exercise 1, what effect would the additions have upon the mean of the series?

8. The thirteen boys of a class of thirty children in a fifth grade made a mean score of 46.4 in an arithmetic reasoning test. The seventeen girls made a mean score of 42.7. What was the mean for the entire class?

9. In a certain high school of 386 students, the mean grade points established one year by 54 students participating in forensics or dramatics was 3.26. The mean for the entire high school was 2.77. What was the grade-point mean of students who participated in neither forensics nor dramatics?

10. (a) To assume the midpoints of a series of intervals like 40–49, 50–59, ... to be 45, 55, . . . when in reality they are 44.5, 54.5, . . . will produce what type of error?

(b) The mean computed in this case would be wrong by how much?

(c) Would it be too high or too low?

11. (a) Compute the mean of the twenty-one scores of Exercise 12 of Chapter 1.

(b) Does the rounding of the scores to the nearest integer have a compensating effect? If so, why?

12. The tabulation below shows the number of books read in one year by the freshman English students of a high school:

No. Books	f
27–29	3
24–26	6
21–23	8
18–20	12
15–17	16
12–14	13
9–11	9
6– 8	6
	73

Find the mean number of books read by these students.

13. The semester marks (grades) of a high school science department are classified in the following table:

Marks	f	$\% f$
A (4)	16	11.43
B (3)	38	27.14
C (2)	54	38.57
D (1)	26	18.57
F (0)	6	4.29
	140	100.00

Find the mean by use of the actual frequencies and again, for a check, by use of the percentage frequencies.

14. What is the value of $x - x'$ for any measure of the following series?

$$11, 8, 11, 10, 12, 8, 9, 12, 7, 10$$

(Remember that x is a measure's deviation from the mean while x' is its deviation from an assumed mean. In dealing with the series you are expected to use the most logical integer for your assumed mean.)

CHAPTER 3

OTHER MEASURES OF CENTRAL TENDENCY

As suggested in the preceding chapter, the arithmetic mean does not meet all the demands which may be placed upon an average. Other measures of central tendency are now to be considered.

The Mid-measure.—The mid-measure or mid-score is the measure which rests at the middle of a series of measures when the measures have been arranged in some regular order (either ascending or descending). In a strict application of the definition only a series of an odd number of measures could have a mid-measure, but the definition is generally liberalized to accept as the mid-measure of an even-numbered series the average of the two measures at the middle. The examples which follow illustrate the two situations:

Odd number of measures: 26, 23, 23, 22, 19, 17, 17. Here the mid-measure is 22.
Even number of measures: 27, 24, 23, 22, 18, 16. Here the mid-measure is 22½ (the average of 22 and 23).

The Mode.—In statistics the term mode retains its common meaning—fashion or prevailing custom. The modal score is the score which represents the prevailing fashion, or it is the most frequent score. When intervals have been used to group a range of scores, the mode may be expessed in terms of an interval—the most fashionable interval.

In this form the mode is a very rough measure of central tendency. It may be determined by inspection, and has little value in exact statistical work. In fact, it may be misleading in the case of a distribution which fails grossly to approximate a normal curve. Before naming the modal interval in such a situation, it is often advisable to smooth the curve by revising the frequencies of each interval to equal the average number of frequencies of the interval concerned and its two adjacent intervals. In revising the frequencies in the top interval or the bottom interval, the frequencies are doubled and added to the frequencies of the one adjacent interval. This may be seen in Table XVII, which shows the annual salaries of a group of high school English teachers. In the column of smoothed frequencies below, the value $2\frac{2}{3}$ was obtained by taking one third of $2 \times 2 + 4$, the value $4\frac{1}{3}$ was obtained by taking one third of $2 + 4 + 7$, and so on.

TABLE XVII. SMOOTHING A DISTRIBUTION TO FIND MODE

Salaries	f	Smoothed Frequencies
1800–1899	2	$2\frac{2}{3}$
1700–1799	4	$4\frac{1}{3}$
1600–1699	7	$9\frac{2}{3}$
1500–1599	18	$13\frac{2}{3}$
1400–1499	16	17
1300–1399	17	15
1200–1299	12	13
1100–1199	10	$9\frac{1}{3}$
1000–1099	6	$6\frac{1}{3}$
900– 999	3	4
	95	95

Inspection of the actual frequencies reveals that the mode is the interval 1500–1599. However, the modal interval is lowered to 1400–1499 as a result of smoothing the curve. Perhaps the latter interval is the better representation of central tendency. The smoothing process may be repeated a second or a third time. However, further smoothing of the frequencies in the illustration would not change the mode.

It is also of interest to note that a distribution may be bimodal or multi-modal. When such is the case, the smoothing process should not be carried far enough to obscure trends truly characteristic of the data.

In a strictly mathematical sense the mode may be defined as a *point* on the scale of measures. The advantages of knowing this exact point, however, are seldom worth the labor necessary to find it. This labor involves the writing of the equation of the best fitting line and, by the use of calculus, finding the first derivative of the equation. Thus, the point on the base directly above which the curve makes its turn at its highest position is determined.

The Median.—The mean as a description of the central tendency of a heterogeneous group of measures is often unsatisfactory. To the average reader it may be highly misleading. If a statement is made to the effect that the mean wealth of A, B, C, and D is $250,001.50, the impression would probably be gained by the untrained student that the group is comparatively well off financially. Yet the facts may be that A has $1,000,000, B has $3, C has $2, and D has $1. Since 75% of the group are practically penniless, the use of a quarter of a million dollars for the central tendency of wealth is very misleading.

It should be remembered that the value of every measure is taken into account in finding the mean. This fact permits a few extreme measures to have a large influence on the mean. On the other hand, the median is unaffected by extreme measures. For this reason the median will serve better for many purposes as a central tendency to describe the wealth of the group mentioned above. The median is the point on the scale of measures below which (or above which) half the measures lie. The median wealth, therefore, of our four individuals is $2.50, this being the point on the scale below which two of the individuals lie. For most purposes, the median describes the present group much better than does the mean.

The Median Computed from Tabulated Data.—The definition of the median is the guide to its computation from a frequency table. A clear understanding of the limits of each interval in the table is necessary. Since the median may fall at any point on the scale, regardless of the nature of the data, the scale must be considered continuous.

The three important steps in the computation of the median will now be shown:

TABLE XVIII.   SCORES ON KNOWLEDGE OF LITERATURE; SIXTH GRADE
(All Scores Integers)

Scale of Scores	f
75–79	2
70–74	
65–69	4
60–64	5
55–59	7
50–54	9
45–49	8
40–44	6
35–39	3
30–34	2
25–29	1
	47

By ascending the scale

$$\text{Md.} = 49.50 + \frac{\frac{47}{2} - 20}{9} \times 5 \text{ or } 51.44$$

By descending the scale

$$\text{Md.} = 54.50 - \frac{\frac{47}{2} - 18}{9} \times 5 \text{ or } 51.44$$

1. To find the number of measures which must lie on each side of the median divide N by 2, ($\frac{47}{2} = 23\frac{1}{2}$ here).

2. (a) Beginning at the bottom ascend the scale, interval by interval, as far as possible; i.e., until ascent through another interval would leave more than $\frac{N}{2}$ cases (23½ here) below. Here the point on the scale is reached which separates interval 45–49 from interval 50–54. This procedure leaves twenty measures below. This point is 49.50, which must serve as a point of reference for any further ascent; or

(b) Beginning at the top descend the scale, interval by interval, as far as possible; i. e., until the descent through another interval would leave more than $\frac{N}{2}$ cases above. Here the point on the scale is reached which separates interval 55–59 from interval 50–54. There are eighteen measures above. This point is 54.50, which must serve as a point of reference for any further descent.

3. (a) It is now necessary to note the number of measures necessary to complete $\frac{N}{2}$ cases ($23\frac{1}{2}-20=3\frac{1}{2}$ in this instance). Counting upward from the point previously reached, 49.50, should be continued into the interval 50–54 far enough to place $3\frac{1}{2}$ more measures below. (Here it is necessary to assume that the nine measures in interval 50–54 are equally spaced throughout the interval.) The additional distance ascended therefore must be $\frac{3\frac{1}{2}}{9}$ of the width of the interval ($\frac{3\frac{1}{2}}{9} \times 5 = 1.94$ in this instance) which must be added to 49.50 ($49.50 + 1.94 = 51.44$, the median) ; or

(b) It is now necessary to note the number of measures necessary to complete $\frac{N}{2}$ ($23\frac{1}{2}-18=5\frac{1}{2}$ in this instance). Counting downward from the point previously reached, 54.50, should be continued into the interval 50–54 far enough to place $5\frac{1}{2}$ more measures above. [See 3 (a) above for necessary assumption here.] The additional distance descended therefore must be $\frac{5\frac{1}{2}}{9}$ of the width of the interval ($\frac{5\frac{1}{2}}{9} \times 5 = 3.06$ in this instance) which must be subtracted from 54.50, ($54.50 - 3.06 = 51.44$, the median).

Of course only one of the processes, either ascending or descending, is necessary to find the median, though use of both furnishes a good check.

In dealing with the mean, emphasis was given to the importance of determining the midpoint of the interval which seems best suited to the method used for locating or defining the interval; in dealing with the median, emphasis is now shifted to the point of separation of two adjacent intervals. A correct computation of the median depends upon a correct determination of the point separating two intervals. From Table XVIII let us magnify for analysis the important interval, 50–54. Figure 8 shows the analysis.

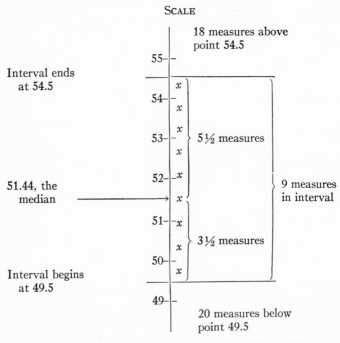

Figure 8.   Analysis of Interval in Which Median Lies

Some students may consider the point on the scale reached after ascending through interval 45–49 to be 50. Such a contention is as illogical as the contention that 49 should be considered the point reached. From the nature of the data of Table XVIII, the point 49.50 is the logical position on the scale to consider as a point of separation between the two intervals, and, therefore, as the point reached after ascending the greatest height on the scale possible by movements of whole intervals.

As a guiding policy in computing the median, the point of division between two intervals should be determined by locating the half-way point between the highest measure possible in the lower interval, and the lowest measure possible in the higher interval. This point of separation is easily determined when the numbers defining an interval have been written to indicate merely the lowest and the highest measures to be included within the interval. It will be half the sum of the top figure in one interval and the bottom figure in the next higher.

When other plans of indicating intervals have been used, one must locate the points of separation of intervals by a consideration of the nature of the measures tabulated and the plan of tabulation.

To illustrate variety in computation of medians, further solutions are given in Tables XIX, XX, and XXI.

TABLE XIX. HEIGHTS OF BOYS MEASURED TO NEAREST HALF INCH

Scale of Heights	f
63½	2
63	3
62½	5
62	6
61½	8
61	5
60½	2
60	2
59½	1
	34

Starting at the bottom of Table XIX, we can ascend the scale through four intervals by moving a whole interval at each step. From the manner in which the data were observed, we know we have reached the point 61.25. We must continue ⅞ of the distance through the next interval, 61½, which is one-half inch wide. We then have

$$\text{Md.} = 61.25 + (⅞ \times ½) \text{ or } 61.69 \text{ inches}$$

Starting at the top of Table XX and descending the scale through four intervals, we reach the point 74.95 $\dfrac{(74.9+75.0)}{2}$, above which we have 23 measures, leaving us

TABLE XX. SCORES ON A GENERAL ACHIEVEMENT TEST

(Each score is the average of ten divisions of the test)

Scale of Scores	f
84.0–86.9	3
81.0–83.9	4
78.0–80.9	8
75.0–77.9	8
72.0–74.9	10
69.0–71.9	9
66.0–68.9	7
63.0–65.9	3
60.0–62.9	2
	54

$\frac{4}{10}$ of the width of the fifth interval yet to descend. Since the intervals are three scale units wide, we must subtract from 74.95 the value $\frac{4}{10} \times 3$, or 1.2, which gives a median of 73.75. In short, the computation becomes:

$$74.95 - \left(\frac{27 - 23}{10} \times 3 \right) = 73.75$$

Again, starting at the bottom of Table XXI and ascending the scale through six intervals, we reach the point 499.50. Below this point there are eleven incomes. Passing now into the

TABLE XXI. ANNUAL EARNED INCOME OF TWENTY-SIX HEADS OF FAMILIES HAVING CHILDREN IN FOURTH GRADE

(Incomes were stated in whole dollars)

Scale of Incomes	f
1000 and up	9
750–999	2
500–749	4
400–499	2
300–399	3
200–299	2
150–199	1
100–149	1
Below 100	2
	26

next interval far enough to get the remaining two incomes to make the necessary thirteen, and assuming that the four incomes in the next interval are equally spaced, we advance a distance of $\frac{2}{4} \times 250$ or 125 scale units (dollars in this case) to the correct point. The median is found to be $499.50 + 125$, or 624.50. Incidentally this is the midpoint of the interval 500–749.

In Table XXI it will be noticed that intervals of varying sizes were used. Also it should be observed that the upper limit of the top interval is not definite, and that the lower limit of the bottom interval is not definite. In computing the median of the distribution, these conditions offer no obstacles. The computation was concerned with the size of only one interval—the one in which the median fell, 500–749, the width of which is 250.

This computation illustrates an important advantage of the median over the mean. Denied access to the original twenty-six incomes, and given only this table with which to work, it would be impossible to find the mean, whereas the median may be found readily.

The Inter-Quartile Mean.—This measure of central tendency combines some of the advantages of both the mean and the median, and at the same time avoids some of the disadvantages of both. It is found by taking the mean of the middle 50% of the measures. It is necessary to discard both the upper 25% of the measures and the lower 25%. When the inter-quartile mean is desired, it is best to do the necessary discarding of measures to be rejected before tabulating.

Example: 192, 150, 143, 106, 78, 74, 71, 69, 66, 66, 65, 61, 57, 52, 43, 38.

The highest four scores and the lowest four scores are now rejected and the common average or the mean is found for the remaining eight scores. The common average here is 68.75. When tabulated as shown on the following page, the mean of the eight measures may be found to be 68.87. Either of these results is called the inter-quartile mean.

A modification of this measure of central tendency is often made by finding the mean of measures remaining, after reject-

Scale	f
78–80	1
75–77	
72–74	1
69–71	2
66–68	2
63–65	1
60–62	1
	—
	8

ing any arbitrary percentage of measures at the top and at the bottom of a series.

The Normal Zone.—Neither the mean nor the median will satisfy all the needs of a central tendency in considering norms. If one should weigh a large number of boys, all of whom were the same height and the same age, one would find a considerable range in weights. The mean of the distribution of weights may be spoken of as a norm, but when so referred to there should be a clear understanding of its meaning. It is nothing more than the mean weight of boys of the specified height and age. In dealing with the mean here as a norm, there is danger that it may be thought of as the one and only desirable weight for a boy of the specified height and age. Use of the mean in this sense would necessitate the classification of every boy of the group as either overweight or underweight. A report to a parent that his boy is overweight or underweight, even though the amount was small, might carry the implication that a defect existed which required correction.

Obviously there is need here for the establishment of a zone with the mean at its center within which a boy may be referred to as normal weight. This is called the *normal zone* for weight. Three classifications are thus permitted—overweight, normal weight, and underweight.

The problem of establishing normal zones as measures of central tendency is a different one for each field of measurement. While some features of the problem may necessarily be decided arbitrarily, other features may be determined as a result of research in the particular field of measurement. Doctors, nurses, and physical-education experts may decide on the width of the normal-weight zones; school administrators may decide on the width of at-age zones for grades; and test specialists may determine logical at-grade zones for their test scores.

The study of rate of change, overlapping, and other characteristics of any certain trait is important as a guide to specifying normal zones. In dealing with age-grade data, a span of

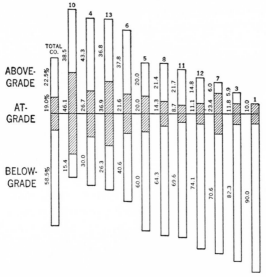

Figure 9. Report of Seventh-Grade Testing Program for Blank County

eighteen months, overlapping six months upon the next span above, is usually accepted as satisfactory for a given grade. All children within the span are counted as of normal age. In similar manner, one of the present writers, in dealing with state-wide test scores, established for the various grades score-zones within which a child may be said to be at-grade. The width of the normal zone for each grade was determined by taking a segment of the scale one and one half times the distance between the means of two successive grades. The segment was then adjusted on the scale so that its midpoint rested at the mean for the grade. This arrangement, of course, will make the at-grade zone for a given grade extend a fourth of its width above the lower limit of the zone for the grade above, and extend a fourth of its width below the upper limit of the zone for the grade below.

These zones permit the classification of all pupils as either above-grade, at-grade, or below-grade. Numbers of pupils falling into these classifications may be converted to percentages. The percentages may then be compared with corresponding percentages for other schools or with normal percentages.

The plan provides very simple means of reporting test results in comparable forms. Figure 9 is such a report of test results for a small county.

The Geometrical Mean.—Only passing mention will be made here of the geometrical mean, for it has relatively little utility in educational statistics and educational research. In educational research its use is confined largely to determining ratios of increase and in finding comparative indices. In the series 4, 6, and 9, six is the geometrical mean as may be demonstrated by the relationship $\frac{4}{6} = \frac{6}{9}$. In this series the geometrical mean may be found by the use of logarithms, as follows:

$$\log 4 = .6021$$
$$\log 6 = .7782$$
$$\log 9 = .9542$$
$$3)\overline{2.3345}$$

Antilog   .7782 = 6, the geometrical mean of the series

The value 6 is less than 6.33, the arithmetic mean of the series. For any series the geometrical mean is always smaller than the arithmetic mean. The computation of the geometrical mean is indicated by the formula:

$$\text{G. M.} = \text{antilog of } \frac{\log X_1 + \log X_2 + \ldots + \log X_n}{N} \qquad (5)$$

The formula may be applied to a series of measures of any length. However, the fact that the logarithm of a variable approaches minus infinity as the variable approaches zero causes the geometrical mean to become zero (or meaningless) if any term in the series is zero.

The following example illustrates one use of the geometrical mean: In a school survey of a city, ratios of increase in post office receipts were accepted as one index of the city's stability. The ratios of increase at five-year intervals over a period of twenty-five years were computed to be 1.37, 1.72, 1.32, 1.22, 1.07. To express these in the form of a single index the geometrical mean was found as follows:

$$\log 1.37 = .1367$$
$$\log 1.72 = .2355$$
$$\log 1.32 = .1206$$
$$\log 1.22 = .0864$$
$$\log 1.08 = .0334$$
$$\frac{.6126}{5} = .1225$$

Antilog .1225 = 1.326, the geometrical mean

The Harmonic Mean.—The harmonic mean is the reciprocal of the arithmetic mean of the reciprocals of the measures. Its formula may be stated

$$\text{H. M.} = \frac{N}{\left(\dfrac{1}{X_1} + \dfrac{1}{X_2} + \cdots + \dfrac{1}{X_n}\right)} \tag{6}$$

For the series 4, 6, and 9 the harmonic mean will be

$$\text{H. M.} = \frac{3}{(\frac{1}{4} + 1/6 + 1/9)} \quad \text{or} \quad \frac{3}{.5278} \quad \text{or } 5.68$$

This value is the smallest of the three types of means for the series, the others being

G.M. = 6.00
M = 6.33 (arithmetic mean or common average)

The harmonic mean is used but little by the average principal or classroom teacher. In educational research this measure of central tendency may serve the purpose of making comparable the results of two studies which employed unlike techniques of measurement.

For example, if a teacher of typing has kept a record of her students' scores in terms of number of seconds (time) required to write each word (average for each student for a period of one minute as 1.78, 1.92, 2.12, etc.), and later discovers an extensive tabulation of typing records in terms of number of words (rate) per minute, she will be able, by use of the harmonic mean, to make conversions that will bring the two records into direct comparison. The constant here is sixty seconds, and the relationship may be expressed by

$$M_t = 60 \frac{1}{\text{H. M.}_r} \tag{7a}$$

$$\text{or } M_r = 60 \frac{1}{\text{H. M.}_t} \tag{7b}$$

By computing the harmonic mean of her records, and substituting the value in Formula (7b), she can solve for M_r, which will be the arithmetic mean for the data she would have if she had recorded it on the rate basis. This mean for her class will then be comparable with the mean of the more extensive data.

Utility of Measures of Central Tendency.—In making a choice of central tendency, one should be governed by the nature of the data being treated, the purpose of finding the central tendency, the ease of computation, and, if a report is to be made in terms of an average, the interpreting ability of those who are to receive the report. In discussing the methods of computing the various types of central tendency, the writers have tried to place each in a setting which is illustrative of its particular usefulness. This statement should not be taken to mean that there is always one and only one central tendency which may be applied properly to a given situation. It is true that the uses of the geometrical mean and the harmonic mean are fairly clearly prescribed in educational statistics. These uses have already been discussed. The mid-measure, the mode, the median, the common average, the mean, the inter-quartile mean, and the normal zone generally have two important uses—to provide a basic point of reference for individual measures of a distribution and to afford means of comparing one distribution with another. Such characteristics of the data as extensiveness, homogeneity, need for permanency, availability of additional measures, and so on are factors to be considered in deciding on the type of central tendency to be used. When the teacher has only a few measures, say a class of fifteen to twenty-five, and his need for a central tendency is merely immediate internal comparison of individuals within the group, the mid-measure should be satisfactory. If he contemplates retaining the data, and expects to accumulate more data of similar nature to be combined into a larger report, he should find the mean.

When data necessarily contains extreme measures, the median furnishes a more practicable point of reference for individual measures or for another distribution. In classifying data for statistical treatment, one should, so far as possible, keep the data in homogeneous groups. Then the mean should be found in order to utilize its many advantages, such as algebraic rigidity, low sampling fluctuations, and simplicity. For example, in a study such as salaries in the education profession, it would be better, perhaps, to make several separate tabulations to preserve homogeneity in each. Instead of throwing all salaries into one table, separate tabulations should be made possibly for teachers of the following classifications: elementary, junior high school, senior high school, principals, superintendents, college professors, and college administrators.

The treatment of heterogeneous data as a unit cannot always be avoided. The world demands to know the central tendency of wealth of its citizens, the central tendency of incomes, and so on. When such information must be given it should be given in such form as to insure the sanest interpretation possible. For heterogeneous data the median, in many cases, is better than the mean for a sane interpretation.

Exercises and Problems

1. Rearrange the series of scores below and determine the mid-score:

37, 34, 31, 43, 40, 28, 41, 23, 31, 34, 21, 26, 28, 25.

2. (a) What are the modes in the distribution of test scores shown below:

Scores	f
55–59	4
50–54	7
45–49	14
40–44	10
35–39	11
30–34	10
25–29	14
20–24	8
15–19	5

(b) Execute one smoothing process and note the changes in mode, if any, which result.

(c) Execute a second smoothing process.

3. Find the median height of the thirty-four boys of Table XIX by starting at the top of the scale and descending to the median.

4. Find the median of the fifty-four test scores of Table XX by ascending the scale.

5. Find the median income of the heads of the twenty-six families of Table XXI by descending the scale.

6. Integral scores on a test of knowledge of health rules are tabulated below. Find the median.

Scale of Scores	f
75–99	2
50–74	2
40–49	5
30–39	8
25–29	7
20–24	5
15–19	4
10–14	3
	36

7. A Challenge: Try to find the mean of the distribution of Exercise 6. No liberties should be taken with the table—do not combine intervals.

8. The table below is a distribution of ages recorded on September 1, according to ages on last birthday.

(a) Find the median of true ages on September 1.

Ages	f
14	3
13	6
12	9
11	12
10	8
9	5
8	2
	45

(b) Also find the median of true ages on March 1 of the following year.

9. A Challenge: See if you can find the median of the measures tabulated below. All measures are integers.

Scale of Measures	f
20 and up	20
15–19	8
10–14	5
5–9	4
	37

10. In predicting future school enrollment of a city it is desired to find a composite ratio from a number of ratios of the city's growth and development over a period of twenty years. For this purpose it is thought best to reject erratic or unstable ratios. From the data below find the proper composite ratio—the inter-quartile mean (use common average) : Building permits 1.13, U. S. Post Office receipts 1.18, telephones 1.32, gas meters, 1.76, electric meters 1.26, automobile registrations 1.88, bank deposits 1.38, population 1.31.

11. In a state-wide, achievement-testing program, scores of 55 to 63 inclusive were established as the normal or at-grade zone for the seventh grade at the end of the school year. Twenty-four per cent of the seventh-grade pupils of the state were above this zone, 52% were in the zone, and 24% were below it. Using the data given below for School A, make a chart comparing School A with state-wide results.

	State-Wide Percentages	School A	
		No.	%
Total	100	84	
64 and up	24	16	
55–63	52	37	
54 and below	24	31	

12. (Omit if you are unfamiliar with the use of logarithms.) Over a period of ten years the annual ratios of increases in total enrollment of a school system were:

$$1.05, \ 1.04, \ 1.04, \ 1.03, \ 1.02, \ 1.02, \ 1.01, \ 1.02, \ 1.02, \ 1.03.$$

(a) Compute the geometrical mean of this series.

(b) Assuming that this index will remain constant, predict the enrollment for the school year ten years hence. (The enrollment for the last school year of the ten-year series was 3280.) The prediction for each of the next ten years may be made by starting with 3280, and multiplying ten successive times by the geometrical mean. If the enrollment for only the tenth year is to be predicted, it may be found by multiplying 3280 by the tenth power of the G. M.

Logarithms may be employed here to great advantage as follows:

$$3280 \times (G. \ M.)^{10}$$
$$\log 3280 =$$
$$10 \times \log (G. \ M.) = \underline{\hspace{4cm}}$$
$$\text{Sum} =$$

The antilogarithm of this sum will be the predicted enrollment for the tenth year.

13. The teacher of typing referred to in the discussion of harmonic mean has a class of ten students who, in a one-minute test, made the following record in average number of seconds per word written without error:

$$1.6, \ 1.9, \ 2.1, \ 1.9, \ 2.2, \ 2.5, \ 1.7, \ 1.5, \ 1.8, \ 1.8.$$

(a) Find the harmonic mean to two decimal places.

(b) Convert to an arithmetic mean for the class on basis of number of words per minute.

14. In Exercise 6 one of the five scores in interval 40–49 is 46.

(a) If this score had been 80, what effect would the change have produced on the median?

(b) Would changing the value of this score from 46 to 23 affect the median?

(c) Will either of these changes affect the mean? Make a general statement concerning the effect on the median produced by changing the value of a measure.

CHAPTER 4

PERCENTILES

In previous chapters the importance of central tendency as a point of reference for individual measures has been referred to repeatedly. A measure of central tendency helps to give meaning to a raw measure or to a single score. For example, if a child presents a report to his mother that he took a test in arithmetic and made a score of 48, the mother has no means of interpreting the score. She does not know whether the score is good, bad, or indifferent. Now if the child also supplies his mother with the mean, the median, or some other central measure for the class, the score of 48 takes on meaning to a certain degree. Let us say the median, 36.76, for the class was supplied the mother. She now knows at least that her child's score was among the upper 50%. The value 36.76 is the point on the scale below which 50% of the scores lie. For this reason it may be called the fiftieth percentile. Of course, the fiftieth percentile and the median are one and the same.

The Quartiles.—The twenty-fifth percentile and the seventy-fifth percentile (sometimes designated Q_1 and Q_3 respectively) are, statistically speaking, two very important points on a scale. Q_1 is the point below which 25% of the measures lie, and Q_3 is the point below which 75% of the cases lie.

In the case of the child's report, let us suppose the teacher provides the following information:

Child's score...48
Q_3 (the seventy-fifth percentile) for the class...........46.76
Md. (the fiftieth percentile) for the class................36.76
Q_1 (the twenty-fifth percentile) for the class...........26.76

The mother's opportunity to interpret her child's score of 48 is now considerably improved. She is definitely informed that the score is among the upper 25%.

The median or fiftieth percentile separates the lower half of the class from the upper half; the seventy-fifth percentile, the median, and the twenty-fifth percentile together give three points on the scale of scores which separate the scores into four groups, with one fourth of the class in each. Now suppose the

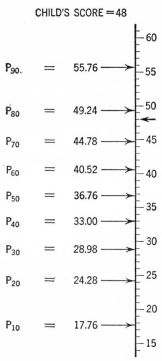

CHILD'S SCORE = 48

P_{90}.	=	55.76 →
P_{80}	=	49.24 →
P_{70}	=	44.78 →
P_{60}	=	40.52 →
P_{50}	=	36.76 →
P_{40}	=	33.00 →
P_{30}	=	28.98 →
P_{20}	=	24.28 →
P_{10}	=	17.76 →

Figure 10. Decile Points
NOTE: P_{90} should be read the ninetieth percentile.

analysis of the scores of the class is carried forward another step by using ten instead of twenty-five as the percentage of scores between the points of reference. This procedure determines the deciles. Their values, together with the child's score furnished the mother, are shown in Figure 10.

The mother is now in a position to make a fairly accurate interpretation of her child's score. It stands between P_{70} and

P_{80}. In other words, it is in the third group from the top when the whole class is divided into ten equal groups.

It is clear that this process of analysis could be carried to any degree of fineness desired. Ninety-nine points on the scale— one for each whole percentile—could be given, such as

$$P_{99} = 71.25$$
$$P_{98} = 67.21$$
$$P_{97} = 64.65$$
$$P_{96} = 62.72$$
$$\ldots \quad \ldots\ldots$$
$$\ldots \quad \ldots\ldots$$
$$\ldots \quad \ldots\ldots$$
$$P_{78} = 48.21$$
$$P_{77} = 47.71$$
$$\ldots \quad \ldots\ldots$$
$$\ldots \quad \ldots\ldots$$

From this analysis, the score of 48 is identified as belonging between P_{78} and P_{77}. Approximately 77% of the class made lower scores than the child in question.

Definition of Percentiles.—At this point in the discussion, no one should experience any difficulty in formulating a definition for percentile. A percentile is a point on the scale of a distribution of measures below which a given percentage of the measures lie. For example, the fiftieth percentile is the point on the scale below which 50% of the measures lie; the thirty-seventh percentile is the point on the scale below which 37% of the measures lie, and so on. (Technically, this definition requires only the lower half of an individual score's space on the scale of scores to lie below the point of its percentile equivalent.) It should be noted carefully here that a percentile is a *point* on the scale and not a percentage. It is *the point* below which a given percentage of measures lie.

Computation of Percentiles.—To anyone who has mastered the computation of the median, the computation of percentiles will be easy. The median is the fiftieth percentile. Its computation is begun by taking 50% of the N, and is continued by proceeding up the scale until a point is reached below which that number of measures lie. To find the thirty-seventh percentile, the computation is begun by taking 37% of N, and is continued by using exactly the same steps as those employed for computing the median.

TABLE XXII. COMPUTATION OF DECILE POINTS ON A SCALE OF MENTAL-ABILITY SCORES

Scale of Scores	f	Cum. f
69–71	1	400
66–68	2	399
63–65	9	397
60–62	15	388
57–59	12	373
54–56	31	361
51–53	37	330
48–50	34	293
45–47	36	259
42–44	63	223
39–41	48	160
36–38	34	112
33–35	31	78
30–32	29	47
27–29	9	18
24–26	6	9
21–23		3
18–20	1	3
15–17	2	2
	400	

It is possible that for some special purpose only one percentile on a scale is desired, in which case a cumulative frequency column need not be made. However, when a series of percentiles on the scale of a distribution is to be found, time will be saved by expressing the cumulative frequencies as explained in a previous chapter. While the cumulative frequency column is not essential here, its use will avoid the necessity of repeatedly totaling the same portions of the frequency column.

Table VIII of Chapter 1, which is here repeated, is a distribution of scores made by four hundred high school seniors on a mental-ability test. In order to acquaint these seniors with their relative performances on the test, each of them is to be supplied with his own raw score, and the deciles for the whole distribution are to be published on a bulletin board. For purposes of reporting to the students, deciles will afford a sufficiently accurate interpretation. See Table XXII.

The following steps must now be taken to find the deciles:

$$10\% \text{ of } 400 = 40$$
$$P_{10} = 29.50 + \frac{40 - 18}{29} \times 3 \quad \text{or } 31.78$$

$$20\% \text{ of } 400 = 80$$
$$P_{20} = 35.50 + \frac{80 - 78}{34} \times 3 \quad \text{or } 35.68$$

$$30\% \text{ of } 400 = 120$$
$$P_{30} = 38.50 + \frac{120 - 112}{48} \times 3 \quad \text{or } 39.00$$

$$40\% \text{ of } 400 = 160$$
$$P_{40} = 41.50 + \frac{160 - 160}{63} \times 3 \quad \text{or } 41.50$$

$$50\% \text{ of } 400 = 200$$
$$P_{50} = 41.50 + \frac{200 - 160}{63} \times 3 \quad \text{or } 43.41$$

$$60\% \text{ of } 400 = 240$$
$$P_{60} = 44.50 + \frac{240 - 223}{36} \times 3 \quad \text{or } 45.92$$

$$70\% \text{ of } 400 = 280$$
$$P_{70} = 47.50 + \frac{280 - 259}{34} \times 3 \quad \text{or } 49.35$$

$$80\% \text{ of } 400 = 320$$
$$P_{80} = 50.50 + \frac{320 - 293}{37} \times 3 \quad \text{or } 52.69$$

$$90\% \text{ of } 400 = 360$$
$$P_{90} = 53.50 + \frac{360 - 330}{31} \times 3 \quad \text{or } 56.40$$

The deciles may now be assembled into a more compact form for posting on the bulletin board as shown on page 71.

These results may be read as follows. 90% of all scores were below 56.40; 80% of all scores were below 52.69; and so on.

If code numbers were used instead of names at the time of the examination, individual scores may be reported by publica-

Deciles on the Scale of Mental Ability Scores

$$P_{90} = 56.40$$
$$P_{80} = 52.69$$
$$P_{70} = 49.35$$
$$P_{60} = 45.92$$
$$P_{50} = 43.41$$
$$P_{40} = 41.50$$
$$P_{30} = 39.00$$
$$P_{20} = 35.68$$
$$P_{10} = 31.78$$

tion of the list on the bulletin board. Each student needs only his own score and the deciles to make an intelligent interpretation of his outcome on the examination.

The Percentage of Measures Below a Given Point on the Scale.—In previous computations we have had given a percentage of measures or scores below a certain point on a scale and have wished to find the point. The reverse of this problem is to have given a point on the scale and to wish to find the percentage of measures or scores below it. For example, in Table XXII, let us take the point 52.3 on the scale of scores and find the percentage of scores below it. We must first find the *number* of scores below the point in question. From the cumulative frequency column we see that below the point 50.5 there are 293 scores. The point 52.3 lies $^{18}/_{30}$ of an interval above 50.5,

$$\left(\frac{52.3 - 50.5}{3} = \frac{1.8}{3} \text{ or } \frac{18}{30} \right)$$

If we assume that the thirty-seven scores in interval 51–53 are evenly spaced from 50.5 to 53.5, then $^{18}/_{30}$ of them or 22.2 will lie below the point 52.3. Thus we have a total of 315.2 scores (293 + 22.2), or 78.8% of the total below the point 52.3.

The Percentile Graph.—A principal or a teacher will seldom have occasion to find the percentage of measures lying below a specific point on a scale when that point is any other than either the midpoint of an interval or the top point of an interval. The determination of a series of such percentages is necessary to the construction of a percentile graph from which any percentile score may be read.

For illustration, let us again take the data of Table VIII and observe how easy it is to find the percentages of scores lying below the top points of the successive intervals.

TABLE XXIII. CONVERSION OF CUMULATIVE FREQUENCIES TO PERCENTAGES

Scale of Scores	f	Cum. f	Cum.* % f
69–71	1	400	100.00
66–68	2	399	99.75
63–65	9	397	99.25
60–62	15	388	97.00
57–59	12	373	93.25
54–56	31	361	90.25
51–53	37	330	82.50
48–50	34	293	73.25
45–47	36	259	64.75
42–44	63	223	55.75
39–41	48	160	40.00
36–38	34	112	28.00
33–35	31	78	19.50
30–32	29	47	11.75
27–29	9	18	4.50
24–26	6	9	2.25
21–23		3	.75
18–20	1	3	.75
15–17	2	2	.50

400

* 100% of the scores lie below the top of interval 69–71 (71.5); 99.75% of them lie below the top of interval 66–68 (68.5); and so on.

By using for the axes of a graph the two variables, scale of scores and cumulative percentage frequencies, it is now possible to construct a percentile graph by drawing a smooth curve through the twenty points (nineteen plus the starting point) which have been located. Before beginning the construction of the graph, the coordinates of the points should be assembled as shown on the following page.

Large cross-section paper should be used for making the graph. The paper should provide at least one hundred spaces (two hundred are better) on the percentile axis and at least

Scale of Scores	Cum. % f
71.5	100.00
68.5	99.75
65.5	99.25
62.5	97.00
59.5	93.25
56.5	90.25
53.5	82.50
50.5	73.25
47.5	64.75
44.5	55.75
41.5	40.00
38.5	28.00
35.5	19.50
32.5	11.75
29.5	4.50
26.5	2.25
23.5	.75
20.5	.75
17.5	.50
14.5	.00

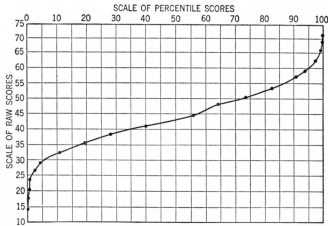

Figure 11. Percentile Graph for Converting Raw Scores to Percentile Scores

sixty spaces (one hundred and twenty are better for this case) on the raw score axis. Space on this page forbids the use of such a large graph, but the method of constructing the graph is shown in Figure 11.

By use of this graph, it is now possible to convert any raw score to its percentile equivalent. Careful draftsmanship on a larger sheet of graphic paper will make it possible to convert any raw score to the nearest whole percentile score. For the use of the principal or the teacher, accuracy to whole or integral percentile scores is usually sufficient.

In dealing with as many as four hundred scores, each of which is to be converted to a percentile score, much time will be saved by using the graph to make a scale of percentile equivalents for the entire scale of raw scores. In this way repeated tracing of the same score on the graph will be avoided.

From a graph larger than the one shown in Figure 11, the percentile equivalents of the raw scores were found to be as follows:

Raw Scores	Percentile Score Equivalents
67–71	100*
65–66	99
64	98
63	97
62	96
61	95
60	94
59	93
58	92
..	..
..	..

* A percentile score of 100 is technically impossible under the implications of the definition. The raw scores of 67 to 71 are assigned the percentile score of 100 here merely because more than 95.5% of the scores are lower than 67. It was decided earlier to express these percentile scores to the nearest whole number.

To be sure, the graph may be used to convert percentile scores of the distribution to raw scores, although the reverse process is usually the one desired. To say that a child's percentile score is 92, means that 92% of the scores were lower than his score.

A percentile score therefore is self-identified. It needs no accompanying statement of medians, quartiles, or other percentiles to locate it. In making a permanent record of a child's score, the percentile score would serve the purpose much better than the raw score. A few years after the record is made a raw score of 58 seen on a record card probably would be meaningless, but a percentile score of 92 would be very significant.

The graph of Figure 11 could have been made by finding the percentages of frequencies below the midpoints of the various intervals. To find the percentages would require first the cumulative frequencies to midpoints of intervals. The scale of raw scores and the scale of percentile scores would be the same here as in Figure 11, but the set of points located would be different. This set of points would be:

Scale of Scores	Cum.* % f
70	99.750
67	99.500
64	98.125
61	95.125
58	91.750
..	.....
..	.....
Etc.	Etc.

* Frequencies cumulative to midpoints of intervals.

and the smooth curve through them would coincide exactly with the curve shown in Figure 11. Either of these methods of making the curve is satisfactory, but use of both methods to increase the number of points is of no advantage, for a straight line from the bottom of an interval to its top will pass through the midpoint.[1]

Weaknesses of Percentile Measures.—The most serious weakness of the percentile score is its failure to indicate relative distance from the mean of a distribution. This weakness is

[1] Of course, if all the measures within an interval are to be assigned the same percentile value, that value should be determined by the percentage of measures below the midpoint of the interval.

While it is true that on a percentile graph the straight line from the bottom of an interval to its top will pass through the point representing its midpoint, it does not follow that the straight line between the midpoints of two adjacent intervals will pass through

largely overcome by the accumulation of a very large mass of data which is approximately normal in frequency and which leaves no gaps on the scale. To clarify this statement refer again to Table XXIII, and assume that the following changes are made in the data : each score of sixty or more is increased by exactly six points. These changes will cause two blank intervals to appear, but otherwise will have no effect on the table. The upper part of the table now appears as follows :

Scale of Scores	f	Cum. % f
75–77	1	100.00
72–74	2	99.75
69–71	9	99.25
66–68	15	97.00
63–65		93.25
60–62		93.25
57–59	12	93.25
54–56	31	90.25
. . . . .	. .	. . . . .
. . . . .	. .	. . . . .
. . . . .	. .	. . . . .

A raw score of 66 will now have exactly the same percentile value that a raw score of 60 formerly had. The fact that this score has been increased is not revealed by its percentile equivalent.

Notwithstanding this defect, the percentile score serves the purposes of making a permanent record of much school data in

the point which separates the two intervals. For that reason, slight absurdities may appear in a graph constructed as a series of straight lines between midpoints of intervals.

Figure 12. Portion of Percentile Scale Magnified for Analysis

To illustrate such absurdity, let us magnify a small portion of the percentile graph of Figure 11, which magnified portion will include intervals 51–53, 54–56, and 57–59.

In Figure 12 points A (59.5, 93.25), B (56.5, 90.25), and C (53.5, 82.50) represent the tops of intervals 57–59, 54–56, and 51–53, respectively. The percentile readings for these three points are exactly 93.25, 90.25, and 82.50, respectively. This statement cannot be questioned for the points are points of separation between intervals and no interpolation is required to read these percentages. However, points D (58, 91.75) and E (55, 86.375) which were located by use of cumulative percentage frequencies to midpoints of intervals 57–59 and 54–56 are interpolated on the percentile axis. The graph made on the midpoint basis will give us a reading of percentile 89 for a raw score of 56.5, whereas we *know* that the score of 56.5 has a percentile equivalent of 90.25.

a form which has greater usefulness than the raw score. Items on a child's personnel record card must be self-explanatory if they are to be of greatest value. To find recorded upon a child's card the fact that when in the sixth grade he made a score of 43 on a certain standardized achievement test would be of no value unless one took the trouble to look up the normal distribution of sixth-grade scores on that test. If this raw score of 43 had been converted to a percentile score, say 78, and recorded as a percentile score, the examiner of the child's record sees at once the child's sixth-grade achievement level.

Percentile Rank.—Let us suppose that A was ranked 12 in a certain endeavor, and that B was ranked 12 in another endeavor. There is danger that we might be misled into assuming that A and B were equally proficient in their respective endeavors. Let us make further inquiry. The ensuing investigation brings out the facts that in A's endeavor there were thirteen individuals involved, while in B's endeavor there were more than seven thousand individuals involved. The significance of the rank 12 in A's case is quite different from the significance of it in B's case. Not until the numbers of cases involved were revealed, did the two ranks assume proper meaning.

In the statistics of education it is frequently necessary to compare an individual who has been ranked in one group with an individual who has been ranked in another group involving a number unequal to the first group. Also it often becomes necessary to find average rankings of individuals who were ranked in two or more different groups. Absolute rank cannot be used for such purpose unless, of course, the N's are constant for the groups. The difficulties suggested here may be overcome by use of percentile rank.

Percentile rank provides a plan for equally distributing the ranking positions upon a scale one hundred units in length. For example, if there are twenty measures to be ranked, the space from 95 to 100 on the scale is reserved for rank 1, and the midpoint of this space (97.5) is the point position (percentile rank) of rank 1. The space for rank 2 will be from 90 to 95, the midpoint of which is 92.5 (the percentile rank for rank 2).

These processes may readily be generalized into the expression

$$P.R. = 100 - \left[\frac{\frac{100}{N}}{2} + \frac{100\,(R-1)}{N} \right]$$

which in turn may be simplified into the formula

$$P.R. = \frac{100\,(N-R)+50}{N} \qquad (8)$$

To confirm the percentile rank of 92.5 found above for rank 2 let us substitute in Formula (8). Here $N = 20$ and $R = 2$.

$$\begin{aligned} P.R. &= \frac{100\,(20-2)+50}{20} \\ &= \frac{1850}{20} \\ &= 92.5 \end{aligned}$$

Again using the formula to find the percentile rank for rank 12.5 in a distribution of twenty measures

$$\begin{aligned} P.R. &= \frac{100\,(20-12\frac{1}{2})+50}{20} \\ &= \frac{800}{20} \\ &= 40 \end{aligned}$$

Application of the Graph to Percentile Rank.—Although the formula may be used for all of the measures of a distribution, it is useful chiefly for making a graph for converting absolute ranks to percentile ranks. The nature of Formula (8) indicates that the line connecting the points will be a straight line, so it will be necessary to locate only two points to construct the graph. In this case let us use the formula to find the percentile ranks for rank 1 and for rank 20. These points are

Absolute Rank	Percentile Rank
1	97.5
20	2.5

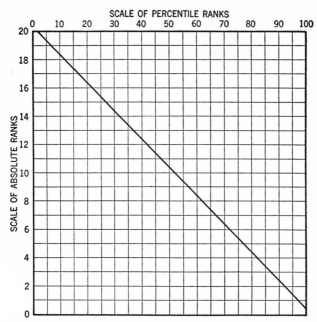

Figure 13. Conversion of Absolute Ranks to Percentile Ranks

TABLE XXIV. PERCENTILE RANKS OF SCORES ON A VOCABULARY TEST

Scores	Rank	Percentile Rank
35	5	77.5
31	8	62.5
42	1	97.5
20	17.5	15.0
24	14	32.5
31	8	62.5
40	2.5	90.0
27	11	47.5
20	17.5	15.0
36	4	82.5
40	2.5	90.0
28	10	52.5
20	17.5	15.0
26	12.5	40.0
14	20	2.5
31	8	62.5
23	15	27.5
33	6	72.5

and a straight line drawn through them (Figure 13) makes the necessary graph which may be used for converting any absolute rank of the twenty measures to an equivalent percentile rank.

The complete set of measures, the ranks, and the percentile ranks of Figure 13 are shown in Table XXIV.

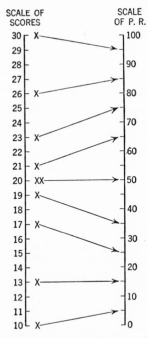

Figure 14.   Space Distortions Resulting from Percentile Ranking

NOTE: The ten scores for which percentile ranks were found are indicated by x's on the scale of scores.

For accurate determination of percentile ranks, graphic paper should be used which will provide at least one hundred units of space on the percentile-rank scale.

The percentile graph of Figure 11 was a curve, while the graph of Figure 13 is a straight line. This difference reflects a serious objection to percentile rank. The objection is the same as that registered previously against ranking, since it arbitrarily equalizes the spaces between measures.   In a normal distribution there is a tendency for measures to be spaced close together in the vicinity of the mean, with a gradual lengthening of space between measures nearer the extremes. Figure 14 shows the distortion of space produced by percentile ranking.

In spite of these defects the percentile rank is often highly useful, if not indispensable, in statistical work.

Exercises and Problems

1. Define percentile.

2. Can you indicate the importance or relative value of a raw score of 63?

3. When informed that the group of scores to which the score of 63 belongs has a Q_3 of 82, an Md. of 66, and a Q_1 of 51, are you able to interpret the score of 63? State your interpretation.

4. From the distribution of social studies test scores (all scores are integers) given below, determine the following points on the scale of scores:
(a) Q_3, the Md., Q_1, and $P_{12.5}$.
(b) The deciles.

Scale of Scores	f
90–94	2
85–89	3
80–84	3
75–79	4
70–74	2
65–69	3
60–64	6
55–59	8
50–54	9
45–49	8
40–44	10
35–39	9
30–34	7
25–29	3
20–24	3
15–19	2
	82

5. In the distribution of test scores given in Exercise 4, what percentages of scores lie below the following points on the scale? (a) 39.5; (b) 42; (c) 41.5; (d) 55.75.

6. The table below is a report of scores made on a general achievement test by the sixth grade of a small city school system. Make a graph for converting raw scores to percentile scores for the pupils' permanent records. Indicate for each raw score from 30 to 79 its percentile equivalent expressed to the nearest whole percentile.

Scores	f
75–79	6
70–74	14
65–69	23
60–64	47
55–59	50
50–54	78
45–49	52
40–44	36
35–39	24
30–34	10

7. If A was ranked 4.5 in a contest of nine contestants, and if B was ranked 6.5 in a contest of fourteen contestants, which made the better showing? To answer this question it is necessary to find the percentile ranks for A and for B.

8. By use of a percentile graph, convert the following absolute ranks into percentile ranks.

Absolute Rank	P.R.
5	
8	
1.5	
9	
5	
7	
1.5	
5	
12	
3	
10.5	
10.5	

9. Two vocal-music contestants, A and B, entered three different contests. In the first contest there were forty-two contestants, in the second seventeen, and in the third twenty-two. A's rankings on the three contests were 11, 7.5, and 5, while B's were 17.5, 6, and 8.5. Find the average percentile rank for A and for B. Which made the better showing? Here it is unnecessary to make percentile graphs. The formula should be used to find the percentile rank for each of the six absolute ranks. Some such systematic arrangement as the following will help to make the problem clear:

		Contestants			
		A		B	
Contests	N	Ab. rank	%ile rank	Ab. rank	%ile rank
1st	42	11		17.5	
2nd	17	7.5		6	
3rd	22	5		8.5	
Total P.R.					
Average P.R.					

CHAPTER 5

MEASURES OF VARIABILITY

If a statement is made that the mean achievement score of Miss Smith's pupils is the same as the mean achievement score of Miss Jones' pupils, one might be misled into assuming greater similarity of the two groups of pupils than is justified by the statement. The only fact given is that the means are equal. The two groups may be quite dissimilar in other respects. It is possible that scores 35, 36, and 37 only were made by Miss Smith's pupils while scores of 33, 34, 35, 36, 37, 38, and 39 were made by Miss Jones' pupils. Under these circumstances the means of the two groups may be exactly the same, but the variability of Miss Jones' pupils is greater than the variability of Miss Smith's pupils.

Variability refers to the amount of dispersion. If individuals of the group tend to cluster closely to the central tendency, the variability is small; if they scatter widely from the central tendency, the variability is large. To be useful statistically, however, the variable characteristic of data must be expressible in terms of a single measure. This measure is never a point on the scale, but is a distance (linear unit) on the scale.

Fundamentally, the three important uses of a measure of variability are (1) to help describe a group of data, (2) to furnish a unit of measurement for measuring the distance from the central tendency to any individual score or point on the scale of scores, and (3) to furnish a unit of measurement for measuring the distance between any two scores or points on the scale of scores.

Respecting the second and third uses mentioned, emphasis needs to be given to the fact that a measure of variability is a linear unit. Even though the unit may be found as a distance between two specific points on a scale, it must not be thought of as being required to remain in that position. It, having once been determined, becomes a measure like a foot, a yard, or a rod, and can be applied to measure distances between any two points on the scale.

The Range.—Absolute range refers to the full length of the scale required to record the data. For Miss Smith's pupils this measure of variability is three (the distance from 34.5 to 37.5), and for Miss Jones' pupils it is seven. The fact that only two measures, the highest and the lowest, fix the range of a distribution of measures renders it of little or no use in educational statistics. In the field of meteorology in which temperatures are dealt with, in the field of industry in which prices are dealt with, and in fields of similar character, range is often of considerable importance.

In chance sampling, the absolute range is subject to greater fluctuations than any other measure of variability. This fact would indicate that it defines poorly the characteristic it purports to define.

Range Between Paired Percentiles.—In a manner similar to that used in finding absolute range, the range between any two percentiles may be found. While it is true that the mere naming of a series of percentiles indicates characteristics of variability, quintiles, deciles, or other percentiles should never be referred to as measures of variability. Such percentiles are points on the scale, whereas variability must be expressed as a distance on the scale. Various measures of variability may be determined by finding the distance between certain pairs of percentiles. For example, in the preceding chapter the decile points on the scale of mental-ability scores were found to be as follows:

$$P_{90} = 56.40$$
$$P_{80} = 52.69$$
$$P_{70} = 49.35$$
$$P_{60} = 45.92$$
$$P_{50} = 43.41$$
$$P_{40} = 41.50$$
$$P_{30} = 39.00$$
$$P_{20} = 35.68$$
$$P_{10} = 31.78$$

Now the distance between P_{90} and its converse companion, P_{10}, $(56.40 - 31.78 = 24.62)$ is a measure of variability. Likewise, the distance between P_{80} and P_{20} (17.01), or the distance between P_{70} and P_{30} (10.35), is a measure of variability. The distance between P_{67} and P_{33} is also a measure of variability. The use of any of these distances as a measure of variability would be better, for most purposes, than the use of the absolute range.

Quartile Deviation.—It is obvious from the preceding paragraph that many different measures of variability could be determined from a given distribution of data. This fact would suggest a need for a common practice. In this connection, the distance from P_{75} to P_{25} has several advantages as a measure of variability. These two points are uninfluenced by the upper 25% of the measures and the lower 25% of the measures—sections of the scale where the measures are most likely to be more widely spaced and therefore subject to greater chance fluctuations. At the same time P_{75} and P_{25} are wide enough apart to provide a substantial value for a measure of variability. For certain practical reasons one half this distance between the quartiles has been adopted as the measure of variability most commonly found when dealing with percentiles. This measure is called the *quartile deviation* or the *semi-interquartile range* (half the range between the quartiles), and it may be found by the formula

$$Q = \frac{Q_3 - Q_1}{2} \tag{9}$$

On the scale of the four hundred mental-ability scores of the preceding chapter the Q_3 or P_{75} is 51.07, and the Q_1 or P_{25} is 37.44. By substituting these values in Formula (9) we have

$$Q = \frac{51.07 - 37.44}{2} \quad \text{or } 6.82$$

The two important uses of this quartile deviation are easily seen. In the first place, the length 6.82 helps describe the entire distribution by informing us that a zone extending 6.82 score units above and below the median will include approximately 50% of all the scores (exactly 50% if the distribution is normal in form). In the second place, the length 6.82 becomes a linear unit with which we may measure the distance between any two points on the scale. For example, if we wish to know in terms of this important unit the position of a score of 62 on the scale, the position here will be measured from the median, 43.41. The distance in scale units from 43.41 to 62 is 18.59 which, divided by 6.82, gives 2.73 Q's. (A score of 2.73 Q's below the median will be written −2.73 Q's.)

Since the full length of a scale of normally distributed measures is usually about 8 or 9 Q's, a statement of the number of Q's of difference between any two scores is more meaningful than a statement of actual difference between the raw scores. For example, a score of 58 may be described as being 1.61 Q's above a score of 47, for the 11 scale units of difference make 1.61 Q's.

Average Deviation.—Average or mean deviation is exactly what the expression implies—the average or mean of the deviations of the measures from their central tendency. The expressions average deviation (A.D.) and mean deviation (M.D.) are both used for the same purpose in the literature of statistics. They refer to the same measure of variability.

In dealing with average deviation, the sum of all the deviations is found without regard to sign. It is the average of all the deviations that we are seeking, and a minus deviation is just as much a deviation as a plus one. Keeping in mind this neglect of signs, then, the fundamental formula becomes

$$\text{A.D. (or M.D.)} = \frac{\Sigma x}{N} \tag{10a}$$

The use of this formula may be illustrated by the following simple series of measures the mean of which is 15:

$$X: 7, 9, 12, 13, 15, 17, 18, 21, 23$$
$$x: 8, 6, \ \ 3, \ \ 2, \ \ 0, \ \ 2, \ \ 3, \ \ 6, \ \ 8$$
$$\Sigma x = 38 \text{ and } N = 9$$
$$\text{A.D.} = \frac{38}{9} \ \text{ or } 4.22$$

The average of the deviations is 4.22.

Of course the average deviation may be taken from the median, or from any other central tendency which may be expressed as a *point* on the scale of measures. The mean, however, is by far the most frequently used.

The fundamental formula as stated above is seldom convenient to use for the reason that the mean of a series is seldom a convenient integer. The series above, with a mean of 15, was specially provided for use of illustration. Data encountered in its natural setting is more likely to have a mean involving decimals, such as 14.73 or 15.27. Each deviation in such cases will have two decimal places. While the fundamental formula can be used in any situation, it is generally better to modify it to permit the use of a convenient integral assumed mean, with proper compensation for the error thus introduced.

In the series below, both forms of the formula are applied to find the average deviation:

$$X: \quad 12, \quad 9, 10, \quad 8, 11, 10, 11, \quad 9, 11, 10$$
$$x: \quad 1.9, 1.1, \quad .1, 2.1, \quad .9, \quad .1, \quad .9, 1.1, \quad .9, \quad .1$$

(True mean = 10.1)

$$\text{A.D.} = \frac{\Sigma x}{N} \quad \text{or} \quad \frac{9.2}{10} \quad \text{or .92}$$

To avoid the inconvenience of taking the deviations from the true mean, we may take the deviations from an assumed mean, say, of 10. Now for every measure which lies above the true mean (four of them here), we shall be taking a deviation too large. For every measure below the true mean (six of them here), we shall be taking a deviation too small. The amount of error in each deviation is exactly the value of the true mean (10.1) minus the assumed mean (10.0), which is also referred to as the correction factor, c (+.1 in this case). Since the error in the deviation of a measure above the mean will offset the error in a deviation of a measure below the mean, we need be concerned only with the difference (if any) between the number of measures below the mean and the number above. Designate these numbers as N_b and N_a respectively. The formula then becomes

$$\text{A.D.} = \frac{\Sigma x' + c(N_b - N_a)}{N} \tag{10b}$$

which may be applied to the series above.

$$\text{X}: 12, 9, 10, 8, 11, 10, 11, 9, 11, 10$$
$$x': \ \ 2, 1, \ \ 0, 2, \ \ 1, \ \ 0, \ \ 1, 1, \ \ 1, \ \ 0$$

$$\text{Tr.M.} = 10.1$$
$$\text{A.M.} = \underline{10.0}$$
$$c = \overline{+.1}$$
$$N_a = 4$$
$$N_b = 6$$

$$\text{A.D.} = \frac{9 + .1\,(6-4)}{10} \ \text{ or } \ \frac{9.2}{10} \ \text{ or } .92$$

The difference between the true mean and the assumed mean must be found by subtracting the assumed mean from the true mean, and this difference must be treated algebraically.

Formula (10b), when written in the symbols commonly used with tabulated data, becomes

$$\text{A.D.} = \frac{h\,\Sigma fd \ (\text{non alg}) + c(N_b - N_a)}{N} \tag{10c}$$

or if it is desired to avoid the necessity of actually finding the true mean it may be written

$$\text{A.D.} = h \cdot \frac{\Sigma fd \ (\text{non alg}) + \dfrac{\Sigma fd \ (\text{alg})}{N}(N_b - N_a)}{N} \tag{10d}$$

Note: Herein h is the height or width of intervals, Σfd (non alg) means the sum of the fd's without regard to signs and Σfd (alg) means the algebraic sum of the fd's. In using this formula the true mean may be found and used to determine the number of measures above and below it. However, N_a and N_b may be determined by inspection without actually finding the true mean. For greatest convenience in determining N_a and N_b by inspection, the assumed mean should be taken at the midpoint of the interval in which the true mean lies. This leaves the measures of only one interval in doubt as to whether they go above or below the mean. The sign of the sum of the fd's will indicate the position of the true mean with respect to the midpoint of the interval in question, and will thus permit an inspectional placement of the measures in that interval.

The series of ten measures with which we have just been dealing, when tabulated, takes the form of

Scale	f	d	fd
12	1	+2	+2
11	3	+1	+3
10	3	0	
9	2	−1	−2
8	1	−2	−2
	10		

$$\Sigma fd \text{ (non alg)} = 9$$
$$\Sigma fd \text{ (alg)} \quad = +1$$
$$h \ = 1$$
$$N \ = 10$$
$$N_b = 6$$
$$N_a = 4$$

When the values computed from the table are substituted in Formula (10d), we get

$$\text{A.D.} = 1 \cdot \frac{9 + \dfrac{+1}{10}(6-4)}{10} \quad \text{or } .92$$

One additional comment should be made on the method of finding average deviation of data which have been tabulated. All of the measures of an interval must be interpreted as resting at the midpoint of the interval. Therefore, all of the measures in the critical interval must either go above the true mean or all must go below it. They must not be divided.

TABLE XXV. COMPUTATION OF AVERAGE DEVIATION

Scores	f	d	fd
40–44	3	+2	6
35–39	7	+1	7
30–34	10	0	
25–29	8	−1	−8
20–24	5	−2	−10
	33		

$$\Sigma fd \text{ (non alg)} = \ 31$$
$$\Sigma fd \text{ (alg)} \quad = -5$$
$$h \ = \ 5$$
$$N \ = \ 33$$
$$N_a = \ 20$$
$$N_b = \ 13$$

Let us take an example to illustrate the most common method of finding average deviation. Formula (10d) will be used. The scores in Table XXV are scores on an English test made by thirty-three high school students on an objective teacher-made test. All scores are integers.

The fact that the algebraic sum of the fd's is -5 tells us that the true mean is lower than the assumed mean, and therefore that the ten measures which rest at the midpoint of interval 30–34 (our assumed mean) must all go with the seven and three to be counted above the true mean.

$$\text{A.D.} = 5 \times \frac{31 + \frac{-5}{33}(13 - 20)}{33}$$

$$= 5 \times \frac{31 - .1515\,(-7)}{33}$$

$$= 5 \times \frac{32.0605}{33} \quad \text{or } 4.86$$

The use of average deviation in the study of educational problems is diminishing. Its use is now largely confined to expressing the variability of short series, or of series which do not fall into the normal frequency distribution.

In spite of the simplicity of the idea of average deviation, its computation from tabulated forms of data presents some complications. No doubt this is one reason for its lack of popularity. Among other reasons for failure of average deviation to receive general acceptance as a measure of variability is the fact that, in a normal distribution, the percentage of measures which lie within a distance of one A.D. of the mean fails to be an easily remembered value (57.51%). The percentage of measures within a distance of one Q of the mean (50%) is much simpler to apply and much easier to remember. On the other hand, the average deviation has an advantage over the quartile deviation for some requirements in that it is influenced by all the measures of the distribution.

The A.D., like the Q, is a unit of linear measure on the scale of a distribution.

Standard Deviation.—Of the various measures of variability, standard deviation is by far the most useful. Standard deviation, or S.D., may be defined here as the square root of the average of the squares of the deviations of the measures from the mean. (In computing S.D. the deviations are never taken from the Md., nor from any other central tendency except the mean.) In a normal frequency curve, this value can be shown to equal the distance from the Y_0 ordinate to the second turning point in the curve (the first turning point being where the curve crosses the Y axis). The proof is by use of the second derivative of the equation of the normal frequency curve. Such proofs are beyond the scope of this book, but for those who have had a little calculus and who have an interest in such proofs, the equation of the normal frequency curve is presented in a subsequent chapter which deals with the normal frequency curve.

Lower-case sigma (σ) is used to designate standard deviation quite as frequently as S.D. is used for that purpose.

In converting the above definition of S.D. into a fundamental formula we have

$$\text{S.D. (or } \sigma) = \sqrt{\frac{\Sigma x^2}{N}} \tag{11a}$$

We shall now apply this formula to a simple series which has an integral mean of 10:

$$
\begin{aligned}
&X: 13, \ 11, \ 10, \quad 9, \quad 7 \\
&x: \quad 3, \quad 1, \quad 0, \ -1, \ -3 \\
&x^2: \quad 9, \quad 1, \quad 0, \quad 1, \quad 9
\end{aligned}
$$

$$\Sigma x = 0$$
$$\Sigma x^2 = 20$$

$$\text{S.D.} = \sqrt{\frac{20}{5}} \quad \text{or} \quad \sqrt{4}$$
$$= 2$$

By now it should not be necessary to repeat that data encountered in their natural setting are seldom found to be so accommodating in the matter of integral means. The fundamental formula given above holds good in all cases, however inconvenient it may be to apply. For example, let us find σ for the series for which we found the A.D. previously in this chapter:

X: 12,   9,   10,   8,   11,   10,   11,   9,   11,   10
x: +1.9, −1.1, −.1, −2.1, +.9, −.1, +.9, −1.1, +.9, −.1
x^2: 3.61, 1.21, .01, 4.41, .81, .01, .81, 1.21, .81, .01

$$(M = 10.1)$$
$$\Sigma\, x = 0$$
$$\Sigma\, x^2 = 12.90$$

$$\sigma = \sqrt{\frac{12.90}{10}} \quad \text{or} \quad \sqrt{1.29}$$
$$= 1.1358$$

When one performs all of the steps given above, one is easily convinced that there should be a method developed by which deviations may be taken from some convenient integral assumed mean. This has been done and algebraic proof may readily be given to show that

$$\sigma = \sqrt{\frac{\Sigma\,(x')^2}{N} - \left(\frac{\Sigma\,x'}{N}\right)^2} \tag{11b}$$

Note how much simpler the finding of the S.D. for the data becomes when the deviations are taken from an assumed mean, say 10.

X: 12,   9, 10,   8,   11, 10,   11,   9,   11, 10
x':   +2,   −1,   0,   −2,   +1,   0,   +1,   −1,   +1,   0
$(x')^2$:   4,   1,   0,   4,   1,   0,   1,   1,   1,   0

$$\Sigma\, x' = +1$$
$$\Sigma\,(x')^2 = 13$$

$$\text{S.D.} = \sqrt{\frac{13}{10} - \left(\frac{1}{10}\right)^2} \quad \text{or} \quad \sqrt{1.30 - .01} \quad \text{or} \quad \sqrt{1.29}$$
$$= 1.1358$$

In tabulated data it will be remembered that a different series of symbols is used as follows:

In simple series		In table	
$\Sigma\, x'$	=	$\Sigma\, fd$	Both of these expressed
$\Sigma\,(x')^2$	=	$\Sigma\, fd^2$	in terms of intervals

Also, since when dealing with tabulated data the deviations are usually expressed in terms of intervals greater than one, the size of the interval must be introduced into the formula. The formula for tabulated data then becomes

$$\text{S.D. (or } \sigma) = h \sqrt{\frac{\Sigma f d^2}{N} - \left(\frac{\Sigma f d}{N}\right)^2} \qquad (11c)$$

In practical use, Formula (11c) will fill the need for computing standard deviation far more frequently than either (11a) or (11b) for the reason that most data will be tabulated. Let us tabulate the data given above and apply Formula (11c) in finding the S.D.

ILLUSTRATION A

[Use of Formula (11c)]

Scale of Measures	f	d	fd	fd^2
12	1	+2	+2	4
11	3	+1	+3	3
10	3	0		
9	2	−1	−2	2
8	1	−2	−2	4
	10		+1	13

$$\text{S.D.} = 1 \times \sqrt{\frac{13}{10} + \left(\frac{+1}{10}\right)^2}$$

$$= 1.1358$$

Previously, the suggestion was made that in finding the mean of tabulated data the sum of the fd's should be divided by N before multiplying by h. The advantages of this procedure over finding the product of Σfd and h before executing the division by N are now obvious. When data have been tabulated, one almost invariably needs to know both the mean and the standard deviation. Since $\dfrac{\Sigma fd}{N}$ appears in the formula for standard deviation as well as in the formula for the mean, its value once found may be used in both.

[Use of Formula (11c). Scores made on a general achievement test by a fourth-grade class. All scores are integers.]

Scale of Scores	f	d	fd	fd^2
50–54	3	+2	+6	12
45–49	5	+1	+5	5
40–44	7	0		
35–39	8	−1	−8	8
30–34	3	−2	−6	12
25–29	2	−3	−6	18
	28		−9	55

Formula (11c): $\sigma = h\sqrt{\dfrac{\Sigma fd^2}{N} - \left(\dfrac{\Sigma fd}{N}\right)^2}$

Substituting: $\sigma = 5\sqrt{\dfrac{55}{28} - \left(\dfrac{-9}{28}\right)^2}$

$= 5\sqrt{1.964 - (-.321)^2}$

$= 5\sqrt{1.964 - .103}$

$= 5\sqrt{1.861}$

$= 5 \times 1.364$

$= 6.72$

To find the mean involved in Illustration B it is necessary only to substitute values already found, as follows

$M = \text{A.M.} + h\dfrac{\Sigma fd}{N}$

$= 42 + 5 \times (-.321)$

$= 42 - 1.61$

$= 40.39$

The Systematic Error in the Standard Deviation.—In an earlier discussion on means, it was pointed out that the center of gravity of the measures in an interval is assumed to rest at the midpoint of the interval. Although the assumption is false, the resulting errors are compensating ones when a mean is being computed. In computing a standard deviation from a tabulation, however, the distances from the mean of the distribution to the midpoints of the consecutive intervals are squared. Regardless of whether the interval is above or below the mean of the distribution, the assumed distance is always slightly longer than the distance from the mean of the distribution to the true center of gravity of the interval. The result is a systematic error which constantly produces a value for the standard deviation slightly too large.

The error is generally ignored in computing standard deviation of data commonly found in the classroom or in the principal's office. Formula (11c) is sufficiently accurate for most data of these types. For very exact work, however, a corrected formula is used which contains the Sheppard's correction and which compensates for the over-value introduced. The formula is

$$\sigma = h \sqrt{\frac{\Sigma fd^2}{N} - \left(\frac{\Sigma fd}{N}\right)^2 - .0833} \tag{11d}$$

A unit of standard deviation is longer than a unit of either quartile deviation or average deviation. About two thirds (68.26%) of the measures will lie within a distance of one S.D. of the mean of a normally distributed group of data.

Combining Standard Deviations.—Somewhat similar to the combining of means, the standard deviations of the parts of a whole group of data may be combined to find the S.D. of the whole group. To do this it is necessary to know the mean and the number of cases for each part, as well as the standard deviation. The formula is

$$\sigma_T = \sqrt{\frac{N_1(\sigma_1^2 + C_1^2) + N_2(\sigma_2^2 + C_2^2) + \dots N_n(\sigma_n^2 + C_n^2)}{N_1 + N_2 + \dots N_n}} \tag{12}$$

To use Formula (12) it is first necessary to apply Formula (3) to find the mean (M_T) of the total distribution. Then

$$C_1 = M_1 - M_T$$
$$C_2 = M_2 - M_T$$
$$\text{Etc.}$$

To illustrate the use of the formula, let us suppose that in a certain school the fourth grade is composed of twenty children who have had kindergarten training, and thirty children who have not had such training. Certain computations have already been made for the two separate groups and have yielded the following information: (Subscripts 1 and 2 refer to kindergarten and non-kindergarten, respectively.)

Scholarship Grade Points

	N	M	S.D.
Kin.	20	3.25	1.08
Non.-Kin.	30	2.90	.92

$$N_1 = 20; \qquad M_1 = 3.25; \qquad \sigma_1 = 1.08$$
$$N_2 = 30; \qquad M_2 = 2.90; \qquad \sigma_2 = .92$$

By applying Formula (3), M_T is found to be 3.04.

Then $C_1 = 3.25 - 3.04$ or $+ .11$
and $C_2 = 2.90 - 3.04$ or $- .14$

Now Formula (12) may be applied

$$\sigma_T = \sqrt{\frac{20\,[1.08^2 + .11^2] + 30\,[.92^2 + (-.14)^2]}{20 + 30}}$$

$$= \sqrt{\frac{20 \times 1.1785 + 30 \times .8660}{50}}$$

$$= \sqrt{\frac{49.55}{50}}$$

$$= \sqrt{.991} \quad \text{or } .9955 \text{ or } 1.00$$

Formula (12) can be solved for σ_1 and thereby Formula (13), which follows, can be derived:

$$\sigma_1 = \sqrt{\frac{N_T \sigma_T^2 - N_2(\sigma_2^2 + C_2^2) - N_1 C_1^2}{N_1}} \qquad (13)$$

Formula (13) is to be used when N, M, and σ are known for a total distribution and N, M and σ are known for one part of the distribution. By applying Formula (13), the standard deviation of the other part of the distribution may be found. However, in order to get C_1 Formula (4) must first be applied to find M_1.

Coefficient of Variation.—So far, variability has been dealt with only as an absolute unit on the scale of a distribution. The three principal purposes of such a measure of variability have been shown. However, a third important need for consideration of variability cannot be met by any absolute measure of variability. To illustrate this need let us consider comparatively a load of firewood and a load of telephone poles. The sticks of firewood are in mixed lengths of two feet, three feet, and four feet—one third each. The telephone poles are also in mixed lengths of twenty-nine feet, thirty feet, and thirty-one feet—one third each. Now, although the standard deviations for these two distributions are exactly the same ($\sigma = .82$), no one would contend that the two distributions are equally variable. The load of firewood is highly variable for firewood, but the load of telephone poles is only slightly variable for telephone poles. It would seem that the mean length of the firewood should be a factor in their coefficient of variation, and that the mean length of the telephone poles should be a factor in their coefficient of variation. Although admittedly arbitrary, this coefficient is usually thought of as a ratio between the absolute variability and the central tendency. To avoid the necessity of using decimal fractions to express coefficients of variation, a constant factor (100) is usually introduced uniformly into the ratio, making the general formula read

$$\text{C.V.} = \frac{100 \times \text{absolute variability}}{\text{central tendency}} \tag{14a}$$

One may substitute any absolute measure of variability and any measure of central tendency into the formula, such as

$$\text{C.V.} = \frac{100 \ Q}{\text{Md.}} \tag{14b}$$

$$\text{or C.V.} = \frac{100 \ \text{A.D.}}{\text{Md.}} \tag{14c}$$

$$\text{or C.V.} = \frac{100 \ \text{A.D.}}{\text{M}} \tag{14d}$$

$$\text{or C.V.} = \frac{100 \ \text{S.D.}}{\text{M}} \tag{14e}$$

Formula (14e) is used most frequently for comparing the variability of one group of data with another. Applying it to the problem of the firewood and telephone poles, we have

$$\text{For firewood: C.V.} = \frac{100 \times .82}{3} \quad \text{or } 27$$

$$\text{For telephone poles: C.V.} = \frac{100 \times .82}{30} \quad \text{or } 3$$

By use of this formula the firewood proves to be more variable.

While the true meaning of this coefficient is considerably clouded because of the arbitrary position of the zero, in much educational data it seems to provide the only means of making certain needed comparisons. By no other means could we answer such questions as:

Are mice more variable in weight than elephants?
Are children more variable in height than in weight?
Is intelligence more variable at the age of twelve than at age six?

Exercises and Problems

1. (a) Which of the two following sets of scores has the greater variability if the comparison is made on the basis of absolute range? (Their medians are equal.)

Set A: 45, 36, 35, 33, 33, 32, 30, 28, 27, 20
Set B: 45, 43, 39, 36, 34, 31, 29, 26, 22, 20

(b) Again make the comparison on the basis of quartile deviation:

$$\text{Set A: } Q = \frac{35 - 28}{2}$$

$$\text{Set B: } Q = \frac{39 - 26}{2}$$

2. Find the quartile deviation of the twenty spelling scores which follow: (All scores were integers).

Scores	f
12	1
11	2
10	2
9	4
8	4
7	3
6	2
5	2
	20

3. Find the range of P_{90} to P_{10} in the distribution of Exercise 2.

4. Find the quartile deviation of the following thirty-two scores on knowledge of physical education:

Scale of Scores	f
80 and up	4
70–79	6
60–69	10
55–59	4
50–54	3
45–49	3
Below 45	2
	32

5. Below is a distribution of reading comprehension scores. Each score is an integer.

Scores	f
55–59	4
50–54	8
45–49	12
40–44	12
35–39	10
30–34	8
25–29	4
20–24	2
	60

(a) Find the median.
(b) Find the quartile deviation.
(c) Express the full length of the scale in terms of Q's. (The scale is interpreted to extend from 19.5 to 59.5.)

(d) Of this length how many Q's extend above the median? Below the median?

(e) A score of 52 is how many Q's higher than a score of 36?

6. The X's in this series are spelling scores:

$$X: 8, 9, 7, 5, 11, 8, 9, 6, 8, 7$$

(a) Find the A.D. by use of Formula (10a).

(b) Find the A.D. by use of Formula (10b).

7. (a) Find the average deviation of the scores given in the table of Exercise 5.

(b) Compare the length of the A.D. with the length of the Q.

(c) A score of 47 is how many A.D.'s higher than a score of 39?

8. Using the simple series which follows make the computations called for below:

$$X: 9 \ 8 \ 7 \ 7 \ 6 \ 6 \ 4 \ 3$$

(a) Find the S.D. by taking the deviations from a convenient assumed mean.

(b) Find the S.D. by taking deviations from the true mean.

(c) Tabulate the measures and find the S.D. by using the same assumed mean that was used in (a).

9. Compute the mean and the standard deviation of the reading comprehension scores tabulated in Exercise 5.

(a) Assemble in order the Q, the A.D., and the S.D. for these scores. Note the relative length of these measures of variability.

(b) What is the length of the scale (19.5 to 59.5) in terms of σ?

(c) A score of 53 is how many sigmas above the mean?

(d) Use Formula (11d) to compute the S.D., and note the small difference between this result and the result obtained by Formula (11c).

10. The table which follows is the four-year high school record of a student.

Marks	f
A	4
B	12
C	10
D	5
F	2
	33

(a) Find the mean scholastic point. (Assign scholastic points as follows: A=4, B=3, C=2, D=1, and F=0.)

(b) Find the standard deviation.

11. A Challenge: From the distribution below, find the mean and the standard deviation by taking 51 for the assumed mean. (All scores are integers.)

Scale	f
65–69	2
60–64	4
55–59	6
50–54	8
45–49	5
40–44	4
35–39	3
	32

12. A sixth grade is composed of forty boys and sixty girls. The grade was given a standardized achievement examination. Scores were tabulated by sexes with the results shown below. It is now desired to find the mean and the standard deviation for the total grade:

	N	M	σ
Boys	40	49.2	10.3
Girls	60	54.3	9.4

13. The means and the S.D.'s of the grade points for the total high school and for Student A are given below. Find the coefficients of variation.

	M	σ
Total high school	2.36	1.04
Student A	2.82	.67

14. The fourth grade of a school was given an arithmetic reasoning test and an arithmetic computation test, with the following results:

	M	σ
A.R.	31.13	8.42
A.C.	53.81	8.87

In which of the two subjects is the class comparatively more variable?

CHAPTER 6

THE NORMAL PROBABILITY CURVE AND RELIABILITY

At this point it may be well for the student to rethink the processes which have been considered thus far. These include mere rearrangement, rearrangement by means of intervals, averages, variability, along with others. Each of these processes has served a very definite purpose in making the data in hand more and more understandable for the student. Logically, the next of these processes to be considered is reliability. This type of calculation has to do with sampling. In most of the work which is done in statistics it is impossible to get a total population of any sort. Samples must nearly always be depended upon. It becomes necessary, therefore, to know how the sample is related to the distribution of which it is a part, with respect to its general form, its mean, its sigma, and its other measures. To answer questions of this sort, reference must be made to the theory of probability. Hence, it becomes necessary at this point to include a brief discussion of this topic.

The Normal Probability Curve

It is a well-known fact that a tabulation of the measures of many biological and psychological traits assumes the proportions of the curve just mentioned. Since a vast amount of educational data has to do with biological and psychological traits, statistics in this field finds itself confronted with the problems of the normal probability curve. This curve, along with its equation and the different calculations based upon the equation, becomes a powerful tool in the hands of the statistician for the solution of many important problems in the field of psychology and education.

Some interesting theories have been advanced with respect to the reasons why traits coincide in their measurements to this mathematical curve. No attempt is made here to prove or to disprove these theories. Attention is merely called to the apparent law of nature involved in the curve.

By probability the mathematician means a very definite thing, or it may be said that probability can be given a definite mathematical definition. If a coin is thrown, the probability that heads will show is $\frac{1}{2}$, since there are just two things which can happen. At the same time, the probability that tails will appear is $\frac{1}{2}$; hence $(\frac{1}{2} + \frac{1}{2}) = 1$, which is interpreted as certainty. In other words, when the coin is thrown, it is certain that either heads or tails will appear. From this standpoint it will be seen that certainty can exist in any degree from 0 to 1. In other words, the probability that human behavior is influenced by walking under ladders or leaning against walls is 0, and the probability that the sun will rise tomorrow approaches 1. If it is desired to determine the probability of occurrences with two coins rather than one, this can be done by the binomial expansion $(\frac{1}{2} + \frac{1}{2})^2$. Here the coefficients are 1, 2, and 1. Interpreting this, it is easy to see that if two coins are thrown, four things can happen. There may be two heads, there may be two tails, and either coin may show a head or a tail. Of these four things, there is one chance in four that there will be two heads, two chances in four that there will be a head and a tail, and one chance in four that there will be two tails. From this it is clear that the probability of occurrence when three coins are thrown will come from the expansion of $(\frac{1}{2} + \frac{1}{2})^3$, and so on as the number of coins is increased.

This can be generalized by letting p equal the probability of success in a certain event, and q equal the probability of failure. If there are no other possibilities, the expansion of $(p + q)^n$ will show the total combinations of successes and failures in a series of n independent occurrences of the event. If the probability of success is equal to the probability of failure, and if there are six occurrences of the event, the binomial and its expansion become

$$(\tfrac{1}{2} + \tfrac{1}{2})^6 = (\tfrac{1}{2})^6(\tfrac{1}{2})^0 + 6(\tfrac{1}{2})^5(\tfrac{1}{2})^1 + 15(\tfrac{1}{2})^4(\tfrac{1}{2})^2 + 20(\tfrac{1}{2})^3(\tfrac{1}{2})^3$$
$$+ 15(\tfrac{1}{2})^2(\tfrac{1}{2})^4 + 6(\tfrac{1}{2})^1(\tfrac{1}{2})^5 + (\tfrac{1}{2})^0(\tfrac{1}{2})^6$$
$$= 1/64 + 6/64 + 15/64 + 20/64 + 15/64 + 6/64 + 1/64$$

Now by using the numerators of the successive fractions as frequencies (from which $N = 64$), and by providing seven $(n + 1)$ intervals, we have the following distribution:

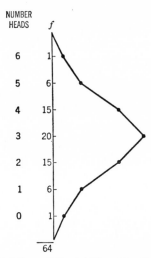

Figure 15. Probability of Heads When Six Coins Are Thrown Simultaneously

It is obvious that if, instead of raising the above binomial to the sixth power, we had raised it to the 100th power or to the 10000th power or to a power infinitely large, the number of points on the graph would have increased, thus reducing the space between the points until the points would merge into a continuous curve. The short, straight lines in Figure 15 would then disappear and the graph would become a continuous curve.

It can be shown that the equation of this curve is

$$y = \frac{N}{\sigma \sqrt{2\pi}} \, e^{\dfrac{-x^2}{2\sigma^2}}$$

in which N is the total area under the curve, e is 2.7183 (the Naperian base of logarithms), π is 3.1416, and σ is a unit of linear measurement on the base. For convenience in expressing areas in terms of percentages let us assign the value of 100 to N. By substituting these values in the equation above and writing the "e" factor in reciprocal form, the equation becomes

$$y = \frac{100}{\sqrt{2 \times 3.1416}} \times \frac{1}{2.7183^{\frac{x^2}{2}}}$$

$$= \frac{39.89}{2.7183^{\frac{x^2}{2}}}$$

In this equation any value may be substituted for x and the corresponding value may be found for y. The labor of finding the y values corresponding to substituted x values will be greatly reduced by converting the exponential equation to logarithmic form as follows:

$$\log y = \log N - \tfrac{1}{2}\log(2\pi) - \frac{x^2}{2} \log e$$

$$= \log 100 - \tfrac{1}{2}\log 6.2832 - \frac{x^2}{2} \log 2.7183$$

$$= 2.00000 - .39914 - .21715x^2$$

$$= 1.60086 - .21715x^2$$

Because of the fact that the x in the equation is squared, a value expressed as either plus or minus when substituted for x will yield only one value for y, which condition produces a symmetrical curve about the Y_0 ordinate.

When x is	y is
.0	39.89
± .5	35.21
±1.0	24.20
±1.5	12.95
±2.0	5.40
±2.5	1.75
±3.0	.44
±3.5	.09

(See Table E for a more complete statement of these values)

A smooth graph constructed through the points indicated above is a normal frequency curve. Of course, no finite value for x will reduce the value of y to 0. Therefore, we may say that the curve will never touch the x axis. Figure 16 shows the graph constructed through the fifteen points previously located.

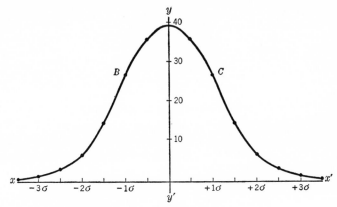

Figure 16. The Normal Frequency Curve

The tendency of certain human traits to conform to this curve is so marked, that the failure of a group of test scores to take on this general form is usually taken by the statistician as evidence that either the test was not a satisfactory one or the sample of individuals was not representative.

It should be remembered that there is only one normal frequency curve. Several normal curves placed on the same base with their y axes coinciding will all have the same proportions. They could differ only in height. The ratio of the height of one to the height of another from any point on the base will equal the ratio of the area of the one to the area of the other. In Figure 16 the area is 100. (The area here is equivalent to a hundred small rectangles each being one sigma long and one unit of the y axis wide.) If we should place upon the same base a normal curve enclosing an area of 200, it would stand exactly twice as high at every point. Therefore, if we reduced the y units by one half in the second curve it would shrink to fit exactly on the first curve. The unit σ is the length of a line which can be drawn from the turning point (B or C in Figure 16) to the y axis.

Areas may be determined mathematically for any segment of the normal curve which is bounded on one side by the y axis. For example, the truncated section of the area from the origin to $+.5\sigma$ may be shown to equal 19.15% of the curve's total area.

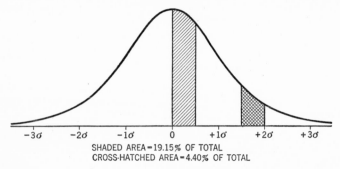

SHADED AREA = 19.15% OF TOTAL
CROSS-HATCHED AREA = 4.40% OF TOTAL

Figure 17.   Areas of Truncated Sections of the Normal Frequency Surface

After having determined and tabulated a series of these areas, all measured in terms of sigmas from the origin, the area of any truncated section may be determined by merely adding or subtracting two areas as the situation may require. The area of the cross-hatched section of Figure 17 is dependent upon the area from 0 to $+2\sigma$ (47.72%) and the area from 0 to $+1.5\sigma$ (43.22%). Here subtraction is indicated and the difference, 4.40%, is obtained.   Tables of areas and ordinates will be found in the final pages of this book (Table E).

The curve can be used in other ways.   It is possible to find the height at any point on the base (y value), to test any curve with respect to its resemblance to the normal probability curve, and to determine the average x value for any part of the curve. These devices, along with others, are used in dealing with many of the problems which are to follow.

Reliability

The idea of reliability arises in all statistical situations which involve the concept of sampling.   Although this concept may apply to practically all statistical computations, the student is best prepared, perhaps, at this stage to attack the subject in its

relation to means. In any statistical situation involving the
mean, there is usually a true mean and an obtained mean. The
true mean would be found if all the cases involved in any type
of statistical problem were used. If one were seeking the true
average height of Siamese twins, N would be very small, but if
one were seeking the true average height of all persons on the
earth, N would be very large—so large that dealing with a problem of this type would not be practicable.

Another important fact concerning populations is that often
they are shifting. If one were seeking the true average reading
rate of fourth-grade children in the United States, one would
be confronted with the fact that many children who are now in
the fourth grade will soon cease to be fourth-grade children,
and that many others who are not now in the fourth grade will
soon be enrolled in this school grade.

These points, along with others, make it very difficult to
obtain a true mean in many types of statistical work. The in-
vestigator is forced to deal with the mean of a sample, and to
relate the obtained mean to the true mean by means of the law
of probability. This is called determining the reliability of the
mean.

Since there are few problems of this type which allow access
to the total parent populations, it seems best to approach the
problem of the reliability of the mean through an experiment.

An Experiment.—A population of numbers (each number
was typed on a slip of paper and placed in an individual capsule,
so that the number was visible through the transparent capsule)
was placed in a box. Rules for drawing were imposed by which
the population was made infinite or inexhaustible. This was
accomplished by returning each capsule to the box after each
draw so that it would have an opportunity to be drawn on the
next trial. The mean of this population was 5 and the standard
deviation was 2. This may be called the parent population, and
the measures may be called the true mean and the true standard
deviation. From the box a sample of one capsule was drawn,
the number on the capsule was recorded, the capsule was returned to the box, and the box was shaken. This process was

repeated ten thousand times with results as indicated in Table XXVI.

TABLE XXVI. DISTRIBUTION OF TEN THOUSAND SAMPLES OF ONE MEMBER EACH FROM AN INFINITE PARENT POPULATION

Scale of Numbers	f	$\% f$
10	88	1
9	272	3
8	696	7
7	1220	12
6	1645	16
5	2152	22
4	1620	16
3	1241	12
2	706	7
1	256	3
0	104	1
	10,000	100

$$M = 5.00$$
$$\sigma = 2.00$$

When the frequencies are reduced to percentages and the percentages are rounded to the nearest integer, the resulting distribution has a mean of exactly 5 and a standard deviation of exactly 2. It will be remembered that these are the same values that were given for the mean and standard deviation of the parent population. As a matter of fact, the distribution of percentage frequencies of Table XXVI is the parent population, and we may say, therefore, that the standard error of a *sample of one* is the same as σ of the parent population. By this statement we mean that since a series of *samples of one* drawn at random from the parent population will have a mean of 5 and a standard deviation of 2, there are approximately two chances in three ($\frac{68.26}{100}$ to be exact—the proportion of area within one sigma of the mean) that the number on any capsule drawn at random will be within two points of the mean of the parent population. In other words, in drawing a *sample of one,* the freedom of the sample to deviate from the mean of the parent population is as great as the deviation of the parent population. To use another terminology, the reliability of this sample is the least possible, being limited only by the extremes of the parent population. It would, therefore, be a serious mistake to draw one sample of one member from an unknown parent population, and from the one sample reach very definite conclusions about the parent population. In the capsule experiment, suppose that the first number drawn had been a *nine;* if we had decided at that point that the box contained a population of *nines* and had drawn no more samples, a serious blunder would have been made.

Let us proceed now to draw from the box *samples of two* (two capsules in each sample), and record only the mean of each sample. Means for the first few samples were 6.5, 4.5, 5.0, 4.5, and so on. The means of one hundred samples of two each were tabulated and are recorded here in Table XXVII.

TABLE XXVII. DISTRIBUTION OF MEANS OF RANDOM SAMPLES OF TWO MEMBERS PER SAMPLE FROM AN INFINITE PARENT POPULATION

Scale of Means	f
8.5	2
8.0	
7.5	
7.0	9
6.5	8
6.0	11
5.5	13
5.0	15
4.5	12
4.0	11
3.5	8
3.0	5
2.5	4
2.0	2
	100

M = 4.995
σ = 1.37

The mean of this distribution is 4.995, and the standard deviation is 1.37. The scale of numbers in Table XXVII was made only long enough to include the actual means which occurred from the hundred samples. It is possible, however, that the mean of a random *sample of two* could have been either 0 or 10. Since 1% of the parent population are 10's, the probability that the first member of a sample will be 10 is $\frac{1}{100}$, and the probability that the second member of the sample will be 10 is $\frac{1}{100}$. Therefore, the probability that both members of a sample will be 10's (the only way in which a mean of 10 could occur) is $\frac{1}{100} \times \frac{1}{100}$ or $\frac{1}{10000}$. In the course of drawing 10,000 random *samples of two* we would therefore expect normally to draw one sample with a mean of 10.

In drawing *samples of two* the freedom of their means to deviate from the mean of the parent population is restricted somewhat more than was the case when we were dealing with *samples of one*. We know now that it is safe to place a bet of two to one that the mean of any random *sample of two* will not differ more than 1.37 from the mean of the parent population. Again, the 1.37 may be spoken of as the reliability of the mean.

In similar manner, one hundred random *samples of four* were drawn. The means of the respective samples were tabulated, and the mean and the standard deviation of the distribution were computed. Table XXVIII is a report of the results.

TABLE XXVIII. DISTRIBUTION OF MEANS OF RANDOM SAMPLES OF FOUR MEMBERS PER SAMPLE FROM AN INFINITE PARENT POPULATION

Scale of Means	f
7.00–7.50	5
6.25–6.75	10
5.50–6.00	22
4.75–5.25	33
4.00–4.50	18
3.25–3.75	8
2.50–3.00	4
	100

$$M = 5.08$$
$$\sigma = 1.04$$

Here the mean is 5.08, and the standard deviation is 1.04. The relatively smaller standard deviation of this distribution of means indicates that the mean of a sample of four has less opportunity to vary widely from the mean of the parent population than the mean of a *sample of two*. This measure of reliability makes it safe to place our two-to-one bet that the mean of any random *sample of four* will not differ by more than 1.04 from the mean of the parent population. Of course, there is a one-to-three probability that we may lose this bet, but in a series of trials we expect to win twice the number of times that we lose. The fact that two of our winnings will pay for one of our losses balances the game.

The importance of securing a clear concept of reliability of the mean of a sample justifies going into experimental details once more, we believe, by drawing random *samples of ten* this time. Each sample contained ten members of the capsule population; a hundred samples were drawn; the mean for each sample was computed; and the hundred means were tabulated, as shown in Table XXIX.

TABLE XXIX. DISTRIBUTION OF MEANS OF RANDOM SAMPLES OF TEN MEMBERS PER SAMPLE FROM AN INFINITE PARENT POPULATION

Scale of Means	f
6.1–6.3	3
5.8–6.0	6
5.5–5.7	16
5.2–5.4	17
4.9–5.1	18
4.6–4.8	18
4.3–4.5	14
4.0–4.2	6
3.7–3.9	2
	100

$$M = 5.02$$
$$\sigma = .56$$

The mean of the one hundred means in Table XXIX is 5.02, and the standard deviation of the one hundred means is .56.

This standard deviation is the smallest of the four distributions. The conclusion, of course, is that means of random *samples of ten* find it more difficult to wander away from the mean of their parent population than means of smaller samples. This result, then, is the most reliable of any of the samples chosen.

The experiment was discontinued at this point by the group working with it. It could have been continued by tabulating the means of one hundred *samples of twenty-five,* or by tabulating the means of one hundred *samples of one hundred,* or by tabulating the means of a series of samples of any size. The mean and the standard deviation for the means of *samples of twenty-five* would approximate 5.00 and .40 respectively, while for *samples of one hundred* the figures would be 5.00 and .20 respectively. Thus it may be seen that the larger the samples in the series the more likely the means of the samples will cluster near the mean of the parent population.

It is clear now that it would be most convenient if this process of sampling could be generalized in some way, so as to give a measure of this variability of means of samples in the same way that σ or Q measures the variability of a distribution. In order to develop this general procedure, the standard deviation of the means of a series of samples may be referred to as standard error (reliability) of the mean (S.E.$_\text{M}$), sigma of the mean (σ_M), or epsilon of the mean (ε_M). In the experiments described, of course, the standard error of the mean indicates the distance from the mean on the scale within which two thirds (68.26%) of all the means of random samples of the size specified will fall. Many statisticians dislike the use of a probability involving a relation of $\frac{2}{3}$, preferring the convenience of a probability involving a relation of $\frac{1}{2}$. When the latter relation is desired, one should take .6745 of the standard error of the mean. This result is called the probable error of the mean (P.E.$_\text{M}$).

The relationship of the standard deviation of the means of a series of random samples to the standard deviation of the parent population has been shown by mathematical proof to be

$$\sigma \text{ of the means } s_n = \frac{\sigma_{pp}}{\sqrt{N}} \tag{15}$$

in which S_n refers to samples of n members, σ_{pp} is the standard deviation of the parent population, and N is the size of each sample of the series. By use of Formula (15), we are now able to determine the theoretical value for each of our experiments in which an empirical value has been determined. These theoretical values are:

For *samples of one*
$$\sigma \text{ of the means } s_1 = \frac{2}{\sqrt{1}} \quad \text{or } 2.00$$

For *samples of two*
$$\sigma \text{ of the means } s_2 = \frac{2}{\sqrt{2}} \quad \text{or } 1.41$$

For *samples of four*
$$\sigma \text{ of the means } s_4 = \frac{2}{\sqrt{4}} \quad \text{or } 1.00$$

For *samples of ten*
$$\sigma \text{ of the means } s_{10} = \frac{2}{\sqrt{10}} \quad \text{or } .63$$

Let us assemble in Figure 18 the essential material of the previous pages in more compact form for comparative study.

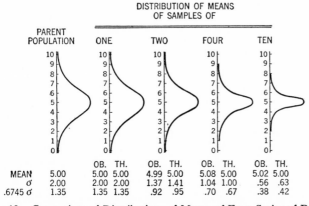

Figure 18. Comparison of Distributions of Means of Four Series of Random Samples Drawn from a Given Infinite Population

NOTE: "Ob." refers to the results observed from the actual drawing and "Th." refers to theoretical expectations by the formula on the preceding page.

From Figure 18 it may be seen that if one draws from the box of capsules a random sample of ten capsules, one may safely wager $68.26 against $31.74 that the mean of the sample one draws will not differ from the mean (5.00) of the box of capsules by more than .63. If the mean of the sample is between 4.37 and 5.63, the sampler wins his wager. If the mean is above 5.63 or below 4.37, he loses. Of course the wager is parimutuel, and if made repeatedly will result in neither loss nor gain for the bettor.

If the sampler prefers, he may wager $1.00 against $1.00 that the mean of the sample of ten which he is about to draw will not differ from the mean of the box of capsules by more than .42. This is obtained by multiplying .63 by .6745. In other words, the probability that the mean of the sample to be drawn will not differ from 5.00 by more than .42 is one half.

When Formula (15) is applied to samples of twenty-five, the result is

$$\sigma \text{ of the means } s_{25} = \frac{2}{\sqrt{25}} \quad \text{or } .40$$

and when applied to samples of one hundred, the result is

$$\sigma \text{ of the means } s_{100} = \frac{2}{\sqrt{100}} \quad \text{or } .20$$

Now if .20 be reduced to a one-to-one bet by multiplying by .6745 it becomes .13, which is very small. Yet if a sample of one hundred be drawn from the box, we can safely wager $1.00 against $1.00 that its mean will not differ from 5.00 by more than .13. With the value of the probable error so small, we may have reasonable confidence that the mean of a single sample of one hundred in this case will fairly represent the central tendency of the total population.

So far, the discussion has been intended to develop the concept of reliability. Many educational problems dealing with reliability of the mean cannot be solved by use of Formula (15). In our experiments we knew the characteristics (mean and S.D.) of our parent population in the first place, and therefore had no real need for trying to determine the mean of this population by use of samples. In actual practice, very often the situation of the experiments is exactly reversed. Frequently, we do not know anything about the parent population, and have no way of learning about it except from the revelations provided by *one* sample which we secure by chance.

Reliability of a Mean.—In order to develop this topic, let us assume that a scientist on a newly discovered continent catches in a trap an animal which has never been seen by civilized men before. The scientist assumes that the animal is one member of a population of animals, and he is eager to know the characteristics (let us confine the discussion to weight) of the population of animals. From the weight of the single member, what conclusions may the scientist draw concerning the mean weight of the whole population? Generalization here would be dangerous, for the captured member which weighs, let us say, twenty-eight pounds may be at either extreme of the total population. If, the next day, the scientist captures a second member which weighs fifty pounds, the mean weight (39 pounds) of the two members has a slightly better chance of representing the mean of the total population than the weight of either taken alone.

Now suppose the scientist builds a special corral into which is driven a random sample of eighty-two members of the animal population. These added to the two already captured now total eighty-four. After tabulating the weights of the eighty-four members, he computes a mean of 40 and a standard deviation of 8. He now has the following information about his sample:

$$N = 84$$
$$M = 40$$
$$\sigma = 8$$

To what degree of certainty can the mean of this sample be accepted as the mean of the total population of animals? Formula (15) calls for sigma of the parent population, but the scientist does not have sigma of the parent population. The situation is saved only by the fact that while there will be variation in standard deviations from chance sample to chance sample, the standard deviation of a sample will generally approximate the standard deviation of the parent population. Actually, the standard deviations of random samples tend to be slightly less than the standard deviation of the parent population. It has been shown mathematically that this slight reduction will be compensated for by using $\sqrt{N-1}$ instead of $\sqrt{N}$ in the denominator of Formula (15). Now by using sigma of the sample to replace sigma of the parent population in Formula (15) and by using $\sqrt{N-1}$ to replace $\sqrt{N}$ the formula becomes

$$\sigma_M \text{ (or S.E.}_M) = \frac{\sigma_S}{\sqrt{N-1}} \qquad (16)$$

or

$$\text{P.E.}_M = \frac{.6745\ \sigma_S}{\sqrt{N-1}} \qquad (17)$$

Applying Formula (16) to the weight of the sample of animals in hand, he has

$$\text{S.E.}_M = \frac{8}{\sqrt{84-1}} \quad \text{or} \quad \frac{8}{\sqrt{83}} \quad \text{or } .88$$

The meaning of this result is that there is (approximately) a probability of two chances in three that the mean weight of the whole class of animals does not differ from 40 pounds by more than .88 pounds. The smallness of this figure (less than one pound) compared with 40 pounds gives us confidence that the mean of the sample adequately represents the mean of the whole population of animals. The standard error then is a measure of reliability.

The scientist does not know, and with the data in hand has no way of knowing, whether the mean weight of the parent population is greater or less than 40 pounds. The probability is one half that it is greater and one half that it is less, for the reason that in the first place the probability that the mean of the sample was above or below the mean of the total population was one half.

If Formula (17) be applied in the animal problem, the probable error will be found to be

$$P.E._M = \frac{.6745 \times 8}{\sqrt{84 - 1}} \quad \text{or } .0740 \times 8 \quad \text{or } .59$$

NOTE: Use of Formula (17) is greatly facilitated by utilizing a table of values of $\frac{.6745}{\sqrt{N}}$ (Table D of this book). Here $\frac{.6745}{\sqrt{83}} = .0740$.

and he is now able to say that there is a probability of ½ that the mean weight of the whole population of animals does not differ from 40 pounds by more than .59 pounds. Also, by use of the table of areas in terms of P.E. deviates from the mean (Table E), he can determine the probability that the mean weight of the total population will lie within any given number of pounds of 40 pounds. For example, several such probabilities are shown in the following summary:

		Probability That the Mean of the Total Group Will Lie	
Distance on Scale from 40 Pounds in Terms of Pounds	Equivalent Distance in Terms of P.E.'s	Within This Range	Outside This Range
.59	1	500/1000	500/1000
1.18	2	822/1000	178/1000
1.77	3	956/1000	44/1000
1.12	1.9	800/1000	200/1000
2.36	4	992/1000	8/1000

Because of the insignificant difference between $\sqrt{N-1}$ and $\sqrt{N}$, when N is larger than twenty-five or thirty, many statisticians omit the -1 from the formula. Since no additional burden of computation is imposed by the retention of the -1, the writers believe it should be retained uniformly, for there is some danger that it may be forgotten in cases in which N is small.

Reliability of the Mean of a Sample from a Restricted Population.—Formulas (15), (16), and (17) have been built upon

the concept of a parent population of very great or infinite proportions. Frequently, samples from restricted parent populations must be dealt with. Naturally in the process of removing
a random sample from a comparatively small parent population,
the character of the remaining parent population is altered pro-
gressively as its members are removed successively. If the first
member drawn is above the mean of the parent population, the
probability is a little better than one half that the second member
of the sample will be below the mean. Thus, as the drawing
proceeds the greater the number of members drawn from one
side of the original parent mean, the greater the probability that
the next member drawn will come from the other side. The
cumulative result of these changing probabilities is to provide
diminishing opportunity for variation of the mean of a random
sample drawn from a restricted parent population. Therefore,
the probable error of such a sample will be less than if it had
been drawn from an infinite parent population. The formulas
which follow should be used for computations of the type discussed here:

$$\text{S.E.}_\text{M} = \frac{\sigma_s}{\sqrt{N-1}}\sqrt{1-p} \qquad (18)$$

$$\text{P.E.}_\text{M} = \frac{.6745\ \sigma_s}{\sqrt{N-1}}\sqrt{1-p} \qquad (19)$$

In Formulas (18) and (19) p is the sample's proportion of
the parent population. To show use of Formula (19), let us
suppose that grade five of a certain school has ninety-three
pupils. In conducting a test survey, a random method is used
to select nineteen of the ninety-three pupils. The test is given
to the nineteen pupils with a resulting mean of 45.70, and a
standard deviation of 8.90. Now the probable error of the
mean, 45.70 is desired. Applying Formula (19), the substitutions are

$$\text{P.E.}_\text{M} = \frac{.6745 \times 8.9}{\sqrt{19-1}}\sqrt{1 - \frac{19}{93}}$$
$$= .1590 \times 8.9\sqrt{1 - .2043}$$
$$= .1590 \times 8.9 \times .892$$
$$= 1.26$$

We may now say that had the test been given to the entire fifth grade of ninety-three pupils, there is a probability of ½ that the mean would not have differed from 45.70 by more than 1.26. The correct reliability for this sample is nearer 1.26 than 1.42, the result which would have been obtained had the parent population been treated as infinite.

Reliability of the Difference Between Two Means.—Returning to the box of capsules, an experimental method was used to observe chance differences which may arise between the means of pairs of random samples. The procedure of this experiment was exactly as before when random samples of ten were being drawn from the box, with this exception: college students, men and women, drew samples of ten in pairs, and only the difference between the two means of a pair of samples was recorded. A schematic method was used in making the draws. When a man and woman stepped forward to draw, the woman always drew her sample of ten first. The mean was computed and retained for reference. Her male companion then drew and computed the mean of his sample of ten. The mean of the man's sample was then placed under the mean of the woman's sample and an algebraic subtraction was made. Thus, some of the differences were positive and some were negative. For example, the results of the drawings by the first five couples were

Mean of Women's Samples	5.1	4.7	5.2	6.1	5.3
Mean of Men's Samples	4.8	5.3	5.4	4.9	5.3
Differences	+.3	−.6	−.2	+1.2	0.0

The drawing was continued until one hundred couples had drawn and one hundred differences had been found. The *differences* were tabulated in intervals of .3, and the mean and standard deviation of the tabulated differences were found. Table XXX shows the complete distribution of the differences.

As would be expected, the mean of these differences appears to approach zero. The standard deviation here is actually the standard error of the difference between the means of two samples of ten. It may also be called $\sigma_{Dif.\ M}$. After the experience we have just described we are no longer surprised when

TABLE XXX. DISTRIBUTION OF ONE HUNDRED DIFFERENCES
BETWEEN MEANS OF PAIRS OF RANDOM
SAMPLES OF TEN

Scale of Differences	f	d	fd	fd^2
2.0 to 2.2	2	7	14	98
1.7 to 1.9	1	6	6	36
1.4 to 1.6	4	5	20	100
1.1 to 1.3	5	4	20	80
.8 to 1.0	8	3	24	72
.5 to .7	10	2	20	40
.2 to .4	15	1	15	15
− .1 to + .1	13	0		
− .4 to − .2	13	−1	− 13	13
− .7 to − .5	11	−2	− 22	44
−1.0 to − .8	7	−3	− 21	63
−1.3 to −1.1	7	−4	− 28	112
−1.6 to −1.4	2	−5	− 10	50
−1.9 to −1.7	2	−6	− 12	72
	100		+13	795

Mean = +0.04
S.D. = .84

a couple step forward and draw two samples with a difference
between their means of as much as .8. As a matter of fact,
differences from zero up to slightly more than this amount will
be expected normally for about two thirds of the draws. Greater
differences will be expected for about one third of the draws.
(Greater differences are to be found at both ends of the scale
of Table XXX, for in dealing with the difference between the
means of two samples it is usually treated as positive. In other
words, if these differences had all been recorded as positive
regardless of their direction, the lower half of the table would
have been thrown into the upper half.)

This experiment is described here for the purpose of acquir-
ing a concept of the correct relations of the factors involved in
reliability of differences between means. The fact that, as a
matter of pure chance, a large range of differences may arise
between means of samples from the same parent population
shows clearly here, but let the slightest difference arise in an

experimental set-up of two groups and someone may try to claim superiority of one group. No such claims should be made until a check has been made on the probability that the observed difference or a greater one could arise as a difference due to chance sampling from one parent population. If the observed difference is readily explainable as a chance difference, no importance need be attached to it.

The importance of this phase of statistics cannot be over-estimated. Progress in education over the last quarter of a century has been dominated by statistical techniques. Particularly have experimental activities taken the form of efforts to measure the superiority of one group over another, of one method of teaching over another, or to measure gains or losses made under certain experimental procedures. In all such work, of course, standard error or probable error of the difference between two means should be employed to detect significance.

For practical statistical work, the cumbersome empirical procedure of our experiment will be replaced by a mathematically determined relationship, which is as follows:

$$\text{S.E.}_{\text{Dif.M}} = \sqrt{\sigma_{M_1}^2 + \sigma_{M_2}^2} \qquad (20)$$

This known relationship permits us to find $\sigma_{\text{Dif. M}}$ when we have only two samples in hand and know nothing about the parent population. As a matter of fact, we need not know that the two samples came from the same parent population. We can use Formula (20) to determine the probability that two such samples might by chance have come from the same parent population, and from this information form a judgment as to whether they probably did come from the same population (in which case their difference is not considered significant) or from two characteristically different populations (in which case their difference is considered significant).

First, however, let us use Formula (20) to check the results of our experiment. In Table XXX we found the actual standard deviation of a hundred differences between means of samples of ten to be .84. Let us determine what the value would have been had the sampling been carried to infinity (the mathematically determined relationship spoken of above). It should be recalled that the standard error of the mean of a sample of ten from our population of capsules was .63, so the substitution in Formula (20) becomes

$$S.E._{\text{Dif.}_M} = \sqrt{.63^2 + .63^2}$$
$$= \sqrt{.7938}$$
$$= .89$$

Our empirically determined sigma, .84, differs but little from the theoretical sigma.

In using Formula (20) it is not necessary that the two samples involved be equal in size. One caution in the use of Formula (20) should be observed, however; the development of the formula assumes no relationship between the members of the two samples. If either positive or negative correlation (a subject to be discussed later) exists between paired members of the two samples, Formula (20) cannot be used.

In dealing with the problem of reliability of a difference between two means, there is one issue on which an arbitrary decision must be made by the statistician. It is the question of how much difference will be accepted as significant. Of course, one can determine mechanically the probability that the existing difference arose by chance, but just how small this probability should be to justify rejection of chance as an explanation cannot be determined mechanically. There is no magical point on the base of the normal probability curve. The suggestion has been made that the third turning point, 1.73σ (found by solving for x with the third derivative of the equation of the normal curve set equal to zero), should be accepted as the point on the base beyond which differences are unlikely to fall by chance and are therefore significant.[1] A difference between two means which amounts to 1.73 times sigma of the difference has a probability of about $\frac{8}{100}$ that it or greater differences could arise between *any two* such chance samples. This difference can be expressed in terms of P.E. units. Here the difference would be 2.56 probable errors of the difference.

[1] C. C. Peters and W. R. Van Voorhis, *Statistical Procedures and Their Mathematical Bases*, p. 346.

To require that the ratio of the difference to the standard error of the difference be 2.78 or 3.00 or even 4.00, as some require, appears to the writers to be somewhat severe. A convenient critical ratio of 2.00 for standard errors or 3.00 for probable errors (these are about equal—3 P.E.'s equal 2.02 S.E.'s) provides a probability of about $^2\!\%_{25}$ that the difference between two means is not explainable as a chance happening. In such cases, it must be recognized that the evidence is not conclusive proof of causes other than chance, but the evidence may be accepted as significant.

An example of one form of treating reliability of a difference between the means of two distributions will now be given. Two sections of the fourth grade in a building have been given the same standardized achievement test. The scores have been tabulated for each section, and the mean and standard deviation for each section has been found. The twenty-eight pupils in Section 1 yielded a mean score of 47.00 and a standard deviation of 13.50, while the thirty-four pupils in Section 2 yielded a mean

TABLE XXXI. SOLUTION OF PROBLEM ON RELIABILITY
OF DIFFERENCE BETWEEN TWO MEANS

	Sec. 1	Sec. 2
N	28	34
M	47.00	44.50
σ	13.50	13.70
P.E.$_M$	1.72	1.59
Dif.$_M$	2.50	
P.E.$_{Dif.}$	2.34	
$\dfrac{\text{Dif.}_M}{\text{P.E.}_{Dif.}}$	1.07	
Probability of Chance	$\dfrac{47}{100}$	
Is Dif. Significant?	No	

score of 44.50 and a standard deviation of 13.70. We now wish to know if the difference, 2.50, between the two means is significant. The steps necessary to answer the question are as shown in Table XXXI on page 125.

The first four steps in the solution of Table XXXI are familiar. Beginning with the fifth step explanations will be made:

Dif.$_\text{M}$ is the value of 47.00 − 44.50.

P.E.$_\text{Dif.}$ is found from $\sqrt{1.72^2 + 1.59^2}$

$\dfrac{\text{Dif.}_\text{M}}{\text{P.E.}_\text{Dif.}}$ IS THE RATIO OF 2.50 to 2.34.   This is sometimes referred to as the critical ratio.

The remaining two steps are usually omitted, for the ratio is all one needs to decide significance. In this case, it falls far short of the value 3.00 previously decided upon as required to show significance. However the next step deals with probability of chance.

Probability of Chance.—This means the probability that differences as great as or greater than the one found here may arise between the means of any two chance samples from the parent population from which these presumably came. The table of P.E. Deviates (Table E) must be referred to and used as given in Figure 19.

Find the area from the mean to 1.07 P.E. This area is 26.50% of total area. This leaves in the plus tail 23.50% (see upper shaded area), but the shaded area below when taken into account adds another 23.50%, making a total of 47.00%. In other words, we may say there is a probability of $^{47}/_{100}$ that a difference as great as or greater than 2.50 may arise between the means of any two similar chance samples from a parent population. *It is therefore so easy for us to explain this difference as a chance happening that there is no need to try to offer any other explanation.* Therefore, it does not appear advisable to say that either of these sections is truly superior to the other.

The step just described is sometimes dealt with in a slightly different manner. Instead of considering the probability of the difference (or a greater one) being a chance difference, which might arise between *any two* random samples, one may consider the probability that in a series of schematic trials the mean of Section 1 will be an amount above the mean of Section 2 equal to or greater than that shown in our problem—in other words, the probability that Section 1 is truly superior to Section 2. Of course, if the mean of all differences between means of samples from parent population of Section 1 and from parent population of Section 2 is zero (one and the same parent population), and if the probable error of these differences is 2.34, then differences favorable to Section 1 would appear only in the upper shaded portion of Figure 19. The probability of that is $\frac{23.5}{100}$.

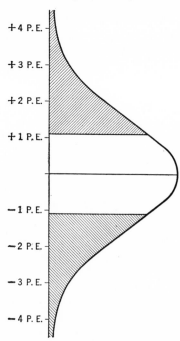

Figure 19. Use of the Normal Frequency Curve to Determine Probability of Chance

Reliability of Other Measures.—A somewhat lengthy discussion has been given on the reliability of means and the reliability of differences between means, for the reason that the concept developed applies to reliability of any measure. The concept includes random sampling and the distribution of the series of means, medians, standard deviations, or any other measure that may be computed. For example, in the capsule experiment, each of the hundred students who drew a sample of ten not only found the mean for his sample, but also found the standard deviation for his sample. When the hundred standard deviations were tabulated, it was found that they made a normal probability distribution whose mean was slightly less than 2.00 (the standard deviation of the parent population), and whose sigma was approximately .42. As will be seen from a formula which follows, these values in theory should be 2.00 and .4472 respectively.

A few formulas are given here for the reliability of some of the other important statistical measures. Others will be given as the need arises.

Reliability of median:

$$\text{S.E.}_{\text{Md.}} = \frac{1.2533\ \sigma_s}{\sqrt{N-1}} \quad \text{or} \quad \frac{.6745}{\sqrt{N-1}} \times 1.86\ \sigma_s \tag{21}$$

$$\text{P.E.}_{\text{Md.}} = \frac{.8454\ \sigma_s}{\sqrt{N-1}} \quad \text{or} \quad \frac{.6745}{\sqrt{N-1}} \times 1.25\ \sigma_s \tag{22}$$

$$\text{S.E.}_{\text{Dif. Md.}} = \sqrt{(\text{S.E.}_{\text{Md.}_1})^2 + (\text{S.E.}_{\text{Md.}_2})^2} \tag{23}$$

$$\text{P.E.}_{\text{Dif. Md.}} = \sqrt{(\text{P.E.}_{\text{Md.}_1})^2 + (\text{P.E.}_{\text{Md.}_2})^2} \tag{24}$$

Reliability of measures of variability:

$$\text{S.E.}_{\sigma} = \frac{\sigma_s}{\sqrt{2\ N}} \tag{25}$$

$$\text{P.E.}_{\sigma} = \frac{.6745\ \sigma_s}{\sqrt{2\ N}} \tag{26a}$$

[Formulas (25a) and (26a) neglect a small correction to compensate for use of σ_s instead of σ_{pp} but it is so insignificant ordinarily that it may be ignored.]

$$\text{S.E.}_{\text{Dif.}_{\sigma}} = \sqrt{(\text{S.E.}_{\sigma_1})^2 + (\text{S.E.}_{\sigma_2})^2} \tag{27}$$

$$\text{P.E.}_{\text{Dif.}_{\sigma}} = \sqrt{(\text{P.E.}_{\sigma_1})^2 + (\text{P.E.}_{\sigma_2})^2} \tag{28a}$$

$$\text{S.E.}_{Q} = \frac{1.1663\ Q}{\sqrt{N}} \quad \text{or} \quad \frac{.6745}{\sqrt{N}} \times 1.73\ Q \tag{25b}$$

$$P.E._Q = \frac{.7867\ Q}{\sqrt{N}} \quad or \quad \frac{.6745}{\sqrt{N}} \times 1.17\ Q \qquad (26b)$$

$$P.E._{Dif._Q} = \sqrt{(P.E._{Q_1})^2 + (P.E._{Q_2})^2} \qquad (28b)$$

$$S.E._{A.D.} = \frac{.7555\ A.D.}{\sqrt{N}} \quad or \quad \frac{.6745}{\sqrt{N}} \times 1.12\ A.D. \qquad (25c)$$

$$P.E._{A.D.} = \frac{.5096\ A.D.}{\sqrt{N}} \quad or \quad \frac{.6745}{\sqrt{N}} \times .76\ A.D. \qquad (26c)$$

$$P.E._{Dif._{A.D.}} = \sqrt{(P.E._{A.D._1})^2 + (P.E._{A.D._2})^2} \qquad (28c)$$

$$P.E._{C.V.} = \frac{.6745}{\sqrt{2\ N}} \times C.V. \sqrt{1 + 2\left(\frac{C.V.}{100}\right)^2} \qquad (26d)$$

$$P.E._{Dif._{C.V.}} = \sqrt{(P.E._{C.V._1})^2 + (P.E._{C.V._2})^2} \qquad (28d)$$

Reliability of a Proportion.—The sampling concept may be applied to proportions in the same manner as it is applied to random sampling of normally distributed parent populations. A brief experiment will be described to illustrate the idea. A small sack of corn consisting of 60% white grains and 40% yellow grains was drawn from repeatedly. At each draw, a sample of five grains was removed and the proportion of white grains was noted and recorded. The sample was immediately returned

TABLE XXXII. DISTRIBUTIONS OF PROPORTIONS OF WHITE GRAINS OF CORN DRAWN IN SAMPLES OF FIVE GRAINS

(100 samples were drawn from the sack which contained 60% white grains)

Number of White Grains	Proportion of White Grains	Observed f	Theoretical f
(5)	1.0	5	7776
(4)	.8	27	25920
(3)	.6	39	34560
(2)	.4	21	23040
(1)	.2	6	7680
(0)	.0	2	1024
		100	100,000
	M_p	.596	.600
	σ_p	.210	.219
	.6745 σ_p	.142	.148

and the sack was shaken before the next draw. Thus an infinite population was provided. The scale used for tabulating the proportions, and the frequency of occurrence of the proportions, is shown in Table XXXII.

The observed frequencies of Table XXXII show the actual occurrence in a hundred samples of the proportions designated in the scale. The theoretical frequencies show the occurrence of the six possible proportions of the scale in a hundred thousand samples as determined by the laws of probability, the general formula for which here is $(p+q)^n = p^n + np^{n-1}q + \ldots$. If a white grain is regarded a success and a yellow grain a failure, then in drawing one grain there is a .6 probability (p) of success and a .4 probability (q) of failure $(.6+.4)^5$ which equals $.07776 + .25920 + .34560 + .23040 + .07680 + .01024$.

Fortunately, we do not need to go through such long and tedious solutions to find the mean and standard deviation of a distribution of proportions. The mean proportion, of course, is always p ($+.6$ in our problem) and the standard deviation of the proportions is

$$\text{S.E.}_p = \sqrt{\frac{pq}{n}} \qquad (29)$$

Substitution of p, q, and n of our problem gives

$$\text{S.E.}_p = \sqrt{\frac{.6 \times .4}{5}} \quad \text{or} \quad .219$$

This is exactly the same result obtained from expanding the binomial $(.6+.4)^5$ and solving for sigma in the usual way. The interpretation is that in making a draw of a sample of five grains the probability is about $\frac{2}{3}$ that its proportion of white grains will not differ from .600 by more than .219. To express the statement in terms of a probability of $\frac{1}{2}$ the formula is

$$\text{P.E.}_p = .6745\sqrt{\frac{pq}{n}} \qquad (30)$$

which may be expressed, for greater convenience, in computation, as

$$\text{P.E.}_p = \frac{.6745}{\sqrt{n}}\sqrt{pq} \qquad (31)$$

If it is desired to express the mean and standard deviation in terms of number of successes instead of proportion of successes, the formulas are

$$M = np \qquad (32)$$

and

$$S.E. = \sqrt{npq} \qquad (33)$$

or

$$P.E. = .6745\sqrt{npq} \qquad (34)$$

The value of np in our problem is $5 \times .6$ or 3 and the value of $\sqrt{npq}$ is $\sqrt{5 \times .6 \times .4}$ or 1.095. Comparison of the scales of numbers and of proportions in Table XXXII will reveal the relationships of Formulas (29), (32), and (33).

Formulas for measuring the reliability of the difference between two proportions are

$$S.E._{Dif._p} = \sqrt{(S.E._{p_1})^2 + (S.E._{p_2})^2} \qquad (35)$$

and

$$P.E._{Dif._p} = \sqrt{(P.E._{p_1})^2 + (P.E._{p_2})^2} \qquad (36a)$$

To illustrate practical application of reliability formulas on proportions, let us suppose that thirty-four of fifty pupils who are known to be superior in spelling were able to spell correctly a certain word. On the other hand, only eighteen of forty-five poor spellers were able to spell correctly the same word. We wish to know if this particular word is truly selective of good spellers or if the difference in proportions of correct spellings by the two types of pupils can be explained readily as a chance happening. For substitution in the formulas, we have

$$N_1 = 50 \qquad p_1 = .68 \qquad \text{and } q_1 = .32$$
$$N_2 = 45 \qquad p_2 = .40 \qquad \text{and } q_2 = .60$$

$$P.E._{p_1} = \frac{.6745}{\sqrt{50}}\sqrt{.68 \times .32} = .0954 \times .4665 \quad \text{or } .045$$

(The values of both factors in the formula may be read from tables provided in this book—Table D and Table F.)

$$P.E._{p_2} = \frac{.6745}{\sqrt{45}}\sqrt{.40 \times .60} = .1005 \times .4899 \quad \text{or } .049$$

(Here the value .049 is the variation from .400 (p_2) which normally may be expected half of the time in random sampling.)

STATISTICS APPLIED TO

.68 − .40 = .28, the difference between the two proportions

$P.E._{Dif._p} = \sqrt{.045^2 + .049^2}$ or .067, the probable error of the difference

.28 ÷ .067 = 4.18, the difference expressed in units of $P.E._{Dif.}$

The ratio of the difference to the probable error of the difference between the two proportions in this case is not likely a chance difference and, therefore, the correct spelling of the word is probably selective of superior students.

By combining Formulas (31) and (36a), a relationship between two proportions may be expressed in a form that will hold the difference between the two proportions equal to any desired constant (s) relative to the P.E. of their difference.[2] As an economy measure, this is highly desirable when pairs of proportions all having the same N are being compared, as in the work of validating test items by comparison of proportions of correct answers made by widely spaced student groups.

The relationship will be

$$p_1 - p_2 = s \sqrt{\left(\frac{.6745}{\sqrt{N}} \sqrt{p_1 q_1}\right)^2 + \left(\frac{.6745}{\sqrt{N}} \sqrt{p_2 q_2}\right)^2}$$

By substituting

$(1 - p_1)$ for its equal q_1
$(1 - p_2)$ for its equal q_2

and g for $\dfrac{.6745s}{\sqrt{N}}$, merely for convenience in computation, and then solving for p_1 the equation becomes

$$p_1 = \frac{2p_2 + g^2 \pm \sqrt{(8g^2 + 4g^4)(p_2 - p_2^2) + g^4}}{2(1 + g^2)} \tag{36b}$$

This formula is general and therefore must be simplified to suit any series of pairs of proportions. For example, let us say, we desire a difference of at least three P.E.'s to show significance $(s=3)$. Also suppose that all groups of the series have forty-six students $(N=46)$.

[2] D. F. Votaw, "Graphical Determination of Probable Error in Validation of Test Items" in *Journal of Educational Psychology*, Vol. XXIV, pp. 682–686.

Then

$$g = \frac{.6745 \times 3}{\sqrt{46}} \quad \text{or} \quad .2982$$

Substituting this value for g in Formula (36b) we obtain

$$p_1 = \frac{2p_2 + .0889 + \sqrt{.7430 \ (p_2 - p_2{}^2) + .0079}}{2.1778}$$

Now the value computed for p_1 when a value for p_2 is substituted will be the least proportion possible to maintain the difference agreed upon as significant. A graph of this equation can be constructed from which any p_1 value can be read for any given p_2 value.[3]

Perhaps the study of reliability as it relates to percentages eventually will do more to discourage injection of mysticism into events than will the study of any other phase of statistics. A conclusion should not be drawn from the mere fact that an event happens, but from the recurrence of the event more frequently than normal expectation. It is not uncommon to read a press dispatch of an accidental death on the day following the victim's dream of death. This leads some to believe the dream portended the death. However, many men dream of death and announce the dream. Also many men die accidentally. These two events are almost certain to happen simultaneously sooner or later. To find the expected frequency of simultaneous happenings, we need only know the average daily proportion of men who dream of death and the average daily proportion of men who lose their lives by accident. The product of these two proportions will give a probability which, though very small, is likely no smaller than the actual occurrence of the two happenings together. Unfortunately, news gatherers do not hunt headlines about men who have "death" dreams but *do not die*.

Permutations and Combinations.—Another important aspect of probability has to do with permutations and combinations. If from a group of n members, sets of r members are removed one set at a time, each set being arranged in every possible

---

[3] J. N. Arnold, "Nomogram for Determining Validity of Test Items" in *Journal of Educational Psychology*, Vol. XXVI, pp. 151–153.

order, and then returned to the group before taking the next set, the total number of different arrangements possible, P, is known as the number of permutations. The formula is

$$_nP_r = n[n-1][n-2] \ldots [n-(r-1)] \tag{37}$$

Suppose, for example, that a boy has five (n) marbles of different colors. He wishes to arrange them in as many different sets of three (r) as possible. He wishes also to arrange each set into as many orders as possible. Applying Formula (37) to the problem we have

$$_5P_3 = 5 \cdot 4 \cdot 3 \quad \text{or } 60$$

Now if the boy is interested only in the number of *combinations*, and takes no account of different orders of arrangement for each set, the formula becomes

$$_nC_r = \frac{n[n-1][n-2] \ldots [n-(r-1)]}{1 \cdot 2 \ldots r} \tag{38}$$

and its application is

$$_5C_3 = \frac{5 \cdot 4 \cdot 3}{1 \cdot 2 \cdot 3} \quad \text{or } 10$$

Many forms of gambling and "fleecing" thrive on the fact that the number of permutations is usually much larger than would appear to the ordinary observer. In the marble problem, the chance probability of getting an arrangement of the red, white, and blue marbles in the order named is $\frac{1}{60}$, yet the accomplishment might appear comparatively easy until tried.

Exercises and Problems

1. Construct a normal probability graph by plotting points at intervals of .25σ's. (The x and y values may be found in Table E.) Let one sigma equal twenty units on the graphic paper. (This will require one hundred and twenty units to provide an x axis six sigmas in length.) The highest point of the graph should be 39.89 graphic paper units high.

2. By an actual count of squares estimate the total area (number of squares) under the curve.

3. By an actual count of squares make estimates of the areas of the following indicated sections:

	Area in Squares	Percentage of Total Area
Total area	. . . .	100
$.00\sigma$ to $+1.25\sigma$	. . . .	. . . .
$+ .75\sigma$ to $+1.50\sigma$	. . . .	. . . .
$- .25\sigma$ to $+ .75\sigma$	. . . .	. . . .
-1.00σ to $+1.00\sigma$	. . . .	. . . .
-2.00σ to -1.00σ	. . . .	. . . .

4. (a) By reference to the table of areas and ordinates, check the approximations you made in Exercise 3.

(b) By use of these tables find the exact area (expressed as percentage) of each of the following sections:

From $.00\sigma$ to $+1.00\sigma$
From $.00\sigma$ to $+1.75\sigma$
From $-.25\sigma$ to $+ .75\sigma$
From $+.50\sigma$ to $+1.50\sigma$
From -1.75σ to $- .75\sigma$
From $+3.00\sigma$ to end of base
From $+2.50\sigma$ to end of base

(c) From $.00\sigma$ to what point on the base will 41.15% of the area be included?

(d) From $+.15\sigma$ to what point on the base lying to the right will 24.27% of the area be included?

(e) From $+.15\sigma$ to what point on the base lying to the left will 26.84% of the area be included?

(f) What percentage of area lies within a distance of one sigma from the mean?

(g) If the mean I.Q. of children in a certain city is 99.5 and the standard deviation of their I.Q.'s is 14, what percentage of the city's children will have I.Q.'s of 107 to 120 inclusive?

5. (a) If a hundred samples of 384 members each were drawn from the box of capsules described in this chapter, and if the hundred means of the samples were tabulated, what standard deviation would you expect the distribution of means to have?

(b) Will doubling the number of samples affect the standard deviation of their means?

6. In a state-wide testing program, the scores (may be accepted as an infinite population) of the fifth grade yielded a mean of 44.8

and a standard deviation of 9.1. Suppose Miss Smith's fifth-grade class of thirty-six pupils makes a mean score of 43.78 on the test.

(a) Should Miss Smith be alarmed about the deficiency of her class?

(b) What is the probability that by pure chance the class could deviate from 44.8 by the amount of difference shown here?

7. In the test program of Exercise 6 the mean score for Miss Jones' fifth-grade class of thirty-six pupils was 47.35.

(a) Is it possible that this high score can be explained as a chance happening?

(b) What is the probability as a pure chance happening that a mean score as great as or greater than the mean of Miss Jones' class may be made by a class of thirty-six pupils?

8. In the test program of Exercise 6 the mean score for Miss Brown's fifth-grade class of thirty-one pupils was 50.40.

(a) Do you believe chance to be a satisfactory explanation for the high mean score?

(b) About what is the probability that a mean score this high or higher would occur by chance?

(c) If chance is not a reasonably acceptable explanation, name a few other *possible* explanations.

9. If the heights of 10,000 twelve-year-old boys who have been chosen at random are found to have a mean of 57 inches and a standard deviation of 6 inches, what is the probable error of the mean?

10. A Challenge: In selecting a group of pupils for an arithmetic teaching experiment it was found, from a preliminary test, that the standard error of the mean score of twenty-five pupils was 1.72. How many pupils will be required to double this reliability? (Doubling the reliability here means reducing the standard error by one half.)

11. In a high school senior class of 435 pupils, a quick survey of achievement in English is desired. From an alphabetical file of the names of the seniors, every fifth name is drawn. The pupils whose names were drawn are assembled and given a standardized test in English with the following results:

$$\text{Mean} = 63.42$$
$$\text{S.D.} = 12.32$$

(a) What is the probable error of the mean?

(b) There is a probability of ½ that the mean for the whole senior class would lie within what limits?

(Before beginning the solution of this problem you should decide on the following points: What is the parent population? The sample? What is the value of *p*? Does the method of securing sample here satisfy the requirement of *random* sampling?)

12. A test on arithmetic computation was given to two sections of the sixth grade. From the following data, determine if the difference between the two sections is significant:

	Sec. 1	Sec. 2
N	31	32
M	52.20	43.70
σ	16.10	15.00

13. (a) Is the difference significant between the means of the two sets of high school grades below?

(b) What is the probability that differences as great as or greater than the difference between the means of these two students may arise between any two chance samples?

S_1: A, C, B, B, D, B, A, F, C, B, A, C, B, A, D, B

S_2: A, B, B, C, C, D, A, B, D, B, C, C, B, D, C, A

14. The median age of 320 girls in the sixth grade of a school is 11.32 years and sigma of their ages is .81 years, while for the 304 boys in the same grade the corresponding values are 11.56 years and .86 years.

(a) Find P.E.$_{Md.}$ of the girls' ages.

(b) Find P.E.$_{Md.}$ of the boys' ages.

(c) Find difference between medians.

(d) Find the P.E.$_{Dif._{Md.}}$

(e) The difference found in (c) is how many times the probable error of the difference?

15 The standard deviation of the twenty-four semester marks (A=4, B=3, C=2, etc.) made by a high school senior, Robert Adams, was .62. The standard deviation of the class was .91. Has Robert been significantly less variable in his scholarship than the total variability of the other members of the class? (Find the standard error for Robert, and the standard error for other mem-

bers together. Then find the difference between the two means, the standard error of the difference, and the ratio of Dif.$_\sigma$ to P.E.$_\sigma$. From this information the question can be answered.)

16. A check-up on the reading habits of seventh-grade pupils revealed that 15.1% of the 558 voluntary reading of those of higher intelligence (upper 25%) was "mystery and detective." Only 4.9% of the 122 voluntary readings of those of lower intelligence (lower 25%) was of the same classification. Is there statistical evidence here that love for the "mystery and detective" type of reading is characteristic of higher intelligence in seventh-grade pupils? (N_1 and N_2 here are the numbers of books read by the respective groups.

$$15.1\% = \text{a proportion of } .151$$
$$4.9\% = \text{a proportion of } .049)$$

17. A Challenge: The senior class of a high school is composed of seventy-eight girls and seventy-two boys. Is there statistical evidence that the survival of girls in the school is better than the survival of boys? (Assume that numbers were equal at the beginning of high school.)

18. A Challenge: A high school which has an enrollment of 956 pupils, 409 of which are boys and 547 of which are girls, publishes an honor roll at the end of the first semester on which are listed the names of fifty-one boys and eighty-six girls. Is the proportion of girls on the honor roll significantly higher than their proportion in the total enrollment? (This problem may be solved by either of two treatments which lead to practically the same results: first, honor students may be treated as a sample from the total enrollment, a restricted parent population, or secondly, the proportion of boys enrolled who made the honor roll may be compared with the proportion of girls enrolled who made the honor roll, both proportions being considered as samples from an infinite parent population.)

19. A Challenge: One unit of a matching test has five questions, but offers ten possible answers with which to match the questions. What is the probability of selecting the five correct answers by pure chance?

20. What is the probability that one will, in succession, cast a "three" with a die, toss "heads" with a coin, and "cut" the seven of spades?

21. Using the data of Exercise 14 of Chapter 5, determine if the coefficients of variability of arithmetic reasoning scores and arithmetic computation scores are significantly different.

22. A Challenge: A true-false test of 110 items (about equally divided between true and false) is given to a class, and the method of determining scores is by the formula $S = R - W$ or $S = N - 2W$. Assuming that no pupil in the class knows the answer to any of the items, and that all pupils respond by guess to all items, answer the following questions:

(a) What is the mean score to be expected for the class?

(b) What is the approximate probability of a score of 8 or more being made by pupil A? (Since the scoring method permits only even-numbered scores, the next lower score possible is 6 and, therefore, the point on the scale of scores which separates 8 and 6 should be considered 7.)

23. A Challenge: Approximately how many items must be provided in a four-response, multiple-choice test to insure a probability of ½ that a student who knows nothing about the subject will not deviate by chance more than two correct answers from the number of correct answers expected of him? Since the next higher number of correct answer deviations possible here is 3, the P.E. should be considered 2.5. The proportion of successes expected is .25 and the proportion of failures expected is .75.)

CHAPTER 7

FURTHER APPLICATIONS OF THE PROBABILITY CURVE

As suggested in the preceding chapter, there are many applications of the probability curve other than reliability. The present chapter considers a few of these applications.

Distribution of Class Marks.—If school marks are true measures of achievement, and if achievement takes the form of normal probability, then it becomes a simple matter to determine the percentage of students to whom each mark should be assigned. If five marks are used, the problem is solved by separating the total area of the normal curve into five truncated sections so that the distances between the true centers of weight of the consecutive sections are equal.[1] These percentages are shown approximately in Figure 20.

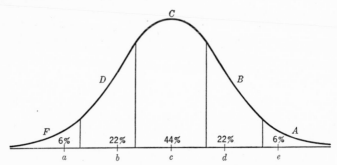

Figure 20. Normal Distribution of School Achievement Marks

In Figure 20, $ab = bc = cd = de$.

Moreover, a is the true center of weight of the section in which it is located, b is the true center of weight of the section

[1] Walter C. Eells, "An Improvement in the Theoretical Basis of Five Point Grading System Based on the Normal Probability Curve" in *Journal of Educational Psychology*, Vol. XXI, pp. 128–135.

in which it is located, and so on. No limits are placed on the ends of the base line.

Although the distribution of marks shown in Figure 20 is in theory correct, perhaps, for ease of computation, it may be better to divide the base into equal segments, say one sigma each, and let the area above each segment represent the percentage for a mark. In this procedure the origin should be used as a point of reference. Figure 21 shows the percentages for the various marks.

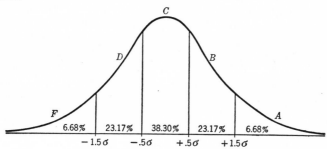

Figure 21. Common Distribution of School Achievement Marks

In this form of distribution the small percentage of cases which lie above $+2.5\sigma$ is thrown into the A's, and the equally small percentage of cases which lie below -2.5σ is thrown into the F's.

In the actual practice of assigning marks to a class no predetermined percentage of F's, D's, C's, B's, and A's should be assigned. To do so would be satisfactory if one had proof that one's class was normally distributed in achievement. Such proof is generally lacking. An illustrative problem will help to make these points clear.

In dealing with an individual class one should first secure for each student a quantitatively expressed measure. This may be a score on a single test or the sum of the scores for several tests and other evaluations. The mean and the standard deviation for these measures should then be computed. All scores lying within one half of a standard deviation above and below the mean should be assigned marks of C; all scores between $+.5\sigma$ and $+1.5\sigma$ should be assigned marks of B; and all scores above

+1.5σ should be assigned marks of A. Of course D's will be assigned to scores lying between −.5σ and −1.5σ, while F's will be assigned to all scores below −1.5σ.

An example of the application of this plan will help to make it clear. Let each of the scores below represent the total accumulated test scores of each of fifty high school seniors in a class in English, at mid-semester.

31, 35, 50, 27, 62, 45, 31, 25, 55, 35, 26, 40, 46, 41, 24, 32, 56, 41, 24, 50, 52, 64, 36, 32, 33, 46, 36, 37, 27, 42, 42, 33, 28, 37, 33, 43, 37, 34, 58, 49, 38, 39, 38, 24, 54, 43, 39, 34, 29, 39.

The teacher of the class is faced with the necessity of turning in to the principal's office a qualitative mark (A, B, C, D, or F) for each student. She will follow the statistical method [2] suggested above by first tabulating the fifty scores.

TABLE XXXIII. SHOWING THE FIRST STEP IN THE CHANGING OF SCORES TO SCHOOL MARKS

Scale	f
60–64	2
55–59	3
50–54	4
45–49	4
40–44	7
35–39	12
30–34	9
25–29	6
20–24	3
	50

The mean of this distribution is 38.90, and the standard deviation is 10.25. With these two facts the points on the scale of scores which separate the successive marks can be found as follows :

Mean + ½ σ or (38.90 + 5.13) = 44.03, the point on the scale of scores which separates the B's from the C's.

Mean − ½ σ or (38.90 − 5.13) = 33.77, the point on the scale of scores which separates the C's from the D's.

[2] F. C. Ayer and D. F. Votaw, "Taking the Guess Out of Grading" in *American School Board Journal*, Vol. 83, No. 4, pp. 35–36.

44.03 + 1 σ or (44.03 + 10.25) = 54.28, the point which separates
the A's from the B's.

33.77 − 1 σ or (33.77 − 10.25) = 23.52, the point which separates
the D's from the F's.

These results may be summarized by indicating between each
pair of marks the point on the scale of scores which separates
the two marks, as follows:

F   23.52   D   33.77   C   44.03   B   54.28   A

With this information before her the teacher is now prepared
to assign a definite mark to each score. For example, 31 = D,
35 = C, 50 = B, 27 = D, 62 = A, and so on. When all of the
scores are converted into marks and the marks tabulated, the
distribution takes the form shown in Table XXXIV.

TABLE XXXIV. DISTRIBUTION OF MARKS FOR A HIGH SCHOOL
ENGLISH CLASS

Marks	f	%f
A	5	10
B	8	16
C	21	42
D	16	32
F	0	00
	50	100

The percentages of the various marks in Table XXXIV do
not conform very closely to the theoretical percentages, but this
lack of conformity should not disturb the teacher. The scores
of the class do not represent a true normal distribution, and
there is no scientific reason for distorting the form of distribution of the class in an attempt to force it into normal shape.
It is interesting to observe that there is no actual score lower
than 24, but the point of division between D's and F's is 23.52.
Therefore, no F's were earned in this class.

**Changing Scores in One Distribution to the Terms of An-
other.**—Occasionally it becomes necessary to change a score in
one distribution into terms of another in order that comparisons
of individual pupils may be made, or that lost scores may be

restored, or that a pupil's score on a test that was never taken may be estimated. Suppose that a fifth-grade child, after having taken Standardized Test R in School A, transfers to School B where Standardized Test S has been given. The principal of School B wishes to record the child's score on Test R in terms of Test S. With the following information he can do this easily.

	Test R	Test S
Fifth-Gr. Mean	26	37
Fifth-Gr. S.D.	8.5	10.6
Child's Score	18	

The problem here is to determine what score will occupy the same relative position in the distribution of Test S scores that 18 occupies in the distribution of Test R scores. The child's score of 18 is 8 score points below $(26-18)$ the mean of Test R, which distance, expressed in terms of sigma of Test R, is $\frac{8}{8.5}$ or $.94\sigma$. The equivalent score which is being sought in the distribution of Test S scores will lie $.94\sigma$ below the mean of Test S. But the standard deviation for Test S scores is 10.6, which multiplied by .94 equals 9.96. When this value is subtracted from the mean, 37, the score 27 (27.04, to be exact) is found. Hereafter the transferred child's score will be treated as 27 instead of 18.

While there are other factors that may be involved in this problem the procedure just outlined here will permit, in many instances, a fair estimate of the score to be recorded.

Other situations which may require the same type of treatment may be seen in such questions as: Is a girl whose height is 61 inches at age eleven relatively taller or shorter than a boy whose height is 62 inches at age eleven? What is the most probable score a pupil would have made on the day he was absent when the test was given? (Of course, previous test scores for the class and for this pupil are known.)

Arbitrary Means and Standard Deviations.—The preceding discussion leads us to a consideration of the general problem of converting the scores of a distribution to a new set of scores having for a mean and for a standard deviation any values previously agreed upon. Conversions of this sort are required in comparing the divisions of a battery test. For example, a general achievement test may be composed of ten divisions. In establishing norms for the tests the tests may be given to a representative sample of the population for whose use they are finally intended. Most likely the ten means computed from the raw scores of the ten divisions will all be different, as also will be the ten standard deviations. To make scores on the ten divisions comparable it will be necessary to decide arbitrarily upon a mean and a standard deviation, and to convert scores from each of the ten divisions to this new distribution.

Steps in the process of conversion are indicated in the following formula:

$$S_a = M_a + \frac{\sigma_a (S_1 - M_1)}{\sigma_1} \tag{39}$$

M_1, σ_1, and S_1, refer respectively to the mean, the standard deviation and any individual score of a known distribution. M_a and σ_a are the mean and the standard deviation arbitrarily decided upon for the new distribution. S_a is the score being sought in the arbitrary distribution, which will be equivalent to S_1 of the known distribution.

To illustrate the use of Formula (39) let us suppose that a high school mathematics teacher has given three tests in the course of a half semester. In order to make the tests have equal weight the teacher wishes to have their standard deviations equal, and in order to be able to make comparisons of relative achievement of a given student on the three tests, or a comparison of two students on two different tests, the teacher wishes to have the three means equal. Data for the three tests are as follows:

	Test 1	Test 2	Test 3
M	54	28	71
σ	18	8	22

The teacher decides upon an arbitrary mean of 60 and an arbitrary standard deviation of 20, so Formula (39), applied to converting the individual scores of Test 1, will become

$$S_a = 60 + \frac{20(S_1 - 54)}{18}$$

Applied to Test 2 the formula becomes

$$S_a = 60 + \frac{20(S_2 - 28)}{8}$$

And applied to Test 3 it becomes

$$S_a = 60 + \frac{20(S_3 - 71)}{22}$$

Let us take two scores from Test 1 (say 72 and 45) and convert them to the new distribution.

$$S_a = 60 + \frac{20(72 - 54)}{18} \quad \text{or} \quad 80$$

$$S_a = 60 + \frac{20(45 - 54)}{18} \quad \text{or} \quad 50$$

Thus it may be seen that a score of 72 of Test 1 is the equivalent of a score of 80 in the arbitrary distribution, and a score of 45 of Test 1 is the equivalent of a score of 50 in the arbitrary distribution. It may be seen also that a score of 36 of Test 2 is the equivalent of a score of 80 in the arbitrary distribution, while a score of 93 of Test 3 is the equivalent of a score of 80 in the arbitrary distribution. When all the scores of the three tests have been converted to the new distribution and recorded, direct comparisons become possible, as may be seen from a small sample of the teacher's register, as shown in Table XXXV.

TABLE XXXV.   RAW SCORES CONVERTED TO ARBITRARY DISTRIBUTION

Names	Raw Scores			Converted Scores		
	Test 1	Test 2	Test 3	Test 1	Test 2	Test 3
J. R. A.	72	36	93	80	80	80
S. G. A.	45	32	49	50	70	40
M. B.	27	20	60	30	40	50
. . . .						
. . . .						

J. R. A.'s three scores which appeared so unequal as raw scores are shown, by conversion, to be exactly equal in relative value. S. G. A. appeared to make the lowest score in the second test when we examine only the raw scores, but actually he was at his best in Test 2. His converted score of 70 was the highest of his three scores. Also, we can now say definitely that S. G. A. in Test 2 was better than M. B. in Test 3, for the two pupils' converted scores for these tests are respectively 70 and 50. The reverse appeared to be the case, however, when comparisons were attempted on the basis of raw scores.

When several scores are to be converted to an arbitrary distribution, much labor will be saved by constructing a graph for the purpose. The graph will be a straight line, since each of the two variables (S_a and S_1) in Formula (39) are of the first degree. Let us illustrate the construction of such a graph by use of the data for Test 2. The equation was previously stated to be

$$S_a = 60 + \frac{20(S_2 - 28)}{8}$$

which reduces to

$$S_a = 2.5\, S_2 - 10$$

and which in turn is the equation to be graphed. In order to save space and to make a more readable and compact graph, it is better to let the scales cross at their mutual means rather than at their zeros. Thus only the useful portions of the two scales will need to be shown. Also the graph will then pass through the point of intersection of the scales. Only one other point will need to be located by substituting in the equation above in order to fix the position of the graph. For safety, however, one should locate two points (one on each side of the intersection of the two scales) by substituting in the equation. If these two points and the point of intersection lie in a straight line it is not likely that an error has been made.

Now, in the equation

$$S_a = 2.5\, S_2 - 10$$

for S_2 substitute 10, and S_a becomes 15. Then for S_2 substitute 40, and S_a becomes 90.

The straight line through these two points will pass through the intersection of the scales. Now from the graph of Figure 22 the arbitrary score equivalent to any raw score can be read.

For example, a raw score of 44 is equal to an arbitrary score

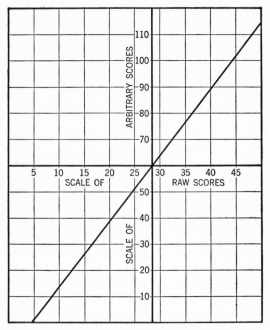

Figure 22. Graph for Converting Scores from One Distribution to Another

of 100, a raw score of 20 is equal to an arbitrary score of 40, and so on.

T-Scores.—If general agreement were entered into in the matter of selecting the mean and standard deviation to be used when converting raw measures to an arbitrary distribution, great advantages would result. To some extent this has been done. Although not the original sense in which the term T-Score was used, it may be used to refer to a distribution of any measures whose *mean is 50* and whose *standard deviation is 10*. Some of the advantages of such an arbitrary agreement are: first, the useful range of scores would practically never fall below zero nor rise above one hundred (these extremes being five sigmas below and above the mean), and secondly, any score from the distribution would carry its own identifications. A report that a child made a raw score of 43 is without meaning, but a report that he made a T-Score of 72 is highly significant. The latter report describes the child's exact position in the distribution of scores. Because of our common understanding that a T-Score distribution has a mean of 50 and a standard deviation of 10 we know that a T-Score of 72 is exactly 2.2 sigmas above the mean—a comparatively high position. Moreover, we can determine the percentage of children who made higher or lower scores.

By reference to the table of areas and ordinates (Table E of this book) in this case we find the percentage of scores higher than 2.2 sigmas to be 1.39.

By substituting 50 for M_a and 10 for σ_a in Formula (39), and by dropping subscripts of other symbols a formula for converting to T-Scores results:

$$\text{T–Score} = 50 + \frac{10(S - M)}{\sigma} \tag{40}$$

In the same manner as described in the discussion of Formula (39) this formula for the T-Scores may be graphed for ready conversion of raw scores to T-Scores.

When and if those who officially handle children's permanent record cards, principals and teachers, understand the meaning of the T-Score it will become a most useful form of record for such measurements as standardized test scores. From the T-Scores immediate interpretations may be made of a child's measure in musical aptitude, mechanical aptitude, achievement, and so on, and without reference to the original distribution of scores.

No doubt the reader has observed a similarity between the percentile score previously discussed and the T-Score. The two forms of records serve very much the same purposes, and, if all distributions were normal, being skewed in neither direction and having no gaps on the scale left unfilled with cases, there would be no need for both the percentile score and the T-Score. However, in the absence of ideally normal distributions there are two important differences between the two measures. First, a T-Score of 50 always represents the mean, whereas a percentile score of 50 may be either above or below the mean, depending on the direction of skewness. Secondly, T-Scores represent on the scale of T-Scores the true relative position of the raw scores on the scale of raw scores, whereas percentile scores have the effect of closing gaps on the scale of raw scores and otherwise distorting the raw score distribution.

Standard Scores.—Another means of expressing a measure so as to give it meaning, or of expressing measures from different distributions so as to make them comparable, is by use of the *standard score*. The standard score may be defined as $\frac{x}{\sigma}$, or the deviation of a raw score from the mean of the raw scores expressed in terms of sigma. For example, in a distribution of raw scores the mean of which is 36 and the standard deviation of which is 8, a score of 44 has a standard score equivalent of $+1.00$ because 44 is one sigma above the mean $(\frac{44-36}{8} = +1.00)$. Some other standard scores of the distribution are

Raw Score	Standard Score
48	+1.50
36	0.00
30	−0.75
26	−1.25
Etc.	

Here, of course, a standard score of zero represents the mean. General use of the standard score has been retarded because of the necessity of using negative values for scores below the mean. In principle there is no difference between the T-Score and the standard score. A standard score can be converted to a T-score by simply multiplying it by 10 and adding 50 to the result. The raw score of 48 as shown above, which equals a standard score of $+1.50$, will equal a T-Score of 65 or $(1.50 \times 10 + 50)$; the raw score of 30 will equal a T-Score of 42.5, or $(-.75 \times 10 + 50)$.

Difficulty of Test Items.—The normative-survey type of research has practically injected a new philosophy into education.

One illustration of this change is the fact that teachers who have learned to think in the language of statistics no longer assign values to their test questions before giving them to their classes. There was a time, for example, when it was not uncommon for the teacher to announce a test consisting of questions or problems with the statement that on Problem 1 ten points would be allowed; on Problem 2, because of its greater difficulty, fifteen points would be allowed; on Problem 3, because of its ease, only five points would be allowed; and so on. Since the teacher had had no previous experience in giving the test, her opinions of the relative difficulty-value of the items were largely arrived at by guess. Difficulty of test items is not to be guessed by the teacher, but is to be determined from the actual responses of pupils. Fundamentally the criterion for relative difficulty is relative numbers of unsuccessful performers. For example, we say that walking a slack wire is difficult, but walking a sidewalk is easy. The basis of our judgment is the fact that a very small percentage of the population can walk a slack wire, but practically the total percentage of population can walk a sidewalk. The greater the percentage of failures, then, the more difficult the item. It does not follow from this statement, however, that the ratio of difficulty of two items will be the same as the ratio of the respective percentages of pupils missing them. A distribution of pupil abilities here, as in most other variable human traits, conforms to normal probability. The normal probability curve must therefore be applied to the solution of relative difficulty as illustrated in Figure 23.

Since we must have a definite point on the limitless base for a point from which to measure, and since there will be some convenience in the use of a base five sigmas in length (a base of five sigmas ignores only about 1.24% of the area), all distances to represent difficulty will be measured from -2.5σ. Now let us suppose that Problem 1 of a test was missed by 80% of a class, and that Problem 2 was missed by 40% of the group. Then the difficulty of Problem 1 is related to the difficulty of Problem 2 as the distance ab in Figure 23 is related to the distance ac when 80% of the curve's area extends to b, and

40% of the curve's area extends to *c*. The problem of finding these two distances is very simple. The table of areas and ordinates must be used, and since this table gives areas only from the mean, points *b* and *c* must first be located in terms of distances from the mean. For example, 80% extends 30% to the right of the mean. Therefore the position of point *b* is $+.85\sigma$. In order to shift zero to our arbitrary starting point (-2.5σ),

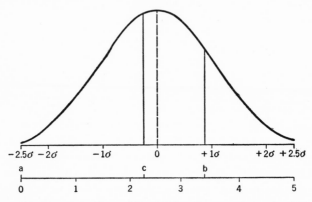

Figure 23. Use of the Normal Probability Curve to Determine Relative
Difficulty of Problems

2.5σ must be added to $+.85\sigma$ making 3.35σ the total length of *ab*. Only 40% missed Problem 2. The area falls short of the mean by 10%. The sigma position of point *c*, therefore, is $-.25\sigma$. Then point *c* is only 2.25σ distant from point *a* ($-.25\sigma+2.50\sigma$). We may now say that with the value 5.00 (the length of the base) representing the maximum value for any problem the value of Problem 1 is 3.35, and the value of Problem 2 is 2.25. If it is desired to allow a maximum value of 10 the values determined for Problems 1 and 2 must be multiplied by 2, which raises them to 6.70 and 4.50 respectively. If the relative difficulty-values are to be expressed as percentile values (maximum of 100), the first values determined must be multiplied by 20.

The entire procedure can be reduced to a mechanical procedure, as follows:

TABLE XXXVI. SUMMARY OF STEPS IN DETERMINING RELATIVE
VALUES OF TEST PROBLEMS

Prob. No.	Percentage Not Know-ing Answers	Less 50%	Corres-ponding σ Value	Plus 2.50 σ	Times 20* (%ile value)	Or Times 2* (decile value)
1	80	+30	+.85	3.35	67	7
2	40	−10	−.25	2.25	45	5

* Percentile values or decile values should be expressed to nearest integer for ordinary uses.

Perhaps the statement should be added here that when deal-ing with objective tests of a large number of items, each of which covers only a small portion of the subject matter, the de-termination of relative values for the items is hardly worth while. Final ranking positions of pupils are affected but little, if any, in such instances. However, distinct refinement of the validity of a test will result from rearranging the items in order of difficulty (beginning with easier items) as determined by per-centages of pupils not knowing the answers.

The Use of Statistical Calculations

Probably the ideal situation in which the teacher can best learn much of statistics as applied to education is in her daily classroom procedure, provided she is expected to do testing and measuring of different types. Such a situation gives a practical basis for many kinds of calculations. Unfortunately, a plan of this type as an element in teacher education is difficult to follow out, and statistics is often learned somewhat apart from the schoolroom and applied later to the problems of the school. Sometimes students reach the present point in their statistical work with interest and success, but the same students often have little or no idea concerning the work done as it relates to them as teachers.

The remaining portion of this chapter is written with the idea of pointing out to inexperienced teachers some of the uses which may be found by them for the different terms and the different calculations considered thus far in the text. Some of the simplest uses of statistics may be found in the one-room country school, where a teacher may have, say, three pupils in the seventh grade. It is just as important for her to do something in the way of testing and measuring as for the teacher in the large urban school to carry out such procedures. If she gives an achievement test to her three pupils in the seventh grade, what can be done with such results, and what meaning will such results have?

DIAGRAM I. ACHIEVEMENT TEST SCORES MADE BY ONE PUPIL

Name __M. S._____ Grade __7_____ Boy or Girl __Girl_____

What is your age? __13_____ When is your next birthday? __October 28_____

Name of your town or district _____

Name of your building _____ Date __May 18_____

Test	Score
1. Choice of Words	55
2. Knowledge of Literature	61
3. Dictation	49
4. Reading: Vocabulary	57
5. Reading: Comprehension	43
Average Reading	50	
6. Social Studies	48
7. Knowledge of Physical Education	45
8. Arithmetic Reasoning	55
9. Arithmetic Computation	44
Average Arithmetic	49.5	

$$9)\ 457$$

Total Average	51
Grade Equivalent	6.1
Age Equivalent	12-10

Data for such a test are shown in Diagram 1 for one pupil, M. S. The statistical calculations here involve the total average, which is obtained by adding the nine partial scores and dividing by 9. It is clear that with only nine scores which are to be averaged for a total score, a sigma or other measure of variation would have little value.

Another calculation which may be of interest to our teacher concerns the average reading score, which is obtained by adding 57, the score on vocabulary, and 43, the score on comprehension. This calculation gives 100, which divided by 2 gives 50. In the same manner the average arithmetic score may be found. From Diagram II the grade equivalent and age equivalent may be recorded. Results for the three members of the class are shown in Diagram III. Note that all possible scores are indicated at the left by a series of class intervals, and that each of the nine tests is designated at the top. Each digit represents a score for one of the pupils. In this tabulation it should be noted that the identity of each child is lost, except for the total average at the right. It is also clear that standard deviations would have little meaning with only three cases, so these results are not calculated.

Diagram II makes it possible to give certain interpretations to the total score. The broken line represents the record of M. S. The results shown indicate that the pupil is below the seventh grade standard for the time of year (seventh grade, eighth month) he was tested, in all tests except two. There is, of course, the possibility that he will attain this standard by the end of the year.

It is probably outside the province of this text to discuss the use of such results as a basis for interviews with parents and pupils and for modification of methods in order to bring about the proper results. The teacher who really comprehends such results and who is to use them to their fullest value will do so at least in part because she has a correct concept of the average as it has been treated in the preceding pages. In this connection attention is called to the fact that the calculations as just described involve only the arithmetic mean. It will probably be advantageous for the student to raise the following questions: first, why do the authors of the text use the mean rather than the median or the mode, and second, what are the advantages and disadvantages of the mean for such work?

It may be profitable to consider a large class from an urban community in much the same way as the preceding group.

DIAGRAM II. INDIVIDUAL EDUCATIONAL CHART

(Also the means for a class may be charted on this page)

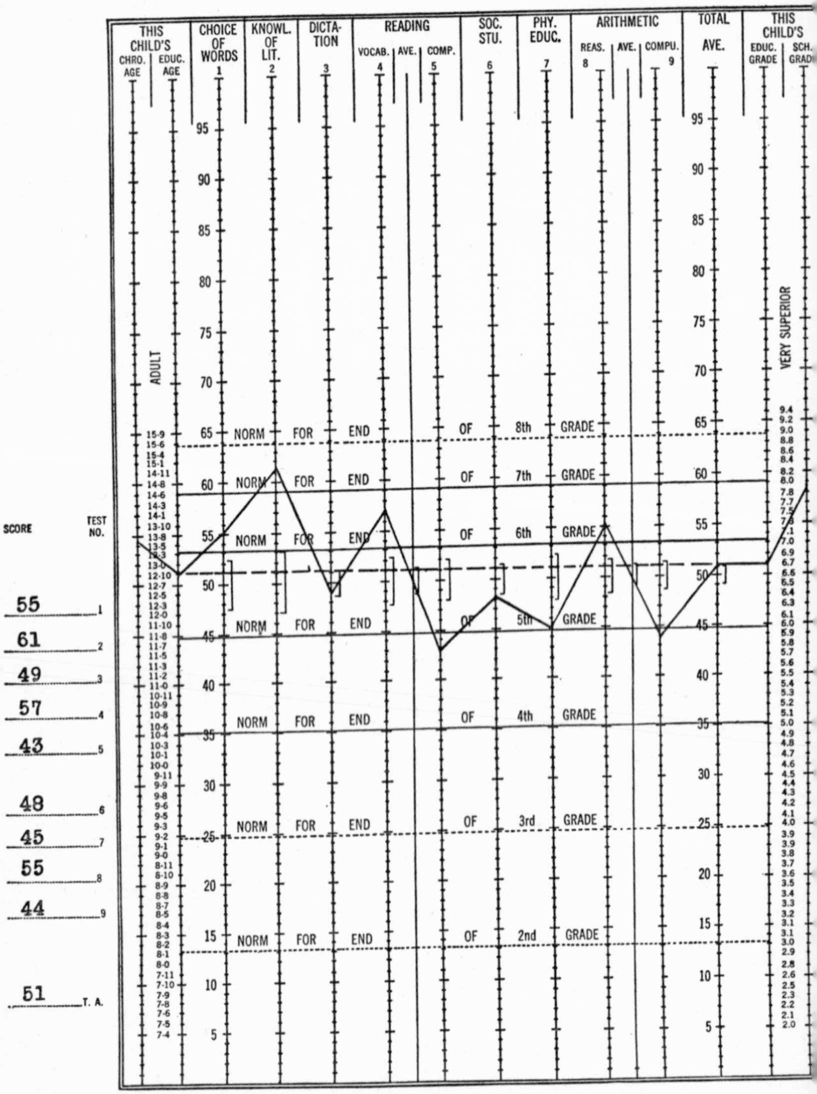

[1] The educational grade and age scales on this Profile Chart indicate the norms for this test.
[2] Ages above 14-6 and below 7.9 are extrapolated.
[3] The short vertical lines are probable errors of the estimated true scores.
[4] The scale of scores for all of the tests has been equated. Thus uniform achievement will indicated for a child if the line connecting his nine score-points is approximately horizontal.

(Courtesy, The Steck Company, Publishers, Austin, Texas)

There would be, of course, a sheet similar to Diagram I showing results for each pupil. Diagram IV is a summary sheet for the entire class of thirty-three pupils. Note that the means have been calculated at the bottom. This is done by taking first the midpoint of the interval concerned as defined by the authors of the test, and multiplying it by the number of cases. Following these operations, the sum of the products is divided by the

DIAGRAM III. DISTRIBUTION OF ACHIEVEMENT TEST SCORES MADE BY THREE RURAL SCHOOL PUPILS (GRADE 7)

Scale of Scores	Test 1	Test 2	Test 3	Test 4	Test 5	Test 6	Test 7	Test 8	Test 9	Total Average
55–59									1	
50–54		1					1	1		
45–49			1	1		1				1
40–44			1	1	1				1	
35–39			1			2	2	2	1	1
30–34	1	2		1						1
25–29					2					
20–24	2									
Totals	3	3	3	3	3	3	3	3	3	3
Means	25.3	38.7	42.0	40.3	32.0	40.3	42.0	42.0	45.3	38.7
S.D.'s										

number of pupils. These calculations may also be carried out by the short method as set forth in Chapter 2. To indicate more clearly the value of these results, the broken line may be drawn across a sheet like the one of Diagram II, which shows the educational profile of pupil M. S. This line will indicate the average scores of the class on each of the nine tests. As before, a broken line may be drawn on a similar sheet for each of the children concerned.

These procedures may seem comparatively simple compared with some of the operations required in the preceding chapters. The important thing about the problem is that the teacher see her results in the proper perspective. In this connection she will need to consider the following questions:

1. The difference in the mean score made by the class (Diagram IV) on Test 1 and Test 2 is *13.8* points. Does this difference have any significance? In other words, is this difference, when expressed in terms of its probable error, too great to be accounted for readily as a chance difference?

2. The difference between the mean of the same class on Test *7* and the norm for the seventh grade is about 4 points. Is this difference significant or reliable?

3. Does the theory of probability as studied in Chapter 6 have any relation to the material as studied in this chapter?

Another approach which this urban teacher may make with respect to these thirty-three children is by means of a percentile curve. This curve is shown in Diagram V, and is discussed

DIAGRAM IV. DISTRIBUTION OF ACHIEVEMENT SCORES MADE BY A CLASS OF THIRTY-THREE PUPILS (GRADE 7)

Scale of Scores	Test 1	Test 2	Test 3	Test 4	Test 5	Test 6	Test 7	Test 8	Test 9	Total Average
95–99		7		1						
90–94		1					1			
85–89	1	1		1	1		2			
80–84		2	1	3	4	4	1			1
75–79		2	2	3	1	2	2	2	1	5
70–74	4	5	4	4	2		2	2	6	3
65–69	5	2	3	4	5	6	10	6	5	2
60–64	5	3	4	4	3	5	3	4	6	6
55–59	5		3	3	5	4	1	7	7	6
50–54	3	2	3	5		4	4	5	2	2
45–49	2	2	6		3	4	3	3	4	4
40–44	3	3	6	1	5	4	2	3	2	3
35–39	1	1	1	3	1		1			1
30–34	1	1		1	2		1	1		
25–29	1				1					
20–24	1	1								
15–19	1									
Totals	33	33	33	33	33	33	33	33	33	33
Means	55.0	68.8	56.7	63.1	58.2	60.2	62.5	57.8	60.4	60.2
S.D.'s	14.9	21.6	12.5	15.5	16.3	12.4	14.4	10.5	10.1	12.1

in Chapter 4. The percentile scores are indicated at the top and raw scores at the left.

The curve was constructed by determining the percentages of scores that lie below the tops of the successive intervals. For example: none lies below point 34.5 of the raw-score scale, 3.0% lie below 39.5, 12.1% lie below 44.5, and so on. If this chart is made fairly accurately, any child can locate his percentile

DIAGRAM V. PERCENTILE GRAPH FOR TOTAL AVERAGE SCORES
OF DIAGRAM IV

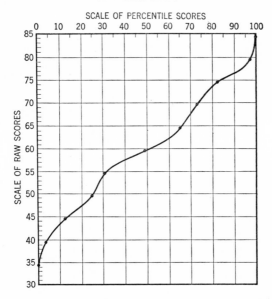

score equivalent for his raw score. This is done by locating the raw score on the scale of raw scores, moving horizontally to the curve, and from this point on the curve moving vertically to the percentile scale. For conferences with parents and pupils this method of interpreting scores has very distinct advantages. Probably a better understanding of the relation of a pupil to his class can be given both to parents and to the individual pupil by this device than by most other plans.

To illustrate further, one pupil made a score of 67. His percentile score is 70, which means that 70% are below him.

The preceding discussion has emphasized the value for the teacher of considering test results in terms of averages and of percentiles. It is apparent that such material is also of interest to the principal. Reference to Diagram IV shows the average of the class in reading comprehension (Test 5) to be 58.2, and shows the standard deviation to be 16.3. Another seventh grade of thirty-three pupils in the same building had an average score of 48.9, with a standard deviation of 15.1. The P.E.$_{Dif.}$ between these scores was found to be 2.65, which when divided into the difference gave 3.5. This indicates that statistically the difference is not likely due to any accident of sampling. The principal immediately began a study to determine why there should be such a wide difference between the two classes. This school system records estimates of intelligence by means of a group intelligence test. He found that the average scores on this intelligence test for the two groups of children were approximately the same. This seemed to place the responsibility on the teacher of the group whose average score was 48.9. A conference with the teacher revealed to her what the principal already knew—that, like many other teachers, she had no organized and systematic program for the teaching of reading. By following a carefully outlined series of readings and by availing herself of summer school courses, she gradually overcame this difficulty and finally became one of the best reading teachers in the system. It is not to be supposed that every reliable difference between two averages could be settled in a clear-cut manner, as the one cited. Usually such differences indicate complicated relations which are difficult to resolve.

Again it is clear that the differences between averages may be of interest to supervisors and superintendents. When such officials have satisfied themselves that differences between grades or schools or communities are statistically reliable, they have a basis for dealing with differences in teaching ability, and differences in groups, along with many other conditions which bring about differences in the accomplishment of children.

In conclusion, emphasis should again be placed upon the fact that the computations involved in the preceding illustrations are relatively simple, but that they have a basis in some of the funda-

mentals of statistics, and that their full appreciation and interpretation by the teacher depend upon many things besides a
knowledge of the simple calculations which are involved in
them.

Exercises and Problems

1. Assign a mark (A, B, C, D, or F) to each of the thirty scores
which follow and tabulate the frequency of marks assigned. Also
indicate the percentages of the class receiving each mark.

68	71	49
109	82	74
86	78	57
60	90	79
107	87	57
83	78	86
84	62	70
92	96	96
86	55	71
88	96	54

(Tabulate scores in intervals of five.)

2. Distribution A has a mean of 42.28, and a standard deviation
of 12.64. Distribution B has a mean of 68.12, and a standard
deviation of 16.24. Find what scores in distribution B are equivalent respectively to the following scores from distribution A: 58,
30, 52.

3. The mean weight of ten-year-old boys is about 72 pounds,
and the standard deviation of their weights is about 16 pounds.
For thirteen-year-old boys the approximate figures for the mean
and the standard deviation are 105 pounds and 20 pounds respectively. If John weighs 84 pounds at the age of ten, about how
much should he be expected to weigh at age thirteen?

4. A test was given a class with the following results:

$$\text{Mean} = 75$$
$$\text{S.D.} = 24$$

The teacher desires to change the scores into a new set with the

$$\text{Mean} = 48$$
$$\text{and the S.D.} = 16$$

Construct a graph for making the conversions and convert the following raw scores:

12,   21,   69,   108

5. The fourth grade of a city took a standardized achievement test with the following results:

Mean = 35.1
S.D. = 8.4

(a) Make a graph for converting the raw test scores to T-Scores.

(b) From the graph make a T-Score scale showing equivalence of all raw scores from 10 to 60. (This plan is more convenient than repeatedly tracing the T-Score value for each child's raw score. There were several thousand children involved here.) Express T-Score to the nearest integer. Use this form:

Raw Score	T-Score Equivalents
60	
59	
58	
Etc.	

6. The following scores were made by thirty-four fifth-grade pupils in a vocabulary test. Tabulate the scores in intervals of three, find the mean and the standard deviation, and find for each score its T-Score equivalent. (Here the graph may be used to advantage.)

33, 21, 27, 45, 39, 12, 16, 30, 24, 43, 19, 28, 31, 22, 36,
44, 25, 29, 34, 10, 26, 38, 49, 47, 35, 23, 17, 32, 27, 31,
29, 20, 41, 25.

7. If John made a T-Score of 58 on a mechanical aptitude test, what percentage of the boys made lower scores than John?

8. A pupil was one of a group which took a test on each of three different subjects. From the information which follows determine his standard score on each test.

Test	(M) Mean for Group	(σ) S.D. for Group	(X) Score for Pupil	(x) X − M	$\left(\dfrac{x}{\sigma}\right)$ Standard Score
A	59.0	15.6	53		
B	34.9	12.0	41		
C	18.6	7.2	28		

9. Find the percentile difficulty-value of the following simple recall test questions, each of which was missed by the percentage indicated:

Problem No.	Percentage Not Knowing Answer
1	60
2	30
3	75
4	16
5	96

10. A Challenge: Make a table for permanent filing which will show the percentile or decile values for percentages not knowing answers as follows: 95, 90, 85, 80, 75, ..., 10, 5. (This will require nineteen computations, but will satisfy practically all ordinary classroom needs.)

CHAPTER 8

CORRELATION

Our previous discussions and problems have dealt with measures of central tendency, measures of variability, and measures of reliability of some one trait. The usefulness of statistics would be greatly limited, however, were it not for methods of determining the relation of one trait to another. To illustrate, it is probably just as important for the teacher to know something of the relationship which exists between intelligence and reading ability, as it is for her to know the mean score of her pupils on an intelligence test or on a reading test. The statistical methods employed for measuring such relations are called correlation.

Next to common average, perhaps, the understanding of the simpler meanings of correlation is more widespread than the understanding of any other statistical term. The technical aspects of its computation and its interpretation, however, are left largely to those with technical training.

Correlation refers to the relationship existing between pairs of measures. Each pair may consist of two measures of different traits for the same individual, two measures of a trait for two individuals who have been paired, or measures of one trait in one of a pair of individuals and a second trait in the other member of the pair.

Let T_1 and T_2 represent measures of two traits. Then the possibilities of pairing may be illustrated as follows:

    (a) T_1—T_2 (of the same individual)
    (b) T_1—T_1 (of two paired individuals), or
    (c) T_1—T_2 (of two paired individuals)

Data of the following type specifically illustrate situation (a): Each child of a class has been given a test in intelligence and a test in vocabulary, with results as follows:

Child	Int. Score	Vocab. Score
A	82	53
B	49	33
C	64	42
—	—	—
—	—	—
—	—	—

Situation (b) may be illustrated by, let us say, intelligence of husbands and wives:

Couple	Intelligence Score of Husband	Wife
A	69	71
B	43	41
C	56	56
—	—	—
—	—	—

Situation (c), which occurs less frequently in educational situations than either (a) or (b), may arise in such forms for example as comparison of sense of rhythm in the male of bisexual twins with the sense of harmony in the female:

Twins	(Male) Rhythm Score	(Female) Harmony Score
A	72	63
B	68	64
C	57	38
—	—	—
—	—	—

In dealing with a problem in correlation, one should analyze the data carefully to decide which of the three situations is represented. While the technique of computation is the same for all three situations, correct interpretation is dependent upon an understanding of the data in hand.

Correlation has been so defined that a perfect relationship of the two sets of measures (often called variables) is +1.00 if they vary in the same direction, and −1.00 if they vary in opposite directions. So far as goodness of relationship is concerned, a correlation of -1.00 is as good as a correlation of $+1.00$. Lack of relationship will be indicated not by negative correlation but by zero correlation.

The extremes of $+1.00$ and -1.00 practically never arise in educational data, so it will be necessary to improvise problems to illustrate these extremes.

Relationship Measured by Rank Difference.—One plan for determining correlation is known as the rank-difference method. This method will be used to introduce the student to the calculations which are used for finding correlation coefficients. The symbol for relationship determined from rank difference is usually given as ρ.

The following improvised data will illustrate the extreme positive case: Ten children were given an arithmetic test and a reading test. The ten pairs of test scores are shown in Table XXXVII.

TABLE XXXVII. SHOWING PERFECT POSITIVE CORRELATION BY THE RANK-DIFFERENCE METHOD

Arith. (X)	Read. (Y)	R_x	R_y	D	D^2
42	51	1	1	0	0
30	48	2	2	0	0
27	46	3	3	0	0
26	43	4	4	0	0
24	40	5	5	0	0
20	38	6	6	0	0
19	31	7	7	0	0
17	30	8	8	0	0
16	27	9	9	0	0
12	22	10	10	0	0
					0

The formula is

$$\rho = 1 - \frac{6\,\Sigma D^2}{N^3 - N} \tag{41}$$

Thus the value of ρ in our problem is found by

$$\rho = 1 - \frac{0}{10^3 - 10} \quad \text{or} \quad +1.00$$

In the above problem the column R_x shows ranks based upon the X scores, and the column R_y shows ranks based upon Y scores. In the D column the differences between the ranks of paired scores are recorded, and in the D^2 column these differences are squared. In our problem the ranking position of each measure in the X column is exactly the same as the ranking position of its companion measure in the Y column. Thus all differences become zero, as do also their squares.

It must not be forgotten here that the value (+ 1.00) found for ρ is really a measure of relationship between the two sets of ranks, rather than a measure of relationship between the two sets of scores. Therefore all the weaknesses of ranking heretofore pointed out will reside in ρ.

To illustrate the extreme negative situation, let us suppose that ten boys about fifteen years of age and of exactly equal height (64.6 inches) are selected. Two measurements for each boy are made—his leg length and his sitting height. The measurements are recorded in Table XXXVIII.

TABLE XXXVIII. SHOWING PERFECT NEGATIVE CORRELATION

Sitting Height (X)	Leg Length (Y)	R_x	R_y	D	D^2
34.1	30.5	1	10	9	81
34.0	30.6	2	9	7	49
33.9	30.7	3	8	5	25
33.8	30.8	4	7	3	9
33.7	30.9	5	6	1	1
33.6	31.0	6	5	1	1
33.5	31.1	7	4	3	9
33.4	31.2	8	3	5	25
33.3	31.3	9	2	7	49
33.2	31.4	10	1	9	81
					330

Substituting in Formula (41) we get:

$$\rho = 1 - \frac{6 \cdot 330}{10^3 - 10}$$

$$= 1 - \frac{1980}{990}$$

$$= 1 - 2 \quad \text{or} \quad - 1.00$$

The value of rho (ρ) may fall at any point between these two extremes. At the half-way point, zero, no relationship is indicated. In the case which follows, nothing more than pure chance seems to be operating to connect the pairs of measures. Data of Table XXXIX were secured by drawing from a hat two numbers simultaneously—one with the right hand and the other with the left. This operation was repeated until ten pairs of numbers were drawn.

TABLE XXXIX.   SHOWING LACK OF RELATIONSHIP OR VALUE OF ZERO FOR RHO

Number Drawn with

Right Hand (X)	Left Hand (Y)	R_x	R_y	D	D^2
17	27	8	9	1	1
12	40	10	5	5	25
26	22	4	10	6	36
19	46	7	3	4	16
16	51	9	1	8	64
20	31	6	7	1	1
32	48	1	2	1	1
27	38	3	6	3	9
24	30	5	8	3	9
30	43	2	4	2	4
					166

$$\rho = 1 - \frac{6 \cdot 166}{10^3 - 10}$$

$$= 1 - \frac{996}{990}$$

$$= 1 - 1.006 \quad \text{or} \quad -.006$$

This small value may be regarded as zero, hence no relationship is indicated.

The computation of rho ignores the original scores or measures, and deals only with the ranks assumed by the scores. It is, therefore, only an approximation of correlation. Rho may indicate a perfect correlation when such does not exist. For a perfect positive correlation, each X measure must occupy exactly the same position in the x distribution that its companion Y measure occupies in the y distribution.

Fundamental Concept of Correlation.—At this point in the discussion perhaps a more exact definition for correlation should be given. By mathematical definition, rectilinear correlation is the slope of the straight line which best fits the y values of the points in a correlation chart. As shown in Figure 24, best fit is effected when the sum of the squares of all the y distances by which the line misses the points is a minimum. (Assume that scales have been equated by making σ_x equal σ_y.)

We may think of the two series in a correlation as the X and the Y series. Thus each pair of raw measures may be shown by use of one point on a graph. By arbitrarily passing the x axis through the mean of the Y data, and by passing the y axis through the mean of the X data, each pair of measures will now be designated by lower-case x and y. (It should be remembered that upper-case X designates a raw measure, while lower-case x designates the deviation of a raw measure from the mean of its group.)

Each point shown in Figure 24 is located by the x and y values of a pair of raw measures. For example, suppose that the series of paired measures were 37–28, 42–31, 39–26, 21–14, and so on, with the mean for the X series being 30 and the mean for the Y series being 20. Then the small x's and the small y's are

Pair	X	Y	x	y
a	37	28	+7	+8
b	42	31	+12	+11
c	39	26	+9	+6
d	21	14	−9	−6
—	—	—	—	—
—	—	—	—	—
—	—	—	—	—

From Figure 24 it is obvious that the line AB is the line of best fit when considering the y value of the points, but line CD is the line of best fit when considering the x value of the points. Fortunately there is no need to deal with both of these lines for the reason that the angle which line AB makes with the x axis is exactly the same as the angle which line CD makes with the y axis. This angle determines the slope of line AB, the slope being the tangent of the angle. Since line AB passes through

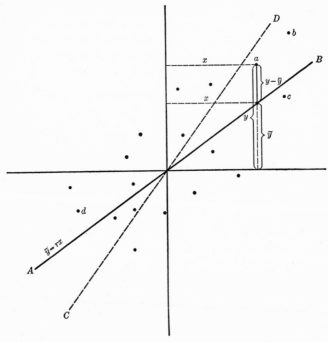

Figure 24. Graphic Illustration of Correlation

the origin, it may be written in terms of one of its points $(x, \overline{y})$ and its slope (r). This equation is

$$\overline{y} = rx$$

To make the units of measure on the two axes common, each term of the equation is divided by its respective sigma, thus:

$$\frac{\overline{y}}{\sigma_y} = \frac{rx}{\sigma_x}$$

Solve for $\overline{y}$

$$\overline{y} = \frac{\sigma_y x r}{\sigma_x}$$

Now $y - \bar{y}$ is the *distance* for point a of Figure 24. According to the theory of least squares, this value must be squared, along with the $y - \bar{y}$ value for each of the other points. Following this operation the sum of these squares is found. All this may be indicated by

$$\Sigma(y - \bar{y})^2$$

or expanded, by

$$\Sigma(y^2 - 2y\bar{y} + \bar{y}^2)$$

Now substituting in this expression the value previously found for $\bar{y}$ we have

$$\Sigma\left(y^2 - \frac{2\, y\sigma_y x r}{\sigma_x} + \frac{\sigma_y{}^2 x^2 r^2}{\sigma_x{}^2}\right)$$

(The next step may be ignored by those having no knowledge of elementary calculus.)

Since the last expression represents the sum of the squares of N distances and this sum was required to be a minimum, it may be set equal to k (or any other symbol) and $\dfrac{dk}{dr}$ (r is our variable) found and set equal to zero as follows:

Deriving

$$\frac{dk}{dr} = \Sigma\left(-\frac{2\, y\sigma_y x}{\sigma_x} + \frac{2\, \sigma_y{}^2 x^2 r}{\sigma_x{}^2}\right) = 0$$

Dividing by 2

$$\Sigma\left(-\frac{y\sigma_y x}{\sigma_x} + \frac{\sigma_y{}^2 x^2 r}{\sigma_x{}^2}\right) = 0$$

Removing parenthesis and replacing summation signs

$$-\frac{\Sigma xy\sigma_y}{\sigma_x} + \frac{\Sigma x^2 \sigma_y{}^2 r}{\sigma_x{}^2} = 0$$

Multiplying by $\dfrac{\sigma_x}{\sigma_y}$

$$-\Sigma xy + \frac{\Sigma x^2 \sigma_y r}{\sigma_x} = 0$$

or $\quad \dfrac{\Sigma x^2 \sigma_y r}{\sigma_x} = \Sigma xy$

Dividing by N, the number of points,

$$\frac{\Sigma x^2 \sigma_y r}{N \sigma_x} = \frac{\Sigma xy}{N}$$

Substituting $\sigma_x{}^2$ in the left member for its equal, $\frac{\Sigma x^2}{N}$,

$$\left(\sigma_x = \sqrt{\frac{\Sigma x^2}{N}} \quad \text{and therefore} \quad \sigma_x{}^2 = \frac{\Sigma x^2}{N} \right)$$

$$\frac{\sigma_x{}^2 \sigma_y r}{\sigma_x} = \frac{\Sigma xy}{N}$$

and cancelling σ_x from numerator and denominator of the left member

$$\sigma_x \sigma_y r = \frac{\Sigma xy}{N}$$

$$\text{or} \qquad r = \frac{\Sigma xy}{N \sigma_x \sigma_y} \qquad\qquad (42)$$

Thus the fundamental formula for correlation is derived. While this formula is seldom directly applied, it should be remembered for its importance as a basic reference. All other forms of formulas for correlation are developed from Formula (42). Useful application of correlation formulas, however, do not necessitate remembering the details of the development just completed.

We shall now take a simple example to illustrate the computation of r.

TABLE XL.   SHOWING CALCULATION OF CORRELATION BY FUNDAMENTAL FORMULA

Child	Spelling Scores	Reading Scores					
	(X)	(Y)	x	y	xy	x^2	y^2
A	13	60	3	10	+30	9	100
B	12	49	2	−1	−2	4	1
C	11	50	1	0	0	1	0
D	10	55	0	5	0	0	25
E	9	51	−1	1	−1	1	1
F	8	40	−2	−10	+20	4	100
G	7	45	−3	−5	+15	9	25
			0	0	+62	28	252

$$M_x = 10, \quad M_y = 50$$

To use the fundamental formula we must know

$$N = 7$$

$$\Sigma xy = +62$$

$$\sigma_x = \sqrt{\frac{\Sigma x^2}{N}} \quad \text{or} \quad \sqrt{\frac{28}{7}} \quad \text{or} \quad \sqrt{4} \quad \text{or} \quad 2$$

$$\sigma_y = \sqrt{\frac{\Sigma y^2}{N}} \quad \text{or} \quad \sqrt{\frac{252}{7}} \quad \text{or} \quad \sqrt{36} \quad \text{or} \quad 6$$

Then
$$r = \frac{+62}{7 \cdot 2 \cdot 6} \quad \text{or} \quad +.7381$$

By making a slight change in the fundamental formula it will be unnecessary to actually find σ_x and σ_y. Formula (42) is

$$r = \frac{\Sigma xy}{N \sigma_x \sigma_y}$$

But
$$\sigma_x = \sqrt{\frac{\Sigma x^2}{N}} \quad \text{and} \quad \sigma_y = \sqrt{\frac{\Sigma y^2}{N}}$$

Substituting these values for σ_x and σ_y respectively

$$r = \frac{\Sigma xy}{N \sqrt{\frac{\Sigma x^2}{N}} \sqrt{\frac{\Sigma y^2}{N}}}$$

or
$$r = \frac{\Sigma xy}{N \sqrt{\frac{1}{N^2}} \sqrt{\Sigma x^2 \cdot \Sigma y^2}}$$

But
$$N \cdot \sqrt{\frac{1}{N^2}} = 1,$$

so the formula becomes

$$r = \frac{\Sigma xy}{\sqrt{\Sigma x^2 \cdot \Sigma y^2}} \tag{43}$$

Formula (43) applied to the problem of Table XL would require only very simple substitution as follows:

$$r = \frac{+62}{\sqrt{28 \cdot 252}} \quad \text{or} \quad \frac{+62}{\sqrt{4 \cdot 7 \cdot 36 \cdot 7}} \quad \text{or} \quad \frac{+62}{2 \cdot 6 \cdot 7} \quad \text{or} \quad +.7381$$

Let us now apply Formula (43) to a problem in which we do not have convenient integers for means. Data of Table XLI are of this type.

TABLE XLI. CORRELATION OF SERIES WITH NON-INTEGRAL MEANS

(Solution a—Using True Means)

X	Y	x	y	xy	x^2	y^2
7	5	+3.1	+1.8	+5.58	9.61	3.24
6	5	+2.1	+1.8	+3.78	4.41	3.24
5	4	+1.1	+0.8	+0.88	1.21	0.64
4	4	+0.1	+0.8	+0.08	0.01	0.64
4	3	+0.1	−0.2	−0.02	0.01	0.04
4	3	+0.1	−0.2	−0.02	0.01	0.04
3	3	−0.9	−0.2	+0.18	0.81	0.04
3	2	−0.9	−1.2	+1.08	0.81	1.44
2	2	−1.9	−1.2	+2.28	3.61	1.44
1	1	−2.9	−2.2	+6.38	8.41	4.48
		0.0	0.0	+20.20	28.90	15.60

$$M_x = 3.9, \quad M_y = 3.2$$

Applying Formula (43)

$$r = \frac{+20.20}{\sqrt{28.90 \times 15.60}} \quad \text{or} \quad + .95$$

The purpose of giving Solution a for Table XLI is to introduce the next formula. A severe burden of computation arises when deviations must be taken from a mean in decimals of one, two, or three places. Facility of computation is greatly improved by always taking the deviations from convenient assumed means which are integers and by using a modified formula which provides appropriate corrections for the false assumptions.

Omitting details of proof the following formula is offered as the most convenient for all purposes:

$$r = \frac{\Sigma x'y' - \dfrac{(\Sigma x')(\Sigma y')}{N}}{\sqrt{\left[\Sigma(x')^2 - \dfrac{(\Sigma x')^2}{N}\right]\left[\Sigma(y')^2 - \dfrac{(\Sigma y')^2}{N}\right]}} \tag{44a}$$

The problem of Table XLI will now be solved by this convenient formula.

TABLE XLII. CORRELATION OF SERIES WITH NON-INTEGRAL MEANS

(Solution b—Using Assumed Means)

X	Y	x'	y'	$x'y'$	$(x')^2$	$(y')^2$
7	5	3	2	+6	9	4
6	5	2	2	+4	4	4
5	4	1	1	+1	1	1
4	4	0	1			1
4	3	0	0			
4	3	0	0			
3	3	−1	0		1	
3	2	−1	−1	+1	1	1
2	2	−2	−1	+2	4	1
1	1	−3	−2	+6	9	4
		−1	+2	+20	29	16

Assumed Mean for X's = 4

for Y's = 3

$$r = \frac{+20 - \dfrac{(-1)(+2)}{10}}{\sqrt{\left[29 - \dfrac{(-1)^2}{10}\right]\left[16 - \dfrac{2^2}{10}\right]}}$$

$$= \frac{+20 - \dfrac{-2}{10}}{\sqrt{\left[29 - \dfrac{1}{10}\right]\left[16 - \dfrac{4}{10}\right]}}$$

$$= \frac{20.2}{\sqrt{28.9 \times 15.6}} \quad \text{or} \quad +.95$$

Formula (44a) is applicable in all situations. It is unnecessary to investigate the means of the X and Y series. In either or both, if the assumed mean taken should happen to be the true mean, either $\Sigma x'$ or $\Sigma y'$ or both will become zero in the formula.

Correlation Found from Tabulated Data.—When the number of pairs of measures is large the arrangement of the data in a series of pairs as shown in Table XLII is very inconvenient. In a long series of pairs of measures ordinarily found in educational situations, many repetitions of measures will occur. Not only would much unnecessary space be required for listing the pairs of measures, but many unnecessary arithmetic operations would be performed in the solution. By tabulating the data, neither more space nor more computation will be required for one thousand pairs of measures than for one hundred pairs.

Again let us take the data of Table XLI and tabulate it for a third solution.

In tabulating data, it is most convenient first to make out a work sheet with cells large enough to contain all the tally marks. Only one tally mark is required for each pair of measures, as is indicated in Figure 25 in which the data of Table XLI are tallied.

X Data

		1	2	3	4	5	6	7
	5						1	1
Y Data	4				1	1		
	3			1	11			
	2		1	1				
	1	1						

Figure 25. Tally Sheet for Tabulating Pairs of Measures

Thus ten tally marks record the ten pairs of measures. When the tallying has been completed, the tally marks in each cell should be totaled and the amount written in the corresponding cell of a new sheet on which the solution is to be executed. The solution is shown in Table XLIII (Solution c).

Every item found in Solution b and substituted in Formula (44a) may be located in the table illustrating Solution c. Therefore Formula (44a) could be applied to Solution c. The application of the formula will be more convenient, however, if we change its symbols to conform to those commonly used in tabulation. The formula will then be

TABLE XLIII.　CORRELATION OF TABULATED DATA
(Solution c)

Y Scale	1	2	3	4	5	6	7	f_y	d_y	$f_y d_y$	$f_y d^2_y$
5						1(+2)	1(+2)	2	+2	+4	8
4				1(+1)	1(+1)			2	+1	+2	2
3			1	2				3	0		
2		1(−1)	1(−1)					2	−1	−2	2
1	1(−2)							1	−2	−2	4
f_x	1	1	2	3	1	1	1	10		+2	16.
d_x	−3	−2	−1	0	+1	+2	+3				
$f_x d_x$	−3	−2	−2		+1	+2	+3	−1			
$f_x d^2_x$	9	4	2		1	4	9	29			
$f_{xy} d_y$	−2	−1	−1	+1	+1	+2	+2	+2			
$f_{xy} d_x d_y$	+6	+2	+1		+1	+4	+6	+20			

X Scale

$$r = \frac{\Sigma f_{xy} d_x d_y - \dfrac{(\Sigma f_x d_x)(\Sigma f_y d_y)}{N}}{\sqrt{\left[\Sigma f_x d^2_x - \dfrac{(\Sigma f_x d_x)^2}{N}\right]\left[\Sigma f_y d^2_y - \dfrac{(\Sigma f_y d_y)^2}{N}\right]}} \tag{44b}$$

Formulas (44a) and (44b) may be written

$$r = \frac{a}{\sqrt{bc}}$$

for brevity and for convenience in referring to the three major parts of the formulas.

Comparison of the identical elements of Formulas (44a) and (44b) are now easy to make, as here illustrated:

Formula (44a)		Formula (44b)		
N	=	N	=	10
$\Sigma x'y'$	=	$\Sigma f_{xy} d_x d_y$	=	20
$\Sigma x'$	=	$\Sigma f_x d_x$	=	−1
$\Sigma y'$	=	$\Sigma f_y d_y$	=	+2
$\Sigma (x')^2$	=	$\Sigma f_x d^2_x$	=	29
$\Sigma (y')^2$	=	$\Sigma f_y d^2_y$	=	16

Now substituting these values in Formula (44b) the result is

$$r = \frac{+20 - \dfrac{(-1)(2)}{10}}{\sqrt{\left[29 - \dfrac{(-1)^2}{10}\right]\left[16 - \dfrac{2^2}{10}\right]}} \quad \text{or} \quad +.95$$

which is the same result obtained when substitutions were made in Formula (44a) of Solution *b*.

In making tabulations, intervals of the two scales do not need to be equal in size. The details of a solution for *r* from tabulated data will now be given to illustrate a general situation.

The solution as shown in Table XLIV divides naturally into three parts determined by the need for finding *a*, *b*, and *c* in the formula $r = \dfrac{a}{\sqrt{bc}}$. Let us take up these parts in reverse order *c*, *b*, *a*. (Of course, *a* is determined partly from values found in the other two parts of the solution.) The introduction of

TABLE XLIV. COMPUTATION OF CORRELATION WITH DATA IN FREQUENCY TABLE (Product-Moment Method)

X (Vocabulary Scores)

Y (Reading Scores)	20–29	30–39	40–49	50–59	60–69	70–79	80–89	90–99	f_v	d_v	$f_v d_v$	$f_v d^2_v$
40–44							1(+3)	2(+6)	3	+3	+9	27
35–39					2(+4)	2(+4)	3(+6)	1(+2)	8	+2	+16	32
30–34				2(+2)	4(+4)	4(+4)	2(+2)		12	+1	+12	12
25–29			3	5	4	3	1		16	0		
20–24		1(−1)	3(−3)	1(−1)	3(−3)	3(−3)			11	−1	−11	11
15–19	2(−4)	2(−4)	4(−8)	2(−4)	2(−4)				12	−2	−24	48
10–14	1(−3)	2(−6)							3	−3	−9	27
f_x	3	5	10	10	15	12	7	3	65		−7	157
d_x	−4	−3	−2	−1	0	+1	+2	+3				
$f_x d_x$	−12	−15	−20	−10		+12	+14	+9	+22			
$f_x d^2_x$	48	45	40	10		12	28	27	210			
$\Sigma f_{xy} d_y$	−7	−11	−11	−3	+1	+5	+11	+8	−7			
$\Sigma f_{xy} d_x d_y$	+28	+33	+22	+3		+5	+22	+24	+137			

$$r = \frac{+137 - \dfrac{-22 \cdot (-7)}{65}}{\sqrt{\left[210 - \dfrac{22^2}{65}\right]\left[157 - \dfrac{(-7)^2}{65}\right]}} \quad \text{or} \quad \frac{+134.63}{\sqrt{202.55 \times 156.25}} = \frac{+134.63}{177.88} \quad \text{or} \quad +.76$$

the figures in parentheses in the cells belongs to part a of the solution, so the c and b parts will be accomplished before the parenthetical figures are written in.

The c part of the solution contains nothing new. It consists simply of the three details involved in preparing to find the standard deviation of a distribution; viz., writing in the deviations, finding the fd's, and finding the fd^2's. Here we work only with the distribution of Y data (f_y).

The b part of the solution is an exact repetition of the c part, except that it deals with the distribution of X data (f_x).

The a part of the solution, which lies for the most part in the bottom two horizontal rows of figures, must take into consideration both frequencies of X and frequencies of Y. The steps are as follows:

1. Each cell frequency is multiplied by its y deviation, and the product placed in a parenthesis in the cell.

2. The parenthetical values are then totaled downward (algebraically) to the column marked $f_{xy}d_y$. This means that a cell frequency (regarded as belonging to both the X frequencies and the Y frequencies) has been multiplied by the y deviation, and the sums of all such products have been kept classified according to their respective x deviations.

3. The third and last step is to multiply the sums of the row marked $\Sigma f_{xy}d_y$ by their respective x deviations. In this manner the last row of figures (marked $\Sigma f_{xy}d_xd_y$) is determined. To be sure, one could attach these two operations at the extreme right, placing them vertically and heading them $\Sigma f_{xy}d_x$ and $\Sigma f_{xy}d_yd_x$ respectively. In that case the order of procedure would be first to multiply each cell frequency by its x deviation, secondly to total the products to the right, and thirdly to multiply the sums by their respective y deviations. The final sums will be exactly as in the procedure first described.

The remainder of the solution, including substitutions and computations, has been shown in connection with both Table XLIII, Solution c, and Table XLIV.

Perhaps an explanation should be made for the disregard of

size of intervals in Formula (44b). In the numerator of the formula the intervals of both scales are involved only as the product of the deviations employed. In the first factor of the denominator the square root of the squares of x deviations appears, and in the second factor the square root of the squares of the y deviations appears. If the actual values of the intervals were introduced into the formula they would appear as

$$\frac{hk}{\sqrt{h^2}\sqrt{k^2}}$$

which, of course, is *one*.

While in no sense is the use of either mechanical aids or tables to be regarded as necessary, the application of either a slide rule or of logarithms to such problems as we are now dealing with will be found to save time. For example, when the solution of Table XLIV reaches the form

$$r = \frac{+134.63}{\sqrt{202.55 \times 156.25}}$$

logarithms may be used as follows : (See Table B of this book.)

log 202.6 = 2.3067   log 134.6 = 12.1290 − 10
log 156.3 = 2.1939   (Sub.)   2.2503
       2)4.5006   9.8787 − 10
         2.2503
     antilog $\overline{1}.8787$ =   .7563
            r = +.76

Since answers correct to the nearest two decimal places are generally sufficiently accurate for correlation, the a, b, and c values could have been expressed here to the nearest integers and solved with a set of tables providing for only three digits. Note the simplicity of the following computation :

$$r = \frac{+135}{\sqrt{203 \cdot 156}}$$

log 203 = 2.3075
                                    log 135 = 12.1303 − 10
log 156 = 2.1931   2.2503
       2)4.5006   9.8800 − 10
         2.2503
                              antilog $\overline{1}.8800$ = .7585
                                     r = +.76

If the student does not now possess the ability to use logarithms it is best, perhaps, that he not attempt to acquire the ability for purposes of use in the exercises of this book.

Summation Method of Computing Correlation.[1]—For those who have access to an adding machine (one which prints the figures on a strip of paper), the summation method is not only fast but it offers few opportunities to make mistakes in computation. Most of the details where danger of error by hand methods is greatest are handled automatically by the adding machine. Let us find the correlation of the data of Table XLV by the summation method.

The formula to be used is Formula (44b). The six items necessary for substitution in the formula are found as follows:

Symbols of Formula (44b)	Equivalent Weights from Summation Table	Values from Table XLV
N	Σf_{x_1} or Σf_{y_1}	65
$\Sigma f_x d_x$	Σf_{x_2}	303
$\Sigma f_x d^2{}_x$	$2\Sigma f_{x_3} - \Sigma f_{x_2}$	$2 \cdot 959 - 303$ or 1615
$\Sigma f_y d_y$	Σf_{y_2}	253
$\Sigma f_y d^2{}_y$	$2\Sigma f_{y_3} - \Sigma f_{y_2}$	$2 \cdot 697 - 253$ or 1141
$\Sigma f_{xy} d_x d_y$	$\Sigma f d_{y_2}$	1314

Making the appropriate substitutions, we obtain

$$r = \frac{1314 - \dfrac{303 \times 253}{65}}{\sqrt{\left(1615 - \dfrac{303^2}{65}\right)\left(1141 - \dfrac{253^2}{65}\right)}}$$

$$= \frac{1314 - 1179.37}{\sqrt{(1615 - 1412.45)(1141 - 984.75)}}$$

$$= \frac{+134.63}{\sqrt{202.55 \times 156.25}} = +.76$$

In Table XLV only those figures are shown which are necessary to be recorded from the adding machine tape. However,

---

[1] Adapted from Chen-nan Li, "Summation Method of Fitting Parabolic Curves and Calculating Linear and Curvilinear Correlation Coefficients on a Scatter-Diagram" in *Journal of the American Statistical Association,* Vol. XXIX, pp. 405-409.

TABLE XLV. SUMMATION METHOD OF FINDING CORRELATION

X (Vocabulary Scores)

Y (Reading Scores)		20–29	30–39	40–49	50–59	60–69	70–79	80–89	90–99	f_{y_0}	f_{y_1}	f_{y_2}	f_{y_3}
		1	2	3	4	5	6	7	8				
40–44	7							1(7)	2(14)	3			
35–39	6					2(12)	2(12)	3(18)	1(6)	8			
30–34	5				2(10)	4(20)	4(20)	2(10)		12			
25–29	4			3(12)	5(20)	4(16)	3(12)	1(4)		16			
20–24	3		1(3)	3(9)	1(3)	3(9)	3(9)			11			
15–19	2	2(4)	2(4)	4(8)	2(4)	2(4)				12			
10–14	1	1(1)	2(2)							3	65	253	697
f_{x_0}		3	5	10	10	15	12	7	3				
f_{x_1}		65											
f_{x_2}		303											
f_{x_3}		959											
fd_{y_0}		5	9	29	37	61	53	39	20				
fd_{y_1}		253											
fd_{y_2}		1314											

in order to give a better understanding of the process the blank spaces of Table XLV are filled in with the cumulative additions to each space in Table XLVI. The columns at the right are added cumulatively downward. For example, the column marked f_{y_1} consists of the cumulative totals of column f_{y_0}, column f_{y_2} consists of the cumulative totals of column f_{y_1}, and so on. In the horizontal rows in the lower part of the table all cumulations are made from right to left. Each of the rows of figures down to f_{x_3} is found by cumulative addition of the row which precedes it. Row fd_{y_0}, however, is found in exactly the same manner as row $f_{xy}d_y$ in Table XLIV. Each value recorded in this row is the sum of the products of the cell frequencies above by their respective y deviations. In this case the zero deviation on the y scale is taken at 7, and on the x scale is taken at 14.5, these points being the midpoints of the intervals next lower than the lowest shown on the respective scales. For con-

TABLE XLVI. SHOWING ALL CUMULATIVE ADDITIONS FOR TABLE XLV

								f_{y_0}	f_{y_1}	f_{y_2}	f_{y_3}
								3	3	3	3
								8	11	14	17
								12	23	37	54
								16	39	76	130
								11	50	126	256
								12	62	188	444
								3	65	253	697
f_{x_0}	3	5	10	10	15	12	7	3			
f_{x_1}	65	62	57	47	37	22	10	3			
f_{x_2}	303	238	176	119	72	35	13	3			
f_{x_3}	959	656	418	242	123	51	16	3			
fd_{y_0}	5	9	29	37	61	53	39	20			
fd_{y_1}	253	248	239	210	173	112	59	20			
fd_{y_2}	1314	1061	813	574	364	191	79	20			

venience the y deviations are given at the left next to the y intervals, and the x deviations are given near the top of the table next to the x intervals. Of course, the lowest two horizontal rows are cumulated from fd_{y_0} as the base row.

When the sub-totaling device is set to function on the adding machine it is unnecessary to record any totals except the last shown for each column or row. Each new column or row may be added cumulatively from the adding machine tape of the last column or row.

Reliability of Correlation.—In a previous chapter on reliability it was shown that the means of samples drawn at random from a parent population will distribute themselves on a scale in a manner which makes it possible to determine the expected variation of these means. Applying the sampling idea to measures of relationship, ρ or r will vary from sample to sample.

In using either the standard error or probable error of ρ or r certain cautions should be held in mind. The development of the reliability formula for r, for example, is based on several assumptions of characteristics of both sets of data which they may not possess. Especially in small samples (N of 30 or less) there is danger that one or more of the assumed characteristics will be lacking.

Formulas for the reliability of ρ are

$$\text{S.E.}_{,\rho} = \frac{1 - \rho^2}{\sqrt{N}} (1 + .086\rho^2 + .013\rho^4 + .002\rho^6) \qquad \textbf{(45a)}$$

$$\text{P.E.}_{,\rho} = \frac{.6745\,(1 - \rho^2)}{\sqrt{N}} (1 + .086\rho^2 + .013\rho^4 + .002\rho^6) \qquad \textbf{(45b)}$$

Many textbooks give

$$\text{P.E.}_{,\rho} = \frac{.7063\,(1 - \rho^2)}{\sqrt{N}} \quad \text{or} \quad \frac{.6745}{\sqrt{N}} \times 1.0471\,(1 - \rho^2) \qquad \textbf{(45c)}$$

for the formula for the probable error of ρ. While this formula will only approximate the value correctly determined by Formula (45b), it is generally acceptable because of its greater simplicity.

Formulas for the reliability of r are

$$\text{S.E.}_r = \frac{(1 - r^2)}{\sqrt{N}} \qquad (46a)$$

and

$$\text{P.E.}_r = \frac{.6745\,(1 - r^2)}{\sqrt{N}} \qquad (46b)$$

Exercises and Problems

1. Find ρ of the following sets of spelling scores made by twenty pupils on two different tests. Also find P.E.ρ.

1st Test X	2nd Test Y	1st Test X	2nd Test Y
36	32	29	21
35	31	28	24
35	30	28	27
34	28	27	32
33	30	27	24
32	27	27	22
31	27	26	24
30	32	26	21
30	29	24	20
30	26	22	18

2. The following pairs of measures are spelling scores and arithmetic scores made by nine pupils.

Spelling	Arithmetic
19	22
18	18
14	17
11	13
10	12
9	11
6	7
2	6
1	2

Find r by use of the fundamental formula.

3. Find the correlation (r) and the probable error of r (P.E.$_r$) for the spelling scores of Exercise 1. Use Formula (44a).

4. Two tests, X and Y, were taken by sixty-four pupils. One pupil made 5 on the X test and 5 on the Y test, two pupils made 5 on the X test and 4 on the Y test, and so on as recorded below for the sixty-four pupils:

X	Y	f
5	5	1
5	4	2
5	3	1
4	5	2
4	4	6
4	3	6
4	2	2
3	5	1
3	4	6
3	3	10
3	2	6
3	1	1
2	4	2
2	3	6
2	2	6
2	1	2
1	3	1
1	2	2
1	1	1
		64

Tabulate these scores in a scatter-diagram of this type:

X Scale

	1	2	3	4	5	
5						
4						
3						
2						
1						

Y Scale

Let the x and y axes intersect at the center of cell 3–3. Now mark a point at each of the five means of the five columns. Draw a line through these points and determine its slope by actual measurement. (This slope will be the y value of any point on the line divided by the x value of the point.) Now in similar manner mark a point at each of the five means of the horizontal rows and draw a line through the points. Compare the size of the angle which this line makes on the y axis with the angle which the other line made on the x axis. (Here divide the x value of any point by the y value of the point.)

By definition the slope of the line you first drew is the correlation of the scores. Corroborate this by actually solving for r by use of Formula (44b).

Give two important reasons why it is not generally convenient to use this graphic method for determining correlation of data tabulated in a scatter-diagram. Would the conversion of both sets of measures to T-Scores overcome one of the difficulties? Explain how.

5. A Challenge: Below is given the records of ten high school boys on two physical tests of strength.

| Push up | Pull up | | Push up | Pull up |
X	Y		X	Y
11	14		11	14
12	13		15	20
6	11		4	9
10	10		11	17
7	9		6	9

Correlate these records by use of

First, Formula (43), which requires that deviations be taken from the true mean;

Second, Formula (44a), which permits deviations to be taken from an assumed mean.

6. Below is a tabulation of one hundred and four pairs of measures of one hundred and four school boys. A measurement to the nearest whole inch was taken for each boy's standing height, and a measurement to the nearest whole inch was taken for each boy's humerus-spread. (Humerus-spread is defined here as the distance between the points of the elbows when the arms are bent at the elbows and the upper arms extended horizontally against a wall or other vertical plane.)

(a) Find the correlation by use of Formula (44b)—Pearson product-moment method.

(b) Find the probable error of r.

(c) Find the mean and the standard deviation of standing heights.

(d) Find the mean and standard deviation of humerus-spreads.

X (Standing Height)

	42–44	45–47	48–50	51–53	54–56	57–59	60–62	63–65	66–68	
36–37									1	1
34–35							3	3	1	7
32–33					1	2	8	2		13
30–31				1	6	10	4			21
28–29			1	5	9	2				17
26–27		1	12	8	2					23
24–25	1	11	5							17
22–23	2	2								4
20–21	1									1
	4	14	18	14	18	14	15	5	2	104

(Y (Humerus-Spread) labels the rows at left.)

7. A Challenge (if you have access to an adding machine) : Find the correlation of the data of Exercise 6 by the summation method.

8.　　　　　　　　　　　　X Measures

	20–24	25–29	30–34	35–39	40–44	
15–17	1					1
12–14		1	1			2
9–11			1	1		2
6– 8			1	2		3
3– 5					2	2
	1	1	3	3	2	

(Y Measures labels the rows at left.)

(a) Find the correlation of the above data by the Pearson product-moment method—Formula (44b)—and again by
(b) The summation method.
The two answers must be exactly the same.

9. A Challenge: In a vocal-music tournament seven judges were used to grade forty-two contestants. Each judge worked independently of the others, judging each contestant by use of a rating sheet. In order to determine the consistency or reliability of the judges' ratings, compare for each contestant his average rating by four judges (taken at random) with his average rating by the other three judges.

Ave. of Four Judges	Ave. of Three Judges				
X	Y	X	Y	X	Y
25	28	31	28	20	22
22	24	31	32	29	25
26	26	33	33	21	24
36	37	22	21	20	26
35	36	28	26	18	24
28	22	20	25	32	29
33	29	34	31	18	20
31	26	34	27	26	27
33	31	22	22	23	20
29	31	34	31	22	20
28	32	39	35	20	23
34	33	24	22	34	34
21	27	28	26	35	35
25	25	18	16	41	41

(a) Find the correlation by the method you think most convenient.

(b) Would you consider the correlation coefficient found an indication of satisfactory reliability of judges?

CHAPTER 9

INTERPRETATIONS AND USES OF CORRELATION

Having learned some of the simple methods of finding correlation, we are now in a position to return to a question about reliability of difference between means. In the chapter on reliability the formulas were given for determining the difference

$$\text{S.E.}_{\text{Dif.}_m} = \sqrt{(\text{S.E.}_{m_1})^2 + (\text{S.E.}_{m_2})^2}$$

and

$$\text{P.E.}_{\text{Dif.}_m} = \sqrt{(\text{P.E.}_{m_1})^2 + (\text{P.E.}_{m_2})^2}$$

between two means. However, the development of these formulas is based on the assumption that there has been no matching of members of the two samples. If matching has been done, the amount of difference necessary to show significance between the two means is reduced in an amount which is related to the correlation existing between the measure of the two samples. Reliability of difference between the means of the two groups should then be found by

$$\text{S.E.}_{\text{Dif.}_M} = \sqrt{(\text{S.E.}_{M_1})^2 + (\text{S.E.}_{M_2})^2 - 2r_{1.2}(\text{S.E.}_{M_1})(\text{S.E.}_{M_2})} \qquad \textbf{(47a)}$$

or

$$\text{P.E.}_{\text{Dif.}_M} = \sqrt{(\text{P.E.}_{M_1})^2 + (\text{P.E.}_{M_2})^2 - 2r_{1.2}(\text{P.E.}_{M_1})(\text{P.E.}_{M_2})} \qquad \textbf{(47b)}$$

In like manner reliability of difference between the standard deviations of two groups which are composed of matched pairs should be found by

$$\text{S.E.}_{\text{Dif.}_\sigma} = \sqrt{(\text{S.E.}_{\sigma_1})^2 + (\text{S.E.}_{\sigma_2})^2 - 2r_{1.2}(\text{S.E.}_{\sigma_1})(\text{S.E.}_{\sigma_2})} \qquad \textbf{(48a)}$$

or

$$\text{P.E.}_{\text{Dif.}_\sigma} = \sqrt{(\text{P.E.}_{\sigma_1})^2 + (\text{P.E.}_{\sigma_2})^2 - 2r_{1.2}(\text{P.E.}_{\sigma_1})(\text{P.E.}_{\sigma_2})} \qquad \textbf{(48b)}$$

Similar to the measurement of reliability of a difference between two means, the measurement of reliability of a difference between two correlations in unmatched series is found by

$$\text{S.E.}_{(r_{1\cdot2} - r_{3\cdot4})} = \sqrt{(\text{S.E.}_{r_{1\cdot2}})^2 + (\text{S.E.}_{r_{3\cdot4}})^2} \qquad \textbf{(49a)}$$

$$\text{P.E.}_{(r_{1\cdot2} - r_{3\cdot4})} = \sqrt{(\text{P.E.}_{r_{1\cdot2}})^2 + (\text{P.E.}_{r_{3\cdot4}})^2} \qquad \textbf{(49b)}$$

Formulas (49a) and (49b) are also generally acceptable for comparing correlations of matched series since these formulas are conservative, and since the computations required for the omitted portion of the formulas for matched series are quite complicated.

In Formulas (47a), (47b), (48a), and (48b) the two groups being compared must have been made up by taking a series of pairs of individuals which have been matched in some manner, and then by systematically placing the first of each pair in one group and the second of each pair in the other group. Differences arising between means or standard deviations of such groups need not be expected to behave as if the groups were pure separate-chance samples from a common parent population. Unless one of the four formulas just given is used instead of formulas previously given for unmatched groups, one is likely to discard a significant difference mistakenly thinking it insignificant. Fortunately such a mistake in choice of formula is always made in the interest of conservatism.

Obviously the four formulas under discussion can be applied only in cases of equal N's for the two groups being compared. The companions of matched pairs of individuals were separated to compose the two groups, so that N for each group will be the same as the number of pairs with which the investigation was started.

Very frequently it becomes inconvenient to compose two groups of matched pairs. In research it often becomes desirable to match two groups on the basis of equal means and equal standard deviations. Here the means of the two groups will be equal at the start of the investigation and the standard deviations of the two groups will be equal, but one group may be larger than the other. At the end of an experimental period when it is desired to determine the difference, and its significance, between the means of the two groups, one of the following formulas should be used:

$$S.E._{\text{Dif.}_m} = \sqrt{\left(\frac{\sigma_1^2}{N_1} + \frac{\sigma_2^2}{N_2}\right)(1 - r^2)} \qquad \textbf{(50a)}$$

or $$P.E._{\text{Dif.}_m} = .6745\sqrt{\left(\frac{\sigma_1^2}{N_1} + \frac{\sigma_2^2}{N_2}\right)(1 - r^2)} \qquad \textbf{(50b)}$$

NOTE: In these formulas r is the correlation between the test scores or other measures used at the start for equating the groups and the final scores or measures used to distinguish between groups.[1]

Now let us go back to Chapter 8 and give examples of the application of each of the probable-error formulas offered:

Use of Formula (45b), Probable Error of Rho.—Suppose that ρ has been found to be .80 for the reading scores and social-studies scores of twenty children. Substituting in Formula (45b) we obtain

$$P.E._{\rho} = \frac{.6745\,(1 - .80^2)}{\sqrt{20}}[1 + .086\,(.80^2) + .013(.80^4) + .002\,(.80^6)]$$

$$= .1508\,(1 - .64)\,[1 + .086(.64) + .013(.41) + .002(.26)]$$
$$= .054\,(1 + .055 + .005 + .001)$$
$$= .054\,(1.061)$$
$$= .0573 \text{ or } .06$$

Had the abridged formula been used the result would have been

$$P.E._{\rho} = \frac{.7063\,(1 - .80^2)}{\sqrt{20}}$$

$$= .0569 \quad \text{or} \quad .06$$

In this instance the difference in computed values of the probable error arising from the use of the two different formulas does not show if rounded to three or fewer decimal places. Ordinarily two decimal places are sufficient to record either a computed value of ρ or the value of its probable error.

Now the value of ρ_{12} for (1), the reading scores, and (2), the social-studies scores, may be written

$$\rho_{12} = + .80 \pm .06$$

[1] For complete discussion on the use of this formula, see E. F. Lindquist: "The Significance of a Difference Between 'Matched' Groups"; in *Journal of Educational Psychology*, Vol. XXII, pp. 197-204. (March, 1931)

which means there is a one-half probability that ρ for the universal data of which these twenty pairs of scores are a sample is within .06 (above or below) of the ρ computed for the sample ($+.80$).

Use of Formula (46b), Probable Error of Linear Correlation, r.—Let us turn to the problem of Table XLIV in which an r of $+.76$ was found for sixty-five pairs of scores made on (1) vocabulary and (2) reading-comprehension tests. Applying Formula (46b) we have

$$P.E._{r_{12}} = \frac{.6745\,(1 - .76^2)}{\sqrt{65}}$$
$$= .0837(.4224)$$
$$= .0354 \text{ or } .04$$

Now the results of both computations may be written

$$r_{12} = +.76 \pm .04$$

and the interpretation is the same as previously stated for ρ.

Use of Formula (47b), Reliability of the Difference Between the Means of Two Groups Composed of Matched Pairs.—Suppose that a new method of teaching arithmetic reasoning in the sixth grade is to be tested for its efficiency. It will be necessary to use two groups for an experiment—one to be taught by traditional methods and one by the new method—for comparative purposes. For the proposed "race" in learning two groups which have reached the same level must be selected. This will be done by giving, let us say, sixty-eight sixth-grade pupils one form of a standardized or otherwise well-prepared test in arithmetic reasoning. The pupils will then be matched in pairs according to equal or approximately equal scores. The pairs will then be separated to compose the two groups. Thus for every pupil in the "traditional" group there will be a pupil of the same arithmetic ability in the "new" group. The two groups of thirty-four pupils each will then be taught for one year by their respective methods.

Now let us suppose that the end of the year has arrived and the results are to be measured. Suppose both groups are given another form of the test previously given, or an entirely new test on arithmetic reasoning. In this test let us suppose the following results are obtained:

TABLE XLVII. SIGNIFICANCE OF DIFFERENCE BETWEEN MEANS OF GROUPS COMPOSED OF MATCHED PAIRS

Groups

	(1) Traditional Plan	(2) New Plan
N	34	34
Mean	51.12	57.42
σ	12.06	14.22
P.E.$_M$	1.42	1.67
r_{12}	.60	
Dif.$_M$	6.30	
P.E.$_{Dif._M}$	1.40	
$\dfrac{Dif._M}{P.E._{Dif._M}}$	4.50	

Herein the r_{12} refers to the correlation found between the scores made on the final test by the pairs previously matched. The complete substitution in Formula (47b) becomes

$$P.E._{Dif._M} = \sqrt{1.42^2 + 1.67^2 - 2(.60)(1.42)(1.67)}$$
$$= \sqrt{4.8053 - 2.8457}$$
$$= \sqrt{1.9596}$$
$$= 1.40$$

The difference between the two means being four and one half times this amount, we can conclude with practical certainty that the higher mean score of the "new plan" pupils was not due to chance. Presumably, since the two groups were started together, the higher mean was due to the superiority of the new plan of teaching.

It is interesting to note here that had we neglected to use the "r" or third term under the radical of the formula in finding the probable error of the difference, we would have found the probable error to be 2.19. The difference 6.30 falls short of being three times this amount, and we would have failed to remove reasonable doubt that chance could explain the difference.

Use of Formula (48b), Reliability of the Difference Between the Standard Deviations of Two Groups Composed of Matched Pairs.—For this illustration let us use the same data of the experiment in teaching arithmetic reasoning, except that in this instance we are interested in noting the change that has taken place in the variability of the two groups. (Their S.D.'s were the same at the start.) For this consideration we need only part of the data from Table XLVII, to which we have added results of additional computations to make Table XLVIII.

TABLE XLVIII. SIGNIFICANCE OF DIFFERENCE BETWEEN STANDARD DEVIATIONS OF GROUPS OF MATCHED PAIRS

Groups

	Traditional Plan (1)	New Plan (2)
σ	12.06	14.22
P.E.$_\sigma$	.99	1.16
r_{12}	.60	
Dif.$_\sigma$	2.16	
P.E.$_{\text{Dif.}_\sigma}$	.97	
$\dfrac{\text{Dif.}_\sigma}{\text{P.E.}_{\text{Dif.}_\sigma}}$	2.23	

Here we have insufficient evidence in the ratio 2.23 to conclude that chance could not explain the difference of 2.16 between the two standard deviations. In this development the key value, .97, was found by substitution in Formula (48b) as follows.

$$\text{P.E.}_{\text{Dif.}_\sigma} = \sqrt{.99^2 + 1.16^2 - 2(.60)(.99)(1.16)}$$
$$= \sqrt{2.3257 - 1.3781}$$
$$= \sqrt{.9476}$$
$$= .97$$

Use of Formula (49b), Probable Error of the Difference Between Two Correlations.—For illustrating the use of this formula let us take the correlation (+.76) and its probable error (.04), which have already been found for (1) vocabulary knowledge and (2) reading comprehension; and in addition let us take the correlation (+.53) and its probable error (.06), which on another occasion were found for (3) knowledge of social studies and (4) arithmetic reasoning. We wish to know if there is a significant difference between the two correlations.

$$r_{12} - r_{34} = .76 - .53 \text{ or } .23$$

Now applying Formula (49b) we have

$$\text{P.E.}_{(r_{12} - r_{34})} = \sqrt{.04^2 + .06^2}$$
$$= \sqrt{.0016 + .0036}$$
$$= \sqrt{.0052}$$
$$= .07$$

Now the difference, .23, is more than three (3.29) times its probable error, and we are justified in concluding that there is but little probability of chance explaining the wide difference between the two correlations. In other words, it is characteristic of vocabulary and reading comprehension to be more closely related than social studies and arithmetic reasoning.

Use of Formula (50b), Reliability of Difference Between Means of Groups Originally Equated on Basis of Equal Means and Equal Standard Deviations.—Here again correlation plays an important part. For this consideration let us suppose that the study previously described is being made on teaching of arithmetic. In this instance, however, groups are not composed of matched pairs, but merely of either equal or unequal numbers with the mean and standard deviation made by the "traditional" group on the initial test the same as the mean and standard deviation made by the "new plan" group. Let us summarize the completed solution in Table XLIX.

TABLE XLIX. RELIABILITY OF DIFFERENCE BETWEEN MEANS OF
MATCHED GROUPS

(No pairing of individuals)

Groups

	Traditional Plan	New Plan
N	36	48
Mean	49.90	55.97
σ	12.30	13.50
r_{IF}	.72	
Dif.$_M$	6.07	
P.E.$_{Dif._M}$	1.32	
$\dfrac{\text{Dif.}_M}{\text{P.E.}_{\text{Dif.}_M}}$	4.60	

In Table XLIX correlation is designated r_{IF} instead of r_{12}. This is to indicate that the correlation was determined for scores of the initial (I) test and the final (F) test. It was by the initial test that the groups were matched; it was by the final test that difference in means was distinguished. Here, of course, the difference is significant and we conclude that the "new plan" is probably superior to the "traditional plan." It is by use of Formula (50b) that the probable error is found here, as follows:

$$P.E._{Dif._M} = .6745\sqrt{\left(\frac{12.30^2}{36} + \frac{13.50^2}{48}\right)(1 - .72^2)}$$

$$= .6745\sqrt{(4.20 + 3.80)(.48)}$$
$$= .6745\sqrt{3.84}$$
$$= .6745(1.96)$$
$$= 1.32$$

These methods of measuring correlation and applying it as an aid to determining significance of various differences are by no means the only methods. However, most requirements of the principal and teacher may be served by the techniques described in this book.

There are so many factors which condition correlation that the mere statement of a coefficient of correlation has little meaning. If the assumed conditions of linearity and normalcy of the sample are approximately present, the relationship indicated by r is entirely satisfactory if applied to the parent population of the sample. However, the presence of these assumed conditions does not insure comparability of a coefficient of correlation of one set of data with that of another.

Moreover the true changes in relationship of data do not affect the coefficient of correlation in such a manner as to enable us to say that the improvement in correlation from .70 to .80 is the same as from .80 to .90, or to enable us to say that .80 is twice as good a correlation as .40.

Coefficient of Alienation.—If correlation is to be interpreted in terms of its efficiency as an instrument of prediction, the coefficient of alienation will serve the purpose of indicating this efficiency better than the coefficient of correlation itself. The coefficient of alienation,

$$\text{C.A.} = \sqrt{1 - r^2} \tag{51}$$

indicates the extent of alienation of the variables. A value of zero for this coefficient will mean that the correlation is perfect ($+1.00$ or -1.00), whereas a value of 1.00 for it will mean that the correlation is zero. To indicate the efficiency of prediction (E.P.) on a percentage basis, some writers use the relationship

$$\text{E.P.} = 100 \, (1.00 - \text{C.A.}) \tag{52}$$

By utilizing Formulas (51) and (52) the low efficiency of prediction possessed by apparently substantial correlations may be seen readily. For example, let us test a correlation of .70 (or $-.70$) in this respect:

$$\text{C.A.} = \sqrt{1 - .70^2} \text{ or } .714$$

Then $\text{E.P.} = 100 (1.000 - .714)$ or 28.6

The efficiency of prediction for a correlation of $+.90$ (or $-.90$) is only about 58, so it may be seen that improvement in efficiency of prediction as correlation changes from .90 to 1.00 is very rapid. Of course, the relationship of the variables C.A. and r in Formula (51) may be shown graphically for ready conversion from the one to the other.

The Coefficient of Correlation as an Index of Reliability.— Consistency or reliability may be indicated by correlation, especially in statistical work dealing with tests and measurement. Here the coefficient of correlation is often called a coefficient of reliability. Reliability is an important characteristic of a test. The user of a test wishes to know if it can be depended upon to secure the same results each time it or another form claimed to be equivalent is used. If a group of pupils is given a test today and again tomorrow, with the results that each child makes the same score on both occasions, perfect reliability would be indicated. If the gains for all children on the second administration were equal, perfect reliability also would be indicated. In either case, of course, the correlation would be $+1.00$.

On the second day a different form may be used, and the scores made on the two forms of the test correlated to determine reliability. If desired, the test may be given only once, and scores made on the first half of it correlated with scores made on the last half to determine reliability. This plan may be modified to correlate scores made on the odd-numbered items with scores made on the even-numbered items. Another slightly modified plan is to correlate scores made on items number 1, 4, 5, 8, 9, etc., with scores made on items number 2, 3, 6, 7, 10, etc. As a matter of fact, two equivalent forms of a test are made by separation of the original items according to the item-numbers suggested above when the original items have been arranged in order of difficulty. The last plan, therefore, is really no different from using two forms of the test to determine its reliability, except that reliability is affected by length of the test. The coefficient of correlation obtained by the split-halves, the odd-even, or the staggered-series indicates the reliability of only half the test. A correction for the coefficient in such cases to make it indicate reliability for the whole test will be given shortly.

Effect on r Caused by Changing Range of Data.—All the weaknesses of correlation conspire to confuse us in interpreting reliability. The knowledge that Test A has a reliability coefficient of $+.92$ while Test B has a reliability of $+.96$, is insufficient evidence to conclude that Test B has the better reliability. Indeed, it is possible that Test A is superior in reliability. For example, suppose that Test A has been validated and normed for the seventh grade only, for which grade the range of talent was comparatively narrow (S.D. $=9.1$), whereas Test B was validated and normed for grades four to seven inclusive. The correlated scores came from all four grades, for which group the range of talent was comparatively wide (S.D. $=13.7$). In order to compare the reliability of the two tests here it is necessary to use a formula for determining an inferred r when the range is changed. One of these is

$$\frac{\text{S.D.}_1}{\text{S.D.}_2} = \frac{\sqrt{1 - r_2^2}}{\sqrt{1 - r_1^2}} \tag{53}$$

Now by the use of this relationship let us determine the correlation which we might reasonably expect if we gave Test A to grades four to seven, instead of confining it to the seventh grade. Then,

$$\frac{\text{S.D.}_A}{\text{S.D.}_2} = \frac{\sqrt{1 - r_2^2}}{\sqrt{1 - r_A^2}}$$

Substituting,

$$\frac{9.1}{13.7} = \frac{\sqrt{1 - r_2^2}}{\sqrt{1 - .92^2}}$$

Solving for r_2,

$$r_2^2 = 1 - \frac{82.81(1 - .92^2)}{187.69}$$

$$r_2 = .9654$$

The inferred r for Test A when applied to a range as wide as that involved in Test B shows Test A to be slightly superior in reliability.

The Spearman-Brown Formula.—It was mentioned previously if a test has only one form, its reliability may be determined from two administrations. Since this would be expensive in time and cost of testing materials, it is usually more convenient to correlate scores on one part of the test with scores on the other part. (Three methods of separating the test into two parts have been mentioned.) Since the correlation coefficient obtained from comparing two halves of the test will represent the reliability of only half the test, an inferred reliability for the whole test should be obtained. The formula used for this purpose is known as the Spearman-Brown prophecy formula, and is often expressed as follows:

$$r_{NN} = \frac{nr_{\frac{N}{n}\frac{N}{n}}}{1 + (n - 1)r_{\frac{N}{n}\frac{N}{n}}} \tag{54}$$

The symbols in the formula and their meanings are

   N = number of items in whole test.
   n = the reciprocal of the fractional part of the whole test used in each of the two variables.
   r_{NN} = the reliability of the whole test.
   $r_{\frac{N}{n}\frac{N}{n}}$ = the reliability of $\frac{1}{n}$ of the items of the whole test.

To show one use of Formula (54) let us suppose that a high school teacher of English has prepared an objective test of sixty items for her classes. After administering the test she correlates scores made on odd items with scores made on even items, and secures a coefficient of $+.77$. Wishing to know the reliability of her whole test she applies the Spearman-Brown formula as follows:

   N = 60 (length of whole test)
   n = 2 (½ of test has been correlated with other ½)
   $r_{\frac{N}{n}\frac{N}{n}}$ or $r_{30.30}$ = $+.77$ (the reliability of ½ of the test)

Then
$$r_{60 \cdot 60} = \frac{2 \, (+.77)}{1 + (2 - 1)(+.77)}$$

$$= \frac{1.54}{1.77} \quad \text{or} \quad .87$$

If the teacher now wishes to know the reliability which her test would possess if she should add thirty more items of measuring quality equal to the sixty she already has, the substitutions in the formula become

$$r_{90 \cdot 90} = \frac{3 \, (+.77)}{1 + (3 - 1)(+.77)}$$

$$= \frac{2.31}{2.54}$$

$$= .91$$

Thus it may be seen that the reliability of the test would be greatly improved by lengthening it, but perfect reliability could never be reached short of making the test infinitely long. This statement raises the question of what length must the test have to meet a given requirement of reliability, let us say, .92. In this case the substitution will be

$$.92 = \frac{n \, (+.77)}{1 + (n - 1) \, (+.77)}$$

and her problem is to solve for n as follows:

$$.92 + .7084n - .7084 = .77n$$
$$.0616n = .2116$$
$$n = 3.435$$

The teacher now knows she must make the whole length of her test 3.435 times thirty items, or 103 items, to insure a reliability of $+.92$.

Estimates by Use of Regression Lines.—Because of the uncertainty of factors which play upon the coefficient of reliability to disturb its significance, many users of tests desire a statement of the actual probable variation from a predicted score. To make this point clear let us first recall that in Figure 24 it was shown that there are always two regression lines for data placed in a scatter-diagram. If there is no correlation one of the lines will coincide with the x axis and the other with the y axis (a slope of zero). If, on the other hand, there is perfect correlation, the two regression lines will coincide with each other, and will bisect the ninety-degree angle of the intersecting axes (a slope of 1.00). Now, it is by use of these regression lines that we are enabled to utilize one of the greatest values of correlation—the value of making predictions or estimates. For greatest convenience in making estimates let us write the equations in terms of actual scores or measurements from the zeros of the two scales. The equations of the regression lines then may be written

$$\overline{Y} = r \frac{\sigma_y}{\sigma_x} X - r \frac{\sigma_y}{\sigma_x} M_x + M_y \tag{55a}$$

$$\text{and } \overline{X} = r \frac{\sigma_x}{\sigma_y} Y - r \frac{\sigma_x}{\sigma_y} M_y + M_x \tag{56a}$$

Although it is good practice always to find the standard deviation for the two variables in a correlation problem, when this has not been done the regression equations may be written as follows:

$$\overline{Y} = \frac{ak}{bh} X - \frac{ak}{bh} M_x + M_y \tag{55b}$$

$$\text{and } \overline{X} = \frac{ah}{ck} Y - \frac{ah}{ck} M_y + M_x \tag{56b}$$

In Formulas (55b) and (56b), a, b, and c are from the simplified formula for correlation,

$$r = \frac{a}{\sqrt{bc}}$$

h is the size of the intervals of the X data, and k is the size of the intervals of the Y data.

To illustrate the use of Formula (55a), let us suppose that in a testing program at the end of the school year, high school seniors have been given both an intelligence test (X) and an English test (Y). The correlation between the two sets of test scores is $+.80$. For the intelligence scores the mean is 141.1,

and the standard deviation is 51.7.   For the English scores the
mean is 92.9, and the standard deviation is 38.7.   When the
principal is recording the results of the tests on the pupils' permanent cumulative record cards he discovers that a few students
failed to take the English tests.   Having no further opportunity
to give the absent pupils the English test but wishing their
records to be complete, the principal decides to record for each
an estimated English score—estimated from the score made on
the intelligence test. He will use Formula (55a) for the purpose
of writing the regression line of Y on X.

The values to be substituted are summarized below:

$$r = .80$$
$$\sigma_x = 51.7$$
$$\sigma_y = 38.7$$
$$M_x = 141.1$$
$$M_y = 92.9$$

Then substituting these values the principal has

$$\overline{Y} = .80 \frac{38.7}{51.7} X - .80 \frac{38.7}{51.7} 141.1 + 92.9$$

$$= .60 X - 84.5 + 92.9$$

$$\text{or } \overline{Y} = .60 X + 8.4$$

This last expression is the equation of the straight line which
comes nearest to passing through the means (properly weighted)
of the columns in the scatter-diagram, and it affords a method
of predicting any individual Y score (English) when the X
score (Intelligence) is known. For example, suppose that one
of the pupils who failed to take the English test has made a
score of 90 on the intelligence test.   The principal then predicts
or estimates an English score for this student by

$$\overline{Y} = .60 \times 90 + 8.4$$
$$= 62.4 \quad \text{or} \quad 62$$

This is the English score he will record for the pupil. In the
same manner he may restore any English score provided he has
the pupil's intelligence score. If many restorations were to be
made, however, economy would suggest that the regression

equation $\overline{Y} = .60\ X + 8.4$ be plotted on the two scales as axes, from which estimates may be made graphically.

The statement that Formula (55a) is for estimating a Y score, when an X score is known should be emphasized again. This formula *cannot* be used for estimating an X score from a Y score. The other regression line which passes through or nearest the weighted means of the horizontal rows of the scatter-diagram must be used for making estimates of X from Y. For example, in the problem of the high school intelligence tests (X) and English tests (Y) Formula (56a) will become

$$\overline{X} = .80\ \frac{51.7}{38.7}\ Y - .80\ \frac{51.7}{38.7}\ 92.9 + 141.1$$

or $\overline{X} = 1.07Y + 41.8$

by which for an English score of, say 130, we may estimate the intelligence score as follows:

$$\overline{X} = 1.07 \times 130 + 41.8$$
$$\overline{X} = 180.9 \quad \text{or} \quad 181$$

A clear understanding of the relationship of the two regression lines offers protection against some common misconceptions regarding prediction. In the first example above, a score of 90 on the intelligence test is almost exactly one sigma below the mean of all intelligence scores, whereas the predicted English score is about eight points above the same relative position on the scale of English scores. In the second example an English score of 130 is approximately one sigma above the mean of all English scores, whereas the predicted intelligence score is about twelve points below the same relative position on the scale of intelligence scores. Applied to comparisons of the heights of fathers and adult sons, between which measurements there is less than a perfect correlation, the principle of regression means:

1. The probability that a father who is taller than average will have a son taller than average is better than one half, and at the same time the probability that the son will be shorter than the father is also better than one half.

2. The probability that a father who is shorter than average will have a son shorter than average is better than one

half, and at the same time the probability that the son will be taller than the father is also better than one half.

3. The average height of a group of sons whose fathers are all the same height and are taller than the average man will be above average, but below the height of the fathers.

4. The average height of a group of fathers whose sons are all the same height and are taller than the average man will be above average height, but below the height of the sons.

Reliability of Estimates from Regression Lines.—Returning now to the subject of reliability of such estimates, unless the coefficient is $+1.00$ or -1.00 we cannot be certain that the actual score will be the same as our predicted score. All $\overline{Y}$ values are on the straight regression line only. The weaker the correlation the greater the possibility, therefore, of an actual score deviating widely from the estimated score. Not every pupil who made an intelligence score of 90 made an English score of 62. The English score of 62 is merely the mean English score of all pupils making intelligence scores of 90. Here, then, we have need for a *standard error* or *probable error of estimate,* and the formulas for these measures of reliability are

$$\text{S.E.}_{(\text{Est. Y})} = \sigma_y \sqrt{1 - r^2} \qquad (57a)$$

and
$$\text{S.E.}_{(\text{Est. X})} = \sigma_x \sqrt{1 - r^2} \qquad (58a)$$

or
$$\text{P.E.}_{(\text{Est. Y})} = .6745 \, \sigma_y \sqrt{1 - r^2} \qquad (57b)$$

and
$$\text{P.E.}_{(\text{Est. X})} = .6745 \, \sigma_x \sqrt{1 - r^2} \qquad (58b)$$

Now applying Formula (57b) to the determination of reliability of the predicted English score of 62, we have

$$\text{P.E.}_{(\text{Est. Y})} = .6745 \times 38.7 \sqrt{1 - .80^2}$$
$$= 15.66 \ \text{ or } \ 16$$

(This is not extremely large when thought of in terms of the S.D. of the Y scores—only about $\frac{2}{5}$ of the S.D.)

We may say, therefore, that there is a probability of one half that the English score of the pupil who made an intelligence score of 90 will not differ from 62 by more than 16. As a matter of fact, 50% of all the English scores which were companions to the intelligence score of 90 were within 16 of 62, 25% of them were 78 or more, and 25% were 46 or lower.

The specific character of this measure of reliability, being in terms of actual score units on the scale of scores, makes its interpretation simple. This probable error, 16, applies to the English score estimated for any intelligence score. It is true, however, that the assumptions of characteristics necessary to applying the probable error of estimate to all portions of the scale alike are seldom entirely justified.

The Regression Line as a Measure of Comparative Change Between the Two Variables.—In Formulas (55a) and (56a) we have already given equations in score form for the two regression lines. These equations may also be written in terms of lower-case x and y; i.e., through the mutual means of the two scales eliminating the constant terms as follows:

$$\bar{y} = \left(r\frac{\sigma_y}{\sigma_x}\right)x \quad \text{or} \quad \frac{ak}{bh}x \tag{59a}$$

$$\bar{x} = \left(r\frac{\sigma_x}{\sigma_y}\right)y \quad \text{or} \quad \frac{ah}{ck}y \tag{60a}$$

In these expressions as well as in Formulas (55a) and (56a) it may be seen clearly that the regression coefficient of y on x is

$$m_{yx} = r\frac{\sigma_y}{\sigma_x} \quad \text{or} \quad \frac{ak}{bh} \tag{59b}$$

and the regression coefficient of x on y is

$$m_{xy} = r\frac{\sigma_x}{\sigma_y} \quad \text{or} \quad \frac{ah}{ck} \tag{60b}$$

In any scatter-diagram the values of these coefficients will have very specific meanings which can be expressed in terms of units on the scales of measures.

The data of Table L, which were taken from an elementary school principal's office, will illustrate the meaning and importance of the regression coefficient. Here all of the pupils have been classified by grade (X) and by age (Y). Ages were taken to the nearest half year as of September 1, of the school year involved.

TABLE L. AGE-GRADE DISTRIBUTION

X (Grades)

		1	2	3	4	5	6	7	8	f_y
	17						1	1		2
	16½								1	1
	16									
	15½						1	2	1	4
	15							3	6	9
	14½						1	3	7	11
	14					1	3	10	18	32
	13½				1	1	3	8	13	26
	13		1			4	4	22	14	45
	12½		1	1	1	3	7	13	5	31
	12			1		4	7	15	1	28
	11½			2	2	6	15	3		28
Y (Ages)	11			1	2	14	15	1		33
	10½		1	2	7	18	7			35
	10		2	7	6	19				34
	9½	1	1	5	17	7				31
	9	1	2	12	19	1				35
	8½	2	4	13	2					21
	8	2	9	21	1					33
	7½	3	23	3						29
	7	7	17	1						25
	6½	23								23
	6	17								17
	5½	4								4
	5									1
	f_x	61	61	69	58	78	64	81	66	538

After executing the various computations involved in finding a coefficient of correlation the principal assembled the following facts

$$r_{xy} = \frac{5698}{\sqrt{2767 \times 14108}} \quad \text{or} \quad .91$$

$M_x = 4.63$ (Mean grade)
$M_y = 10.46$ (Mean age)
$\sigma_x = 2.27$
$\sigma_y = 2.56$

Utilizing Formula (60b) to determine the regression coefficient of x on y, the substitutions are

$$m_{xy} = .91 \frac{2.27}{2.56} \quad \text{or} \quad .81$$

The same result may be obtained by substituting the values of a, c, h, and k in the alternate part of the formula as follows:

$$m_{xy} = \frac{5698 \times 1}{14108 \times \frac{1}{2}} \quad \text{or} \quad \frac{5698}{7054} \quad \text{or} \quad .81$$

If the summation method has been used for finding the correlation, the standard deviation may be found conveniently from these relationships:

$$\sigma_x = h \sqrt{\frac{b}{N}} \quad \text{and} \quad \sigma_y = k \sqrt{\frac{c}{N}}$$

Let us now examine the age-grade table to determine exactly the meaning of this coefficient. Imagine a straight line sloping upward from left to right and passing through (or near) the means of the eight columns. As a point moves along this line, from lower left to upper right, a distance sufficient to elevate it vertically *one unit* (a year in this case), the distance it will have moved horizontally will be *.81 of a unit* (.81 of a grade in this case). All of this reduces to the simple idea that on the average in a time-period of one year, children of this school progress .81 of a grade.

The principal is now ready to compare the *rate of flow* of

pupils through his school with the rate for the entire state, or for another elementary school.

In similar manner the other regression coefficient may be found. It, of course, will indicate the amount of change on the Y scale for a unit of change on the X scale for a point moving on the other regression line.

Correction of Correlation for Attenuation.—In responding to test items a student will make certain chance errors and variations in reaction at one sitting that he might not make at another sitting. In a very long test compensation would result from such errors in so far as measurement of central tendency is concerned. The standard deviation, however, will be increased by such errors regardless of direction for the reason that x's are squared in computing standard deviation. This tendency, in turn, will decrease the correlation as σ's appear in the denominator of the expression for correlation.

To correct for attenuation it is necessary to have the following information

$r_{x_1 x_2}$, the reliability of Test x from two administrations.

$r_{y_1 y_2}$, the reliability of Test y from two administrations.

$r_{x_1 y_2}$, the correlation of the scores of the first administration of Test x and the scores of the second administration of Test y.

$r_{x_2 y_1}$, the correlation of the scores of the second administration of Test x and the scores of the first administration of Test y.

The true correlation of x and y (r_{xy}) will be found by

$$r_{xy} = \frac{\sqrt{(r_{x_1 y_2})(r_{x_2 y_1})}}{\sqrt{(r_{x_1 x_2})(r_{y_1 y_2})}}$$
(61a)

To illustrate the use of Formula (61a) let us suppose that we desire to know the "true r" between

x, a vocabulary test for seventh grade, and
y, a reading-comprehension test for seventh grade.

Both tests have been administered twice to a group of seventh-grade pupils with the following results:

$$r_{x_1 x_2} = .76$$
$$r_{y_1 y_2} = .74$$
$$r_{x_1 y_2} = .68$$
$$r_{x_2 y_1} = .72$$

Substitution in the formula then takes the form of

$$r_{xy} = \frac{\sqrt{.68 \times .72}}{\sqrt{.76 \times .74}} \quad \text{or} \quad .92$$

When only one coefficient of correlation has been determined between the two tests, either $x_1 y_1$ or $x_2 y_2$, it may be assumed to equal approximately the mean proportion of the two correlations, $r_{x_1 y_2}$ and $r_{x_2 y_1}$, and the formula may be modified to appear in the following form:

$$r_{xy} = \frac{r_{x_1 y_1}}{\sqrt{(r_{x_1 x_2})(r_{y_1 y_2})}} \tag{61b}$$

Validity Coefficient.—One form of inferred coefficient of validity of a combination of tests is dependent upon the correlations of each test with the criterion, and of each test with each of the other tests of the combination. The measure becomes an index of validity in a sense when it is used to compare the efficiency of measurement of a portion of a battery of tests with the total battery. In survey testing one might wish, for the sake of economy of time and expense, to administer only three parts of a battery test which consists of nine or ten parts. By use of the formula under discussion one will be able to determine which three parts combined will come nearest to giving the same results as the entire battery.

The formula is

$$\text{V.C.} = \frac{r_{T1} + r_{T2} + \cdots + r_{Tn}}{\sqrt{3 + 2r_{12} + \ldots + 2r_{1n} + \ldots + 2r_{(n-1)n}}} \tag{62}$$

For illustrating the application of this formula let us take the following information from a battery test of nine parts.

Correlation of Parts with Total Test

$r_{T1} = .82$	$r_{T6} = .81$
$r_{T2} = .71$	$r_{T7} = .82$
$r_{T3} = .70$	$r_{T8} = .61$
$r_{T4} = .87$	$r_{T9} = .76$
$r_{T5} = .80$	

Correlation of Certain Parts with
One Another

$r_{4.5} = .76$	$r_{5.8} = .54$
$r_{4.6} = .70$	$r_{5.9} = 61$
$r_{4.8} = .54$	$r_{6.8} = .53$
$r_{4.9} = .57$	$r_{6.9} = .58$
$r_{5.6} = .69$	$r_{8.9} = .56$

Relative to the criterion of the total test what is the measuring efficiency of a combination of parts 4, 6, and 8? The substitutions in Formula (62) are

$$\text{V.C.}_{T(4 \cdot 6 \cdot 8)} = \frac{.87 + .81 + .61}{\sqrt{3 + 2 \times .70 + 2 \times .54 + 2 \times .53}}$$

$$= .895$$

Discrepancies may arise from the use of inferred correlations as, for example, in correcting for attenuation it is possible to obtain an inferred r of more than 1.00. Considerable suspicion is therefore cast upon all inferred correlations. Notwithstanding all these faults such coefficients serve a need not served by any other means, and when used with proper caution and discount for their weaknesses these coefficients have a legitimate place in statistics.

Exercises and Problems

1. Complete the solution suggested by the following information: (The groups were composed of matched pairs.)

	G_1	G_2	
N	61	61	
M	52.4	50.2	
σ	13.3	14.2	
P.E.$_M$			
r_{12}	.58		
Dif.$_M$			
P.E.$_{Dif._M}$			
$\dfrac{Dif._M}{P.E._{Dif._M}}$			

2. A correlation of $+.57$ has been found between vocabulary-test scores and arithmetic-computation test scores, and a correlation of $+.69$ has been found between reading-comprehension test scores and social-studies test scores. In the first correlation 320 pupils were involved, while in the second correlation 378 were involved. Is the difference between the two correlations significant?

3. Each of two groups of boys has a mean I.Q. of 104, and a standard deviation of 14. The first group consisting of 20 boys is sent to a summer camp for 10 weeks, while the second group consisting of 32 boys is sent to a summer school for 10 weeks. At the close of the period the boys are given another form of the intelligence test with the following results:

	Groups	
	School	Camp
N	32	20
Mean I.Q.	106	105
σ	13	14
r_{IF}	.89	

Continue this solution until you have determined the probability that the difference found or greater differences may arise by chance between any two random samples. Do you have evidence here that summer school improved intelligence?

4. For a group of high school students the correlation between freshman school marks and senior school marks was $+.54$, but between sophomore marks and senior marks it was $+.67$. Is prediction of senior marks from sophomore marks as much improved over prediction of senior marks from freshman marks as the change in correlation from $+.54$ to $+.67$ would indicate? Find the efficiency of prediction for each case.

5. A Challenge: Make a graph for determining the efficiency of prediction index for any r.

6. A test which was being standardized for grades four to seven was found to yield a correlation of $+.963$ between two of its forms, administered to 2,800 pupils of the four grades (700 in each). By inference from the following information, find the reliability of the test for each of the four separate grades:

Grade	S.D.	r
4 to 7	13.7	$+.963$
4	8.4	
5	9.1	
6	9.5	
7	9.7	

7. In a vocabulary test of seventy-two items the correlation of scores made on items 1, 4, 5, 8, 9, 12, etc., and the scores made on items 2, 3, 6, 7, 10, 11, etc., is $+.73$. What is the coefficient of reliability of the test?

8. A Challenge: The vocabulary test of Exercise 7 would need to be increased in length to include a total of how many items in order to give the final test a reliability of $+.90$?

9. A certain high school over a period of years has given an intelligence test and an English test to all of its seniors who have indicated intention of attending a nearby college. A composite score is then found for each pupil. After these high school graduates have been in college one year the principal secures the college grade-point average (Y) for each, and correlates the two sets of data.

The summary of the project to date is as follows:

	(X) H.S. Composite Score	(Y) College Grade-point Average
Mean	100	2.26
σ	20	1.04
r_{xy}	.66	

(a) Write the equation for estimating the college freshman grade-point average of a student from his composite English-intelligence score.

(b) From this equation estimate the college freshman grade-point average which may be expected for a high school senior whose composite score is 122.

(c) Write the equation for restoring a composite score for a student whose college freshman grade-point average is known.

(d) Restore the composite score for a student who established a college freshman grade-point average of 3.76.

10. A Challenge: Plot the regression equation $\overline{Y} = .60\,X + 8.4$, and from it determine the estimated companion English test score, Y, for each of the following intelligence-test scores, X 160, 140, 100, 80, 40.

11. (a) Find the probable error of college grade points estimated from high school composite scores of Exercise 9.

(b) Find the probable error of high school composite scores estimated from college grade points of Exercise 9.

12. In equating two forms of a test the author succeeded in securing the following results:

	(X) Form A	(Y) Form B
Mean	48.0	48.1
σ	13.7	13.6
r_{AB}	.963	

(a) Write the equation for estimating a score on Form B when the score on Form A is known.

(b) Determine the probable error of any Form B score estimated by use of this equation.

13. A high school principal wishes to study the relationship between scholarship and absence from classes. He discards from consideration pupils of perfect attendance and those of no more than four days' absence. The data are tabulated below:

X (Scholastic Grade Points)

	0–.3	.4–.7	.8–1.1	1.2–1.5	1.6–1.9	2.0–2.3	2.4–2.7	2.8–3.1	3.2–3.5	3.6–3.9	f_y
45–up	1	1	2			1					5
40–44	2	4	2	1							9
35–39	3	3	1	3	2	1					13
30–34	1		3	2	6	2	2				16
25–29					5	5					10
20–24			1	1	1	4	4	2		1	14
15–19						1	2	3	1		7
10–14					1		1	1	2	2	7
5–9							2	1	3	1	7
f_x	7	8	9	7	15	14	11	7	6	4	88

(Y = Days Absent)

Determine the loss in grade points for absence of one day, five days, ten days.

14. A Challenge: From the data of Exercise 13, estimate the grade-point average to be expected for a pupil who is absent 34 days of the school year. Also find the probable error of your estimate.

15. The reliability ($r_{x_1 x_2}$) of an arithmetic-reasoning test for the range of a grade is .85, and the reliability ($r_{y_1 y_2}$) of an arithmetic-computation test is .87. The correlations between these tests computed for two administrations are

$$r_{x_1 y_2} = .56$$
$$r_{x_2 y_1} = .59$$

Apply correction for attenuation and find the true correlation between the two tests.

16. Would a combination of parts 4, 6, and 9 of the battery test discussed in this chapter give better results than parts 4, 6, and 8 of the sample solution?

CHAPTER 10

OTHER TYPES OF CORRELATION

In a previous chapter it was stated that the formula for computing the Pearson correlation coefficient was developed on the assumption that the two regression lines were straight lines (linear data). However, this assumed condition is not always present in data. If a correlation coefficient is computed under the assumption that relationship of the two variables is linear, when in fact the relationship is curvilinear, scatter of points will be charged against the data in excess of the true scatter from the best fitting curved line. The result will be a coefficient of correlation which is too small. In some instances no relationship may be found when in fact a high degree of association is present.

The Correlation Ratio.—When data are non-linear, Pearson's *correlation ratio,* η (eta), should be used. This ratio may also be used when the relationship is linear, for in that instance η and r will have the same value, as will be demonstrated shortly. The greater the departure of the curve from a straight line the greater the difference between η and r, with η always the larger.

In linear correlation only one coefficient is present. It is the slope of the straight line $\bar{y} = rx$. The angle made by the other regression line and the y axis is equal exactly to the angle between the line $\bar{y} = rx$ and the x axis. These conditions may not hold true in non-linear regressions. The value of eta for each of the two lines of regression must be computed separately because the nature of the two curves may be different. Therefore, in dealing with η it is necessary to employ subscripts to distinguish between the ratios represented by the two non-linear regression lines. η_{yx} indicates the relationship present in considering the curve of the best fitting line through the means of the columns with Y the dependent variable, while η_{xy} indicates

the relationship present in considering the curve of the best
fitting line through the means of the rows with X the dependent
variable. Briefly stated, η_{yx} is the index to the regression of
y on x, and η_{xy} is the index to the regression of x on y.

The method of solution produces a positive result for η
always. Positive or negative relationship between the two variables must be determined by inspection.

In dealing with educational data, the coefficient of correlation, r, is to be preferred when the regression deviates from
linearity no more than might reasonably be expected from a
chance sample. The reason for this preference is that r has
greater usefulness because of the greater ease with which equations of the straight regression line may be written for purposes of making estimates. However, r should not be used
when data are non-linear. Estimates made from the straight
regression lines in such cases may be very much in error.

The term "correlation ratio" is properly used in referring
to η. The ratio referred to by η_{yx} is the quotient obtained by
dividing the standard deviation of the means (weighted) of the
columns by the standard deviation of the total distribution of
Y measures.

Summary of Steps in Finding η_{yx}

1. Find the mean for each column of frequencies. $\overline{Y}_x$ may
be used to designate these means because each is a point on the
regression line.

2. Find the mean for the total distribution of Y data. M_y.

3. From the mean of each column subtract the mean of the
total distribution. $\overline{Y}_x - M_y$.

4. Square each of these differences. $(\overline{Y}_x - M_y)^2$.

5. Multiply each squared difference by the column frequency.
$f_x(\overline{Y}_x - M_y)^2$.

6. Find the sum of the row of weighted squared differences.
$\Sigma f_x(\overline{Y}_x - M_y)^2$.

7. Find the standard deviation of the weighted means.

$$\sigma_{my} = \sqrt{\frac{\Sigma f_x(\overline{Y}_x - M_y)^2}{N}}.$$

This is an application of the general formula

$$\sigma = \sqrt{\frac{\Sigma x^2}{N}}.$$

8. Find the standard deviation of the total distribution of Y data.

$$\sigma_y = h\sqrt{\frac{\Sigma f_y d^2_y}{N} - \left(\frac{\Sigma f_y d_y}{N}\right)^2}.$$

9. Find the correlation ratio.

$$\eta_{yx} = \frac{\sigma_{my}}{\sigma_y}. \tag{63}$$

The probable error of η is found in the same manner as the probable error of r by substituting η for r:

$$\text{P.E.}_\eta = \frac{.6745(1 - \eta^2)}{\sqrt{N}} \tag{64}$$

An improvised problem will now be solved to illustrate the relationship of η and r in a situation of perfect linearity:

TABLE LI. COMPARISON OF η AND r WHEN DATA ARE LINEAR

X Scale

	1	2	3	4	5	f_y	d_y	$f_y d_y$	$f_y d^2_y$
5			1	2	1	4	2	8	16
4		2	6	6	2	16	1	16	16
3	1	6	10	6	1	24	0		
2	2	6	6	2		16	−1	−16	16
1	1	2	1			4	−2	−8	16
f_x	4	16	24	16	4	64		0	64
$\overline{Y}_x$	2	2.5	3	3.5	4				
$\overline{Y}_x - M_y$	−1	−.5	0	.5	1				
$(\overline{Y}_x - M_y)^2$	1	.25		.25	1				
$f_x(\overline{Y}_x - M_y)^2$	4	4		4	4	= 16			

Y Scale

$$\sigma_{my} = \sqrt{\frac{\Sigma f_x(\overline{Y}_x - M_y)^2}{N}} = \sqrt{\frac{16}{64}} \quad \text{or} \quad .5 \qquad \begin{array}{l} M_y = 3 \\ \\ \sigma_y = \sqrt{\frac{64}{64}} \quad \text{or} \quad 1 \end{array}$$

$$\eta_{yx} = \frac{\sigma_{my}}{\sigma_y} = \frac{.5}{1} \quad \text{or} \quad .5$$

$$\text{but } r = \frac{32}{\sqrt{64 \times 64}} \quad \text{or} \quad .5$$

Educational data of such perfect linearity are seldom encountered in a natural setting, though it is true that excessively non-linear data are encountered less frequently in problems of education than in problems of economics, agriculture, physics, and other sciences.

In the problem dealing with intelligence scores and ages which accompanies this discussion, a complete solution of the correlation ratio for each of the two non-linear regression lines is given. This problem was selected for illustration partly because it represents a borderline condition between linearity and unquestioned non-linearity. See Tables LII and LIII.

Test for Linearity of Regression.—If successive random samples are drawn from an infinite parent population which possesses true linear regression, the samples will be found to fluctuate more or less in their degrees of departure from linearity. The probability that the extent of departure for any given sample will reach or exceed any stated amount can be determined from the nature of the distribution of amounts of departures of a large number of samples. Conversely, in dealing with one sample from an unknown parent population, it is possible to determine the probability that the parent population has linearity of regression when the amount of departure from linearity is known for the sample.

Briefly stated: $\eta^2 - r^2$, frequently called zeta (ζ), may be taken as an index to the degree of departure from linearity. Blakeman has developed a formula for determining the probable error of ζ which, when modified slightly in form to permit the use of a table of xi values (Table D in this book), will appear as follows:

$$\text{P.E.}_\zeta = 2 \times \frac{.6745}{\sqrt{N}} \sqrt{\zeta[(1 - \eta^2)^2 - (1 - r^2)^2 + 1]} \qquad (65)$$

TABLE LII.   CALCULATION OF CORRELATION RATIO, ETA—CALCULATION OF η_{yx}

(Distribution of Intelligence Scores)

x axis (Scale of Ages)

y axis (Scale of Scores)	10	11	12	13	14	15	16	f_v	d_v	$f_v d_v$	$f_v d^2_v$
55–59					1	1	2	4	4	16	64
50–54				2	2		1	5	3	15	45
45–49			2	3	5	6	2	18	2	36	72
40–44				5	4	4	2	15	1	15	15
35–39		1	5	8	6	5	1	26	0		
30–34		2	7	5	3	1		18	−1	−18	18
25–29		4	5	2			2	13	−2	−26	52
20–24		4	3	1				8	−3	−24	72
15–19	1	3						4	−4	−16	64
10–14	2	2						4	−5	−20	100
5–9	2							2	−6	−12	72
0–4	3							3	−7	−21	147
								120		−55	721
f_x	8	16	22	26	21	17	10				
$\overline{Y}_x$	7.6	23.3	32.0	38.0	42.0	42.6	43.5				
$\overline{Y}_x - M_y$	−27.1	−11.4	−2.7	3.3	7.3	7.9	8.8				
$(\overline{Y}_x - M_y)^2$	734.41	129.96	7.29	10.89	53.29	62.41	77.44				
$f_x(\overline{Y}_x - M_y)^2$*	5875	2079	160	283	1119	1061	774	= 11351			

* Numbers in this row were rounded off to integers.

$$M_v = 37 + 5 \times \frac{-55}{120} \text{ or } 34.7$$

$$\sigma_v = 5\sqrt{\frac{721}{120} - \left(\frac{-55}{120}\right)^2} \text{ or } 12.04$$

$$\sigma_{mv} = \sqrt{\frac{11351}{120}} \text{ or } 9.73$$

$$\eta_{yx} = \frac{\sigma_{mv}}{\sigma_v} = \frac{9.73}{12.04} \text{ or } .81$$

$$\text{P.E.}_{\eta} = .02$$

TABLE LIII. CALCULATION OF CORRELATION RATIO, ETA—CALCULATION OF η_{xy}

(Distribution of Intelligence Scores)

x axis (Scale of Ages)

y axis (Scale of Scores)	10	11	12	13	14	15	16	f_y	$\overline{X}_y$	$\overline{X}_y - M_x$	$(\overline{X}_y - M_x)^2$	$f_x(\overline{X}_y - M_x)^2$
55–59					1	1	2	4	15.25	2.19	4.7961	19.1844
50–54				2	2		1	5	14.00	.94	.8836	4.4180
45–49			2	3	5	6	2	18	14.17	1.11	1.2321	22.1778
40–44				5	4	4	2	15	14.20	1.14	1.2996	19.4940
35–39		1	5	8	6	5	1	26	13.46	.40	.1600	4.1600
30–34		2	7	5	3	1		18	12.67	−.39	.1521	2.7378
25–29		4	5	2			2	13	12.46	−.60	.3600	4.6800
20–24		4	3	1				8	11.63	−1.43	2.0449	16.3592
15–19	1	3						4	10.75	−2.31	5.3361	21.3444
10–14	2	2						4	10.50	−2.56	6.5536	26.2144
5–9	2							2	10.00	−3.06	9.3636	18.7272
0–4	3							3	10.00	−3.06	9.3636	28.0908
f_x	8	16	22	26	21	17	10	120				187.5880
d_x	−3	−2	−1	0	1	2	3					
$f_x d_x$	−24	−32	−22	0	21	34	30	7				
$f_x d_x^2$	72	64	22	0	21	68	90	337				

$$\sigma_{mx} = \sqrt{\frac{187.5880}{120}} = \frac{1.250}{1.675} \quad \text{or } 1.250$$

$$\eta_{xy} = \frac{\sigma_{mx}}{\sigma_x} = \frac{1.250}{1.675} \quad \text{or } .75$$

$$\text{P.E.}_\eta = .03$$

$$M_x = 13 + \frac{7}{120} \quad \text{or } 13.06$$

$$\sigma_x = \sqrt{\frac{337}{120} - \left(\frac{7}{120}\right)^2} \quad \text{or } 1.675$$

Pearson's product-moment correlation, $r = .73$

$$\text{P.E.}_r = .03$$

In the problem of our illustration the test of linearity would be applied as follows:

$$\zeta = .81^2 - .73^2 \quad \text{or} \quad .1232$$

$$\text{P.E.}_\zeta = 2 \times \frac{.6745}{\sqrt{120}} \sqrt{.1232[(1 - .81^2)^2 - (1 - .73^2)^2 + 1]} \quad \text{or} \quad .0410$$

If ζ, a difference, is now divided by its probable error, the difference is indicated in terms of probable errors. In this case

$$\frac{\zeta}{\text{P.E.}_\zeta} = \frac{.1232}{.0410} \quad \text{or} \quad 3.05$$

The probability that a difference so great as this will arise by chance is so remote (the customary three probable errors being accepted as the criterion, though the actual probability may be found by use of Table E of this book) that non-linearity is accepted as being characteristic of the line referred to by η_{yx}.

A shorter test by Blakeman consists of determining if

$$N(\eta^2 - r^2) < 11.37 \tag{66}$$

If an inequality is found to exist in the direction indicated, the data may be considered to fail in being characteristically non-linear. When the values obtained in our solution for η_{yx} are substituted in this formula,

$$120(.81^2 - .73^2) < 11.37,$$

the direction of the expressed inequality is found to be reversed for

$$14.78 > 11.37$$

and the data may be regarded non-linear, as was decided by use of the longer test.

Similarly, tests of the linearity of the regression of x on y, η_{xy}, may be made as follows:

The longer test:

$$\zeta = .75^2 - .73^2 \quad \text{or} \quad .0296$$

$$\text{P.E.}_\zeta = 2 \times \frac{.6745}{\sqrt{120}} \sqrt{.0296[(1 - .75^2)^2 - (1 - .73^2)^2 + 1]} \quad \text{or} \quad .0209$$

$$\frac{\zeta}{\text{P.E.}_\zeta} = \frac{.0296}{.0209} \quad \text{or} \quad 1.42 \quad \text{(less than 3 P.E.'s)}$$

The shorter test:

$$\text{Is } 120(.75^2 - .73^2) < 11.37?$$

The answer is *yes* for

$$3.55 < 11.37$$

Both the longer and the shorter test in this case leave considerable doubt that the data are non-linear with respect to the regression of x on y. It is probably safer, therefore, to treat this regression as linear.

If the number of pairs of measures in the sample had been, let us say, 1080 instead of 120 (a nine-fold increase), and the pattern of functionality had remained the same, practically all doubt as to the non-linearity of the data would have been removed. In that case r would have remained unchanged in both computations, but $P.E._r$ would have been reduced in each instance to one third of the original computation. The final result then would have been to multiply each of the ratios, 3.05 and 1.42, by three, making them 9.15 and 4.26 respectively.

The Coefficient of Contingency.—Determination of coefficients of correlation so far discussed is dependent upon quantitatively expressed measures of traits. These measures have been tabulated in order according to the scales used for making the measurements. In educational statistics, however, the relationship of unordered characteristics frequently needs to be determined. In order of general usefulness, therefore, the coefficient of contingency stands high.

Principles of probability are employed in determining contingency. For each cell-frequency, it is necessary to determine the extent of departure from the frequency which would be expected for the cell if chance only were operating to determine the frequency. An illustration will offer the best means of explaining the process of finding the coefficient of contingency. For this illustration, let us use the data of forty-eight boys who have been classified into categories both with respect to rate of pulse return and with respect to health. Four categories were used for rate of pulse return to normal after a standardized exercise—rapid, above average, below average, and slow. Only three health categories were provided—excellent, average, and poor. The distribution of cases was as follows:

	S	BA	AA	R	f_y
E		3	4	6	13
A	1	9	8	3	21
P	6	4	4		14
f_x	7	16	16	9	48

Now let us examine the cell representing the intersection of column AA and row E, in which f_{xy} is 4. Since the total of this column is 16, the probability that an individual will fall into it by chance is $\frac{16}{48}$ or .3333. Since the total of the row is 13, the probability that an individual will fall into it by chance is $\frac{13}{48}$ or .2708. The probability of these two events occurring simultaneously if they are independent of each other is $\frac{16}{48} \times \frac{13}{48}$ or .0903. Therefore, from 48 individuals the number expected to fall into this call is .0903×48 or 4.3344. This process may be shortened by $48 \times \left(\frac{16 \times 13}{48^2} \right)$ or $\left(\frac{16 \times 13}{48} \right)$. The cell actually contains 4 individuals, however, so the difference, − .3344, suggests a lack of complete independence in the case of this cell. When the square of this difference is divided by $\frac{16 \times 13}{48}$ or 4.3344, and summed with similarly derived values for the other cells and the sum averaged by division by 48, the result is called the mean-square contingency function. When certain changes are made in this function in order to limit the contingency coefficient within the bounds of 0 to 1, the formula reduces to

$$C = \sqrt{\frac{S - 1}{S}}$$

(67)

The use of Formula (67) is very simple as it requires only one value for substitution. This is the value S which is merely $\Sigma(f^2_{xy} \div f_x f_y)$.

A complete solution is provided for the data on health and rate of pulse return.

TABLE LIV. COMPUTATION OF C, THE COEFFICIENT OF CONTINGENCY

Rate of Pulse Return

		S	BA	AA	R	f_y
	E	f_{xy} f^2_{xy} $f_x f_y$ $f^2_{xy} \div f_x f_y$	3 9 208 .0433	4 16 208 .0769	6 36 117 .3077	13
Health	A	1 1 147 .0068	9 81 336 .2411	8 64 336 .1905	3 9 189 .0476	21
	P	6 36 98 .3673	4 16 224 .0714	4 16 224 .0714		14
	f_x	7	16	16	9	48

NOTE: f_{xy} is the cell frequency—3 in BA—E.

f^2_{xy} is the square of the cell frequency—9.

$f_x f_y$ is the product of the totals for the column and the row which intersect to make the cell—16 × 13 or 208.

$f^2_{xy} \div f_x f_y$ is the quotient obtained by the indicated division—9 ÷ 208 or .0433.

The sum, S, of $(f^2_{xy} \div f_x f_y)$ for all of the cells here is 1.4240 and this value substituted in Formula (67) gives

$$C = \sqrt{\frac{1.4240 - 1}{1.4240}} \quad \text{or} \quad \sqrt{\frac{.424}{1.424}}$$
$$= .55$$

An important advantage of C over the Pearson product-moment r lies in the fact that the characteristics being compared may be unordered. For example, the sample may be divided into such categories as races, color of eyes, language spoken, and so on. In situations of this kind the Pearson r cannot be used. On the other hand C earns for itself some distrust because of its erratic behavior under changed categories. The Pearson r ordinarily changes but little when the size of intervals is increased or diminished. Another shortcoming of C is that a given coefficient may have two different interpretations for two different tables of unequal numbers of categories. As a matter of fact, the value of 1.00 for C should be thought of as the maximum limit for perfect relationship when t, the number of categories, is very large. Therefore C for a given sample must be viewed in the light of the highest possible C attainable for a table of its number of categories. Where t_x and t_y are approximately the same, the maximum value of C is

$$\sqrt{\frac{\frac{t_x + t_y}{2} - 1}{\frac{t_x + t_y}{2}}}$$

If t_x and t_y are equal, the expression changes to $\sqrt{\frac{t-1}{t}}$. From this expression, the following maximum values for C have been worked out:

$\frac{t_x + t_y}{2}$	Maximum Value of C
2	.71
3	.82
4	.87
5	.89
6	.91
7	.93
8	.94
10	.95
13	.96
17	.97
25	.98

A very rough method of correcting C for difference in number of categories in order that comparisons of the C's can be made as though all tables have the same number of categories, is to divide the obtained C by its maximum value. This rough method applies to our problem on health and pulse return as follows:

$$\sqrt{\frac{\frac{t_x + t_y}{2} - 1}{\frac{t_x + t_y}{2}}} = \sqrt{\frac{\frac{4 + 3}{2} - 1}{\frac{4 + 3}{2}}} \quad \text{or} \quad \sqrt{\frac{3.5 - 1}{3.5}} \quad \text{or} \quad .845$$

The value .845 may also be determined by interpolation from the preceding table—3.5, the average of 4 categories and 3 categories, should have a maximum value for C equal to one half of (.82 + .87) or .845.

Then corrected $C = \dfrac{.55}{.845}$ or .65.

The method given for computing C makes no provision for the minus values of C, hence the coefficient can only be taken as a measure of association between the two traits. If a sign is to be attached, it must be determined by observation of the data as they appear in the scatter-diagram. If C is small, this determination is often difficult to make. Then too in many scales, such as rate of pulse return, for example, we are not certain which end to call upper and which lower. In this case it is best, perhaps, to state simply that corrected C equals .65, and that rapid pulse return is associated with excellent health.

Probable Error of the Coefficient of Contingency.—Computation of the probable error of C is longer and more tedious than computation of C itself. Moreover, its value is so nearly that of the probable error of the Pearson r for a sample having the same N and the same coefficient that, except where great exactness is desired, it is not recommended that the computation be made. The formula for the probable error of C is

$$\text{P.E.}_C = \frac{.6745}{\sqrt{N}} \sqrt{\frac{\frac{\psi^3}{S - 1} + 1 - (S - 1)}{[1 + (S - 1)]^3}} \tag{68}$$

The value of S − 1 to be substituted in this formula may be secured from Formula (67). In our illustration this value is

.424. The cube of psi (ψ^3), however, is not so easily found. To obtain the value of ψ^3 each cell must be entered for the value of $\left(f_{xy} - \dfrac{f_x f_y}{N}\right)^3$ and the value of $\left(\dfrac{f_x f_y}{N}\right)^2$ for

$$\psi^3 = \frac{1}{N}\Sigma\left[\frac{\left(f_{xy} - \dfrac{f_x f_y}{N}\right)^3}{\left(\dfrac{f_x f_y}{N}\right)^2}\right]$$

Taking the cells in order of rows the values to be summed are

$$\left(3 - \frac{208}{48}\right)^3 \div \left(\frac{208}{48}\right)^2 = \quad -.1260$$

$$\left(4 - \frac{208}{48}\right)^3 \div \left(\frac{208}{48}\right)^2 = \quad -.0019$$

$$\left(6 - \frac{117}{48}\right)^3 \div \left(\frac{117}{48}\right)^2 = \quad +7.5750$$

$$\left(1 - \frac{147}{48}\right)^3 \div \left(\frac{147}{48}\right)^2 = \quad -.9340$$

$$\left(9 - \frac{336}{48}\right)^3 \div \left(\frac{336}{48}\right)^2 = \quad +.1633$$

$$\left(8 - \frac{336}{48}\right)^3 \div \left(\frac{336}{48}\right)^2 = \quad +.0204$$

$$\left(3 - \frac{189}{48}\right)^3 \div \left(\frac{189}{48}\right)^2 = \quad -.0535$$

$$\left(6 - \frac{98}{48}\right)^3 \div \left(\frac{98}{48}\right)^2 = \quad +14.9190$$

$$\left(4 - \frac{224}{48}\right)^3 \div \left(\frac{224}{48}\right)^2 = \quad -.0138$$

$$\left(4 - \frac{224}{48}\right)^3 \div \left(\frac{224}{48}\right)^2 = \frac{-.0138}{+21.5347}$$

Then $\psi^3 = \dfrac{21.5347}{48}$ or **.449**

We are now ready to substitute the necessary values in Formula (68), as follows:

$$P.E._c = \frac{.6745}{\sqrt{48}} \sqrt{\frac{\frac{.449}{.424} + 1 - .424}{(1 + .424)^3}}$$

$$= .0974 \sqrt{\frac{1.635}{1.424^3}}$$

$$= .0733$$

It should be observed that when both are rounded off to two decimal places, this probable error of C and the probable error of an r of .55 with an N of 48 are the same, .07. When similar comparisons are made for the corrected C (.65) and r, the probable error of r is only .01 less.

Biserial r.—The computation of biserial r is resorted to when relationship is sought between two characteristics, one of which has been measured quantitatively and the other expressed as one of two categories. Although it is not necessary for the numbers of cases falling into the two categories to be equal, it is necessary for the measures of the variable trait to be approximately normally distributed. The formula is

$$r_{\text{bis.}} = \frac{M_{y_2} - M_{y_1}}{\sigma_y} \left(\frac{pq}{z} \right) \tag{69}$$

in which

M_{y_2} is the mean of the second distribution.

M_{y_1} is the mean of the first distribution.

p is the second group's proportion of the total distribution $\left(\frac{n_2}{N} \right)$.

q is the first group's proportion of the total distribution $\left(\frac{n_1}{N} \right)$.

σ_y is the standard deviation of the total distribution.

z is the ordinate which separates the two proportions p and q in a normal frequency area of 1.

To illustrate the solution of $r_{\text{bis.}}$ let us use the following data on relationship between the scholarship of high school students and their service as officers of clubs. Records from a high school principal's office reveal that of 480 seniors, 170 had served as officers of school clubs during one or more semesters. The remaining 310 had had no such service. The scholastic grade-point averages for the two groups have been tabulated separately, as shown in Table LV.

TABLE LV. SHOWING THE COMPUTATION OF BISERIAL r

Grade Points (Midpts. of intervals)	Y_1 Non-Officers	Y_2 Officers	Y Totals
3.9	4	16	20
3.6	8	44	52
3.3	21	62	83
3.0	32	28	60
2.7	53	12	65
2.4	71	5	76
2.1	57	1	58
1.8	29	2	31
1.5	22		22
1.2	10		10
.9	3		3
Totals	$n_1 = 310$	$n_2 = 170$	N = 480

In Table LV

$$M_{y_2} = 3.29, \ M_{y_1} = 2.40, \ \sigma_y = .68$$

$$p = \frac{170}{480} \text{ or } .3542, \ q = \frac{310}{480} \text{ or } .6458$$

z = ordinate which corresponds to area of .1458 (.6458 − .5000 or .5000 − .3542). This ordinate is about .372[1].

These values may now be substituted in Formula (69) as follows:

[1] Table E should be used to determine the height of the ordinate. Since Table E refers to areas in terms of percentages of the total normal frequency surface, the proportions .3542 and .6458 should be thought of as percentages (35.42 and 64.58 respectively). Likewise, the area from the mean to the ordinate, the height (z) of which we are seeking, should be considered 14.58%. By rough interpolation between the ordinates .3752 and .3683 which correspond to the areas 13.68% and 15.54% respectively, the approximate ordinate .372 will be found to correspond to the area 14.58%.

$$r_{bis.} = \frac{3.29 - 2.40}{.68}\left(\frac{.3542 \times .6458}{.372}\right)$$

$$= \frac{.89}{.68} \times \frac{.229}{.372}$$

$$= .81$$

Unlike the probable error of the contingency coefficient, the probable error of biserial r is found easily from values derived in the solution of $r_{bis.}$. The formula is

$$\text{P.E.}_{(bis.\, r)} = \frac{.6745}{\sqrt{N}}\left(\frac{\sqrt{pq}}{z} - r^2\right) \tag{70}$$

Substituting the required values in this formula we have

$$\text{P.E.}_{(bis.\, r)} = \frac{.6745}{\sqrt{480}}\left(\frac{\sqrt{.3542 \times .6458}}{.372} - .81^2\right)$$

$$= .0308\,(1.285 - .656)$$

$$= .02$$

(Table F may be used for finding the value of $\sqrt{pq}$)

The relationship between school club office-holding and scholarship may now be written

$$r_{bis.} = .81 \pm .02$$

As in the case of the contingency coefficient, no sign is used to indicate direction of relationship. This characteristic may be seen from the mean of the group possessing the advantage.

There are other methods of measuring relationship, but they are beyond the scope of an elementary textbook on educational statistics and will be left for the reader to investigate from more extensive treatments of the subject.

Correlation coefficients found by the methods discussed previously are often spoken of as being of zero-order. By this is meant the relationship between two variables was found without the influence of others being taken into consideration. It is possible in many instances that the relation between two variables is influenced by other variables. Statistical techniques have been developed for controlling or holding constant the influence of a third, a fourth, or any other additional number of factors, so that the true relation between the two original variables may be determined more accurately.

Partial Correlation.—To explain the meaning of controlling or holding constant a third variable will require a simple illustration. Three traits of 111 boys have been measured. The traits are

1. Humerus-spread
2. Height
3. Weight

The three possible zero-order correlations have been found to be

$$r_{12} = .96$$
$$r_{13} = .90$$
$$r_{23} = .89$$

Now it is desired to rule out weight, and to find the correlation between (1) humerus-spread and (2) height when these two variables are freed from the "weight" variable. The question is this: Will the correlation of .96 remain unchanged between humerus-spread and height if the measurement of these two traits is based upon a group of boys all of the same weight?

The formula to be used is

$$r_{12 \cdot 3} = \frac{r_{12} - (r_{13})(r_{23})}{\sqrt{1 - (r_{13})^2}\sqrt{1 - (r_{23})^2}} \tag{71a}$$

and the substitutions and solution are

$$r_{12 \cdot 3} = \frac{.96 - (.90)(.89)}{\sqrt{1 - (.90)^2}\sqrt{1 - (.89)^2}} \quad \text{or} \quad .80$$

This is a first-order correlation. By methods already explained, the probable error of this correlation may be found to be .023. The probable error of the correlation r_{12} (.96), when the N is 111, may be shown to equal .005. The difference, .16, between these two correlations is actually 6.67 times the probable error, .024, of the difference. From this fact we may conclude that the presence of the "weight" factor definitely affected the relationship of humerus-spread and height, for the correlation between these two traits was significantly alienated by the removal of the influence of weight.

It should be noticed in Formula (71a) that the grouping of subscripts 12·3 in the left member indicates that the correlation between traits 1 and 2 is to be found with trait 3 held constant. By observing the relationship of the subscripts in the right member to the subscript 12·3, and by changing them rhythmically, formulas may be written for finding the correlation of any two traits with the third held constant as follows:

$$r_{13 \cdot 2} = \frac{r_{13} - (r_{12})(r_{23})}{\sqrt{1 - (r_{12})^2}\sqrt{1 - (r_{23})^2}} \tag{71b}$$

$$r_{23 \cdot 1} = \frac{r_{23} - (r_{12})(r_{13})}{\sqrt{1 - (r_{12})^2}\sqrt{1 - (r_{13})^2}} \tag{71c}$$

The substitution of the zero-order correlations into Formulas (71b) and (71c), and the computation of the other two first-order correlations, follow:

$$r_{13 \cdot 2} = \frac{.90 - (.96)(.89)}{\sqrt{1 - (.96)^2}\sqrt{1 - (.89)^2}} \quad \text{or} \quad .36$$

$$r_{23 \cdot 1} = \frac{.89 - (.96)(.90)}{\sqrt{1 - (.96)^2}\sqrt{1 - (.90)^2}} \quad \text{or} \quad .21$$

From these results it may be seen that if boys of the same height had been measured for the traits of humerus-spread and weight, the correlation would have been .36, or if boys of the same humerus-spread had been measured for the traits of height and weight, the correlation would have been .21. While the difference, .15, between these two correlations is only about two probable errors of the difference, there is a suggestion of the possibility that humerus-spread (a combination measure of growth of bone and of thorax) may be more closely related to weight than height is related to weight.

Computations of this type illustrate the need for using logarithms to save time and to reduce opportunities of error. Of course the "elbow" method can be used for any of these computations, but for those who use logarithms, many short-cuts are possible. To illustrate this, the solution of $r_{13.2}$ by logarithms (see Table C) is given below:

$$\log\sqrt{1 - (.96)^2} = 9.44716 - 10$$
$$\log\sqrt{1 - (.89)^2} = \underline{9.65893 - 10}$$
$$9.10609 - 10$$

$$.90 - (.96)\ (.89)$$

$$\text{or} \quad .90 - .8544 = \quad .0456$$

$$\log .0456 = 18.65896 - 20$$

$$\text{subtract} \qquad \underline{9.10609 - 10}$$

$$\text{antilog} \qquad \overline{9.55287 - 10} = .36$$

In partial correlation, second-order correlations are possible when four variables are involved. The finding of the zero-order and the first-order correlations must precede the computation of second-order correlations. Here the object is to imply the correlation between two variables when the influence of *two other variables* is eliminated. The operations can be described best by illustration. Let us suppose we have given four tests to a group of pupils.

The tests are

      1. Vocabulary
      2. Social studies
      3. Arithmetic reasoning
      4. Arithmetic computation

The zero-order correlations are

$r_{12} = .70$	$r_{23} = .53$
$r_{13} = .54$	$r_{24} = .58$
$r_{14} = .57$	$r_{34} = .56$

By substituting in turn these zero-order correlations in Formula (71a), twelve different first-order correlations may be found. Ordinarily, however, there will be no need for all of these correlations, to meet the requirements of the specific purpose of the partial correlation. Therefore, before going to the trouble of making all the possible first-order correlations, it is best to consider carefully the question to which an answer is sought. Let us say in this case we wish to know the correlation of (1) vocabulary and (2) social studies, when (3) arithmetic reasoning and (4) arithmetic computation are held constant. The formula is

$$r_{12 \cdot 34} = \frac{r_{12 \cdot 3} - (r_{14 \cdot 3})(r_{24 \cdot 3})}{\sqrt{1 - (r_{14 \cdot 3})^2}\sqrt{1 - (r_{24 \cdot 3})^2}} \qquad (72)$$

Now, for the purposes of finding this second-order correlation, we shall need the following first-order correlations:

$$r_{12 \cdot 3} = \frac{.70 - (.54)(.53)}{\sqrt{1 - (.54)^2}\sqrt{1 - (.53)^2}} \quad \text{or} \quad .58$$

$$r_{14 \cdot 3} = \frac{.57 - (.54)(.56)}{\sqrt{1 - (.54)^2}\sqrt{1 - (.56)^2}} \quad \text{or} \quad .38$$

and
$$r_{24 \cdot 3} = \frac{.58 - (.53)(.56)}{\sqrt{1 - (.53)^2}\sqrt{1 - (.56)^2}} \quad \text{or} \quad .40$$

Substituting these values in Formula (72) we have

$$r_{12 \cdot 34} = \frac{.58 - (.38)(.40)}{\sqrt{1 - (.38)^2}\sqrt{1 - (.40)^2}} \quad \text{or} \quad .50$$

It is now clear that the correlation between vocabulary scores and social-studies scores is materially reduced when uninfluenced by arithmetic reasoning and arithmetic computation.

Although the examples used have shown a reduction in correlation between two variables when one or more other variables are held constant, it should not be assumed that a reduction will always result. In some instances, the additional factor or factors actually have the effect of partially alienating the two variables being considered, and therefore when this influence is removed, the effect is to increase the correlation of the two variables. Such a situation may be seen in the following example:

$$\text{If} \quad r_{12} = \quad .24$$
$$r_{13} = \quad .38$$
$$r_{23} = \quad -.28$$

Then

$$r_{12 \cdot 3} = \frac{.24 - (.38)(-.28)}{\sqrt{1 - (.38)^2}\sqrt{1 - (-.28)^2}} \quad \text{or} \quad .39$$

Rhythmical adjustment of subscripts in Formula (72) may be employed to revise the formula for use in finding $r_{13 \cdot 24}$, $r_{14 \cdot 23}$, $r_{23 \cdot 14}$, and so on.

Multiple Correlation.—In multiple correlation, no variable is being ruled out, but the influence of all the variables is being used or measured. The computations of multiple correlations become highly complex when more than three or four variables are involved. In view of that fact, and in view of the further fact that in this elementary treatment the purpose is merely to learn the meaning and application of multiple correlation, the discussion will be limited to three variables. Those who are interested in extending their knowledge of the subject should investigate some of the special methods in use, such as the iteration method, the method by determinants, or the Doolittle method.

There are two aspects of the subject of multiple correlation which will be treated separately here. The first of these is the aspect of determining the correlation coefficient of one variable with the composite of two or more other variables which have been combined in the most effective manner to produce maximum correlation. This aspect of multiple correlation does not provide a means of determining what are the correct weights for the individual variables to be combined; it merely enables us to say what correlation coefficient between the single variable and the combined variables will result if and when the variables of the combination have been properly weighted. For these computations it is necessary to have the zero-order correlations. The formulas for these coefficients are

$$R_{1 \cdot 23} = \sqrt{\frac{(r_{12})^2 + (r_{13})^2 - 2(r_{12})(r_{13})(r_{23})}{1 - (r_{23})^2}} \tag{73a}$$

$$R_{2 \cdot 13} = \sqrt{\frac{(r_{12})^2 + (r_{23})^2 - 2(r_{12})(r_{23})(r_{13})}{1 - (r_{13})^2}} \tag{73b}$$

$$R_{3 \cdot 12} = \sqrt{\frac{(r_{13})^2 + (r_{23})^2 - 2(r_{13})(r_{23})(r_{12})}{1 - (r_{12})^2}} \tag{73c}$$

It should be observed that the third term in the numerator is the same for all three of the preceding formulas. The order of factors in the term was changed to conform with changed subscripts for R.

Let us now apply Formula (73a) to the data previously given for relationship between (1) humerus-spread, (2) height, and (3) weight which were secured by measurements of one hundred and eleven boys:

$$r_{12} = .96$$
$$r_{13} = .90$$
$$r_{23} = .89$$

Suppose that we wish to know what correlation might be obtained by combining on the basis of optimum influence the "height" and "weight" measure for each boy, and by correlating these composite measures with measures of humerus-spread. The substitution will be

$$R_{1 \cdot 23} = \sqrt{\frac{(.96)^2 + (.90)^2 - 2(.96)(.90)(.89)}{1 - (.89)^2}} \text{ or } .965$$

Since $r_{12} = .96 \pm .005$, $R_{1 \cdot 23} = .965 \pm .004$, and $.965 - .96 = .005 \pm .006$, it may be seen plainly that the correlation between (1) and (2) has enjoyed no worthwhile improvement by combining (3) with (2), having been changed less than three probable errors of the difference.

The second aspect of multiple correlation pertains to the actual determination of the weight to assign to each of a number of variables, so that a composite measure of the variables will produce the best correlation possible with another variable. Included in these operations will be the writing of the equation for predicting the most probable value of one variable for given values of a second, a third, or more variables.

It has been shown previously that, in the case of two variables, the equation for predicting the most probable value of X is

$$\overline{X} = r_{xy}\frac{\sigma_x}{\sigma_y} Y - r_{xy}\frac{\sigma_x}{\sigma_y} M_y + M_x$$

When substitutions are made in this equation, it reduces to three terms which may be written

$$\overline{X} = b_{xy} Y + \text{constant}$$

In much the same manner, this method of prediction may be used with three, four, or even more variables. Because of the large number of variables which may possibly enter the equation, they are usually indicated by $X_1, X_2, X_3, \ldots \ldots X_n$ instead of by different letters. Using these symbols, the equation above becomes

$$\overline{X}_1 = b_{12}X_2 + C$$

When three variables are involved, it becomes

$$\overline{X}_1 = b_{12 \cdot 3}X_2 + b_{13 \cdot 2}X_3 + C_1$$

$$\text{in which} \quad b_{12 \cdot 3} = r_{12 \cdot 3}\frac{\sigma_{1 \cdot 3}}{\sigma_{2 \cdot 3}} \tag{74}$$

$$\text{and} \quad b_{13 \cdot 2} = r_{13 \cdot 2}\frac{\sigma_{1 \cdot 2}}{\sigma_{3 \cdot 2}}$$

Moreover

$$\sigma_{1 \cdot 2} = \sigma_1\sqrt{1 - (r_{12})^2}$$
$$\sigma_{1 \cdot 3} = \sigma_1\sqrt{1 - (r_{13})^2}$$
$$\sigma_{2 \cdot 3} = \sigma_2\sqrt{1 - (r_{23})^2}$$
$$\text{and} \quad \sigma_{3 \cdot 2} = \sigma_3\sqrt{1 - (r_{32})^2}$$

Further simplification may be effected with only zero-order coefficients involved, by substituting for $r_{12 \cdot 3}$ and $r_{13 \cdot 2}$ their respective values given in Formulas (71a) and (71b). At first it may appear that these substitutions complicate the formula, but in view of the cancellation of certain factors and combination of others made possible by the substitutions, necessary computations are reduced. When the suggested substitutions are made, Formula (74) changes to

$$\overline{X}_1 = \frac{r_{12} - (r_{13})(r_{23})}{\sqrt{1 - (r_{13})^2}\sqrt{1 - (r_{23})^2}} \times \frac{\sigma_1\sqrt{1 - (r_{13})^2}}{\sigma_2\sqrt{1 - (r_{23})^2}} X_2$$

$$+ \frac{r_{13} - (r_{12})(r_{23})}{\sqrt{1 - (r_{12})^2}\sqrt{1 - (r_{23})^2}} \times \frac{\sigma_1\sqrt{1 - (r_{12})^2}}{\sigma_3\sqrt{1 - (r_{32})^2}} X_3 + C_1$$

which by obvious cancellations and multiplications becomes

$$\overline{X}_1 = \frac{\sigma_1[r_{12} - (r_{13})(r_{23})]}{\sigma_2[1 - (r_{23})^2]} X_2 + \frac{\sigma_1[r_{13} - (r_{12})(r_{23})]}{\sigma_3[1 - (r_{23})^2]} X_3 + C_1 \tag{75a}$$

in which

$$C_1 = M_1 - b_{12\cdot3}M_2 - b_{13\cdot2}M_3$$

Rearrangement of subscripts on a rhythmical plan now produces the following additional formulas:

$$\overline{X}_2 = \frac{\sigma_2[r_{12} - (r_{13})(r_{23})]}{\sigma_1[1 - (r_{13})^2]} X_1 + \frac{\sigma_2[r_{23} - (r_{12})(r_{13})]}{\sigma_3[1 - (r_{13})^2]} X_3 + C_2 \qquad \textbf{(75b)}$$

in which

$$C_2 = M_2 - b_{21\cdot3}M_1 - b_{23\cdot1}M_3$$

and

$$\overline{X}_3 = \frac{\sigma_3[r_{13} - (r_{12})(r_{23})]}{\sigma_1[1 - (r_{12})^2]} X_1 + \frac{\sigma_3[r_{23} - (r_{12})(r_{13})]}{\sigma_2[1 - (r_{12})^2]} X_2 + C_3 \qquad \textbf{(75c)}$$

in which

$$C_3 = M_3 - b_{31\cdot2}M_1 - b_{32\cdot1}M_2$$

In determining the value of C, the factors by which the two means are multiplied are merely the coefficients of the X_1, X_2, or X_3 of the formula.

We are now ready to apply Formula (75a) and for that purpose we shall assemble all the necessary data from the measurements of the one hundred and eleven boys as follows:

	Mean	σ	Correlation
(1) Humerus-spread....	28.32″	3.18″	$r_{12} = .96$
(2) Height.............	51.64″	5.76″	$r_{13} = .90$
(3) Weight...........	71.16 lb.	19.35 lb.	$r_{23} = .89$

$$\overline{X}_1 = \frac{3.18\,[.96 - (.90)(.89)]}{5.76\,[1 - (.89)^2]} X_2 + \frac{3.18\,[.90 - (.96)(.89)]}{19.35\,[1 - (.89)^2]} X_3 + C_1$$

$$= \frac{3.18 \times .1590}{5.76 \times .2079} X_2 + \frac{3.18 \times .0456}{19.35 \times .2079} X_3 + C_1$$

$$= .4222\, X_2 + .0361\, X_3 + C_1$$

The value of C_1 may now be found from

$$C_1 = M_1 - b_{12\cdot3}M_2 - b_{13\cdot2}M_3$$

or $C_1 = 28.32 - .4222 \times 51.64 - .0361 \times 71.16$ or   3.9487

Rounding off all fractions to three decimal places the equation in its entirety becomes

$$\overline{X}_1 = .422X_2 + .036X_3 + 3.949$$

As in the case of the two-variable equation discussed in the preceding chapter, this three-variable equation may be used to make predictions. For example, if we have in hand the facts that a boy's height (X_2) is 55 inches and his weight (X_3) is 83 pounds, we may substitute these values to obtain his humerus-spread (X_1):

$$\overline{X}_1 = .422 \times 55 + .036 \times 83 + 3.949 \quad \text{or} \quad 30.15$$

Again the question of reliability of a prediction arises and we have need for another formula for standard error of estimate or probable error of estimate. In terms of zero-order correlation, the formula for standard error of estimate is

$$\sigma_{1 \cdot 23} = \sigma_1 \sqrt{\frac{1 - (r_{12})^2 - (r_{13})^2 - (r_{23})^2 + 2(r_{12})(r_{13})(r_{23})}{1 - (r_{23})^2}} \tag{76}$$

Since the numerator of the fraction in Formula (76) remains unchanged in computing any one of the three standard errors of estimate, it is often abbreviated to the expression S_{123} and the formulas written:

$$\sigma_{1 \cdot 23} = \sigma_1 \frac{\sqrt{S_{123}}}{\sqrt{1 - (r_{23})^2}} \tag{77a}$$

$$\sigma_{2 \cdot 13} = \sigma_2 \frac{\sqrt{S_{123}}}{\sqrt{1 - (r_{13})^2}} \tag{77b}$$

$$\sigma_{3 \cdot 12} = \sigma_3 \frac{\sqrt{S_{123}}}{\sqrt{1 - (r_{12})^2}} \tag{77c}$$

To express the reliability of estimate in terms of probable errors, it is only necessary to multiply the right member of each of the foregoing formulas by .6745. The formulas then become

$$\text{P.E.}_{1 \cdot 23} = .6745\sigma_1 \frac{\sqrt{S_{123}}}{\sqrt{1 - (r_{23})^2}} \tag{78a}$$

$$\text{P.E.}_{2 \cdot 13} = .6745\sigma_2 \frac{\sqrt{S_{123}}}{\sqrt{1 - (r_{13})^2}} \tag{78b}$$

$$\text{P.E.}_{3 \cdot 12} = .6745\sigma_3 \frac{\sqrt{S_{123}}}{\sqrt{1 - (r_{12})^2}} \tag{78c}$$

Now let us return to the boy whose humerus-spread was estimated to be 30.15 inches from a height of 55 inches and a weight of 83 pounds, to find the probable error of the estimated humerus-spread. For this purpose we shall use Formula (78a) after first finding the value of S_{123}.

$$S_{123} = 1 - (r_{12})^2 - (r_{13})^2 - (r_{23})^2 + 2 (r_{12})(r_{13})(r_{23})$$
$$= 1 - (.96)^2 - (.90)^2 - (.89)^2 + 2 (.96)(.90)(.89)$$
$$= .0142$$

Making appropriate substitutions in Formula (78a) and reducing the expression to a single value, we obtain

$$\text{P.E.}_{.1 \cdot 23} = .6745 \times 3.18 \frac{\sqrt{.0142}}{\sqrt{1 - (.89)^2}}$$
$$= .56$$

Then $\overline{X}_1 = 30.15 \pm .56$

The probable error of the estimate of 30.15 inches for the humerus-spread of the boy in question is .56 inches. This probable error also applies to any estimate which may be made from the equation used in making this estimate. In other words, when a boy's height and weight are known we may estimate his humerus-spread with reasonable assurance that there is a one-half probability that the true measure of that trait will not differ from our estimate by more than .56 inches.

Unless the worker has access to a computing machine for computations of the foregoing type, it is strongly recommended that he utilize tables of logarithms and other tables to reduce labor and possibility of error.

As was the case in the two-variable regression equation, the coefficients in the three-variable regression equation are regression coefficients. In the equation

$$\overline{X}_1 = .422 X_2 + .036 X_3 + 3.949$$

the coefficient .422 indicates the average change in X_1 for a unit change in X_2, and the coefficient .036 indicates the average change in X_1 for a unit change in X_3. Thus it may be seen here that the third variable, weight, has considerable less force than height in determining humerus-spread.

An important value of equations of this type which have been written to fit known relationships of measured traits of a sample in hand lies in their use as instruments to predict one unknown trait for a similar sample in which the remaining traits are known.

Exercises and Problems

1. In a study of character in school children, extent of cheating was measured for comparison with frequency of attendance at moving pictures.

These data for 120 pupils are tabulated as shown in the following arrangement:

x Scale (Frequency of Attendance per Month)

	Never −1*	1	3	5	7	9	11	f_y
8–8.99							1	1
7–7.99							1	1
6–6.99						2	3	5
5–5.99	1					3	3	7
4–4.99	3	3			1	5	2	14
3–3.99	7	6			5	2		20
2–2.99	4	5	2	1	7	3		22
1–1.99		4	4	13	6			27
0– .99			16	7				23
f_x	15	18	22	21	19	15	10	120

(Row label at left: y Scale (Xi Cheating Scores))

* A value of −1 is assigned here to maintain consistency in the scale of frequency of attendance.

(a) Find η_{yx} and its probable error.
(b) Find r and its probable error.
(c) Find ζ for the correlation ratio η_{yx}.
(d) Find the probable error of ζ.
(e) Find the ratio of ζ to its probable error.
(f) Is the regression linear?

You may repeat these operations for η_{xy}.

2. A group of students was classified by use of an ascendance-submission scale into personality categories of ascendant, middle, and submissive. They were also classified into scholarship categories of upper, middle, and lower.

The numbers falling into these classifications are shown in the following table:

Personality

		S	Mid.	A	f_y
Scholarship	Up.	10	14	11	35
	Mid.	17	28	14	59
	Low.	8	17	10	35
	f_x	35	59	35	129

(a) Find the contingency coefficient.

(b) Estimate its probable error.

(c) Do these data prove a relationship between scholarship and the personality trait measured?

3. A Challenge: Using the data of Exercise (2), find the probable error of the contingency coefficient.

4. In an attempt to measure the relationship of kindergarten training and subsequent school success in the elementary grades, an elementary school principal compared a group of pupils who had received kindergarten training with a group which had received no kindergarten training. These groups were of approximately equal socio-economic status. All grades from 1 to 7 were represented in both groups in approximately equal proportions. Scores made on a standardized achievement test were converted to achievement ages which became the measures of achievement. A complete assembly of the data is given in the table at the top of page 246.

(a) Find r_{bis}.

(b) Find the P.E.$_{(bis. \ r)}$.

(c) Interpret your results.

Achievement Ages (Lower limits of intervals)	Y_1 Non-kin.	Y_2 kin.	Y Totals
15		3	3
14		4	4
13	3	5	8
12	4	7	11
11	8	7	15
10	8	6	14
9	8	6	14
8	13	7	20
7	9	7	16
6	6	3	9
5	5	1	6
Totals	64	56	120

5. From the following facts

$$r_{12} = .70 \qquad r_{23} = .53$$
$$r_{13} = .54 \qquad r_{24} = .58$$
$$r_{14} = .57 \qquad r_{34} = .56$$

wherein

1 is vocabulary scores
2 is social studies scores
3 is arithmetic reasoning scores
4 is arithmetic computation scores

(a) Find the correlation between vocabulary and arithmetic reasoning with social studies held constant.

(b) Find the correlation between vocabulary and arithmetic reasoning with arithmetic computation held constant.

(c) Find the correlation between vocabulary and arithmetic reasoning with social studies and arithmetic computation held constant.

6. Using the zero-order correlations given in this chapter for measures of (1) humerus-spread, (2) height, and (3) weight of 111 boys:

$$r_{12} = .96$$
$$r_{13} = .90$$
$$r_{23} = .89$$

(a) Find the value of $R_{2 \cdot 13}$, interpret this coefficient, and determine if combining (1) and (3) changes significantly the correlation of height with either of the two variables taken alone.

(b) Repeat the operations suggested in (a) for the value of $R_{3 \cdot 12}$.

7. A high school principal assembled the following data from experience over a five-year period with the success of his graduates, 366 in number, in a local college:

	Mean	σ	Correlations
1. College grade points (1st semester)..................	2.1	.9	$r_{12} = .72$
2. Psychological Exam. (Given in H.S.)...................	141.1	51.7	$r_{13} = .67$
3. Comprehensive English Exam. (Given in H.S.)............	92.9	38.7	$r_{23} = .80$

(a) Write the equation for estimating a high school pupil's grade-point average in college for the first semester, when his psychological examination score and his comprehensive English examination score are known.

(b) What grade-point average for the first semester may be expected for a high school graduate who will be entering college next fall, and who made a psychological examination score of 116 and a comprehensive English score of 72?

(c) Find the probable error of the estimate made in (b).

APPENDIX

TABLES TO FACILITATE CALCULATIONS

Most of the calculations required in statistical computations are very simple in principle, but many of them are tedious to execute. The processes are not difficult to understand, but some of them require much time to perform and provide many opportunities for arithmetic errors. While every student of statistics should possess the ability to perform all of the arithmetic operations involved in simple statistical formulas, he should also possess the wisdom as well as the ability to utilize labor-saving tables. The tables which follow will be found very useful in lifting the burden of drudgery from statistics.

Table A.—From this table, direct readings of the squares and square roots of all numbers from 101 to 1000 may be made. By proper adjustment of decimal points, direct readings of squares may be made for the numbers from 1 to 100. The square roots of numbers for which this table does not provide direct readings may be found indirectly by entering the table through the *square* column. It should be observed that the digits in the *square* column are grouped in pairs. The two digits of a pair should never be separated by a decimal point.

Examples: To find the value of 87^2 look up the square of 870 which is 756900. Adjust the decimal point two places to the left to account for the loss of one place from 870, and the answer 7569 results. To find the value of $\sqrt{870}$, a direct reading gives 29.496. Also values of $\sqrt{8.70}$ and of $\sqrt{0870}$ may be written 2.9496 and .29496, respectively. However, when the value of $\sqrt{87}$ is sought, the paired arrangement of digits in the *square* column for 870 is disrupted. To find the value of $\sqrt{87}$, therefore, it is necessary to find in the *square* column the closest value to 87 00 00. This is 87 04 89, and it is the square of 933. Thus 9.33 is the square root of 87 (rounded to two decimal places). This table of square roots is particularly valuable for use in the formula for standard deviation.

Table B.—This table of four-place logarithms will be found of great assistance to those not having access to a computing machine. Speed in the processes of multiplication, division, powers, and roots comes from practice in using logarithms.

Example:

$$r = \frac{7433}{\sqrt{8214 \times 9785}}$$

log 8214 = 3.9145	log 7433 = 13.8712 − 10
log 9785 = 3.9905	less 3.9525
2)7.9050	antilog 9.9187 − 10 = .8291
3.9525	r = .8291 or .83, Ans.

Table C.—While Table B may be employed to serve the purposes of all needs for use of logarithms in elementary statistics, Table C may be used to eliminate a *squaring* operation and a *subtracting* operation in any formula in which either $1 - r^2$ or $\sqrt{1 - r^2}$ appears.

Examples:

$$\text{P.E.}_r = \frac{.6745\,(1 - .72^2)}{\sqrt{83}}$$

$$= \frac{.6745}{\sqrt{83}} \times (1 - .72^2)$$

$$= .0740 \times (1 - .72^2)$$

$$\begin{aligned}
\log .0740 &= 8.86920 - 10 \\
2 \log \sqrt{1 - .72^2} &= 9.68268 - 10 \\
\text{antilog} \quad &\overline{8.55188 - 10} = .0356
\end{aligned}$$

or P.E.$_r$ = .0356, Ans.

$$r_{12 \cdot 3} = \frac{.90 - (.72)(.70)}{\sqrt{1 - .72^2}\sqrt{1 - .70^2}} = \frac{.396}{\sqrt{1 - .72^2}\sqrt{1 - .70^2}}$$

log $\sqrt{1 - .72^2}$ = 9.84134 − 10	log .396 = 19.59770 − 20
log $\sqrt{1 - .70^2}$ = 9.85379 − 10	less 9.69513 − 10
9.69513 − 10	antilog 9.90257 − 10 = .7993

or $r_{12 \cdot 3}$ = .80, Ans.

Table D.—The values of $\dfrac{.6745}{\sqrt{N}}$ given in this table are of great importance in dealing with any formula containing the factor $\dfrac{.6745}{\sqrt{N}}$.

Example:

$$P.E._M = \frac{.6745 \times 12.5}{\sqrt{56}}$$

$$= \frac{.6745}{\sqrt{56}} \times 12.5$$

$$= .0901 \times 12.5$$

$$= 1.12625 \quad \text{or} \quad 1.13$$

(Also see first example given in explanation of use of Table C.)

Table E.—When sigma is taken as the unit of measure on the base line, and the area (N) of the normal probability distribution is assigned a value of one square unit, the equation of the normal frequency curve becomes

$$y = \frac{1}{\sqrt{2\pi}} e^{-\frac{x^2}{2}}$$

By changing this equation to a more convenient form and then by substituting successive values for x, corresponding values (ordinates) for y may be determined. These y values are shown in the column marked *ordinate*. The area corresponding to each sigma distance from the mean is expressed as a percentage of the total area. The second portion of Table E differs from the first portion only in the respects that ordinates have been omitted, and distances from the mean on the base have been converted to P.E. units.

By use of the first part of this table a normal frequency curve may be plotted. Also, an area between any two ordinates of the curve may be found by adding or subtracting as the case may require.

Examples:

The area from $.00\sigma$ to $+.65\sigma$ is 24.22%.
The area from -1.15σ to $+1.25\sigma$ is 37.49% $+39.44\%$ or 76.93%.
The area from $+.85\sigma$ to $+2.45\sigma$ is 49.29% -30.23% or 19.06%.

By use of the second part of the table, the probability that a statistic will lie within limits given in terms of the P.E. may be determined.

Examples: If $M = 43.60\pm.35$, the probability that the mean of the parent population from which this sample came will lie between 42.55 and 44.65 (a range of three P.E.'s above and below 43.60) is $\frac{47.85}{50.00}$ or $\frac{957}{1000}$.

If the difference between two means is 9.88, and the P.E. of the difference is 2.6, the probability of a difference as great or greater arising between any two similar chance samples is $\frac{.52}{50.00}$ or $\frac{104}{10000}$ or about $\frac{1}{100}$; and the probability of a difference as great or greater arising between two samples and at the same time favorable to a specified sample is $\frac{.52}{100.00}$ or $\frac{52}{10000}$ or about $\frac{.5}{100}$.

Table F.—This table is of value chiefly in dealing with standard errors or probable errors of proportions:

Example:

$$P.E._p = .6745\sqrt{\frac{.37 \times .63}{41}}$$

$$= \frac{.6745}{\sqrt{41}} \sqrt{.37 \times .63}$$

$$= .1053 \times .4828$$

$$= .0508, \quad \text{Ans.}$$

TABLE A   Squares and Square Roots

No.	Square	Sq. Root	No.	Square	Sq. Root	No.	Square	Sq. Root
101	1 02 01	10.050	151	2 28 01	12.288	201	4 04 01	14.177
102	1 04 04	10.100	152	2 31 04	12.329	202	4 08 04	14.213
103	1 06 09	10.149	153	2 34 09	12.369	203	4 12 09	14.248
104	1 08 16	10.198	154	2 37 16	12.410	204	4 16 16	14.283
105	1 10 25	10.247	155	2 40 25	12.450	205	4 20 25	14.318
106	1 12 36	10.296	156	2 43 36	12.490	206	4 24 36	14.353
107	1 14 49	10.344	157	2 46 49	12.530	207	4 28 49	14.387
108	1 16 64	10.392	158	2 49 64	12.570	208	4 32 64	14.422
109	1 18 81	10.440	159	2 52 81	12.610	209	4 36 81	14.457
110	1 21 00	10.488	160	2 56 00	12.649	210	4 41 00	14.491
111	1 23 21	10.536	161	2 59 21	12.689	211	4 45 21	14.526
112	1 25 44	10.583	162	2 62 44	12.728	212	4 49 44	14.560
113	1 27 69	10.630	163	2 65 69	12.767	213	4 53 69	14.595
114	1 29 96	10.677	164	2 68 96	12.806	214	4 57 96	14.629
115	1 32 25	10.724	165	2 72 25	12.845	215	4 62 25	14.663
116	1 34 56	10.770	166	2 75 56	12.884	216	4 66 56	14.697
117	1 36 89	10.817	167	2 78 89	12.923	217	4 70 89	14.731
118	1 39 24	10.863	168	2 82 24	12.961	218	4 75 24	14.765
119	1 41 61	10.909	169	2 85 61	13.000	219	4 79 61	14.799
120	1 44 00	10.954	170	2 89 00	13.038	220	4 84 00	14.832
121	1 46 41	11.000	171	2 92 41	13.077	221	4 88 41	14.866
122	1 48 84	11.045	172	2 95 84	13.115	222	4 92 84	14.900
123	1 51 29	11.091	173	2 99 29	13.153	223	4 97 29	14.933
124	1 53 76	11.136	174	3 02 76	13.191	224	5 01 76	14.967
125	1 56 25	11.180	175	3 06 25	13.229	225	5 06 25	15.000
126	1 58 76	11.225	176	3 09 76	13.266	226	5 10 76	15.033
127	1 61 29	11.269	177	3 13 29	13.304	227	5 15 29	15.067
128	1 63 84	11.314	178	3 16 84	13.342	228	5 19 84	15.100
129	1 66 41	11.358	179	3 20 41	13.379	229	5 24 41	15.133
130	1 69 00	11.402	180	3 24 00	13.416	230	5 29 00	15.166
131	1 71 61	11.446	181	3 27 61	13.454	231	5 33 61	15.199
132	1 74 24	11.489	182	3 31 24	13.491	232	5 38 24	15.232
133	1 76 89	11.533	183	3 34 89	13.528	233	5 42 89	15.264
134	1 79 56	11.576	184	3 38 56	13.565	234	5 47 56	15.297
135	1 82 25	11.619	185	3 42 25	13.601	235	5 52 25	15.330
136	1 84 96	11.662	186	3 45 96	13.638	236	5 56 96	15.362
137	1 87 69	11.705	187	3 49 69	13.675	237	5 61 69	15.395
138	1 90 44	11.747	188	3 53 44	13.711	238	5 66 44	15.427
139	1 93 21	11.790	189	3 57 21	13.748	239	5 71 21	15.460
140	1 96 00	11.832	190	3 61 00	13.784	240	5 76 00	15.492
141	1 98 81	11.874	191	3 64 81	13.820	241	5 80 81	15.524
142	2 01 64	11.916	192	3 68 64	13.856	242	5 85 64	15.556
143	2 04 49	11.958	193	3 72 49	13.892	243	5 90 49	15.588
144	2 07 36	12.000	194	3 76 36	13.928	244	5 95 36	15.620
145	2 10 25	12.042	195	3 80 25	13.964	245	6 00 25	15.652
146	2 13 16	12.083	196	3 84 16	14.000	246	6 05 16	15.684
147	2 16 09	12.124	197	3 88 09	14.036	247	6 10 09	15.716
148	2 19 04	12.166	198	3 92 04	14.071	248	6 15 04	15.748
149	2 22 01	12.207	199	3 96 01	14.107	249	6 20 01	15.780
150	2 25 00	12.247	200	4 00 00	14.142	250	6 25 00	15.811

Squares and Square Roots

No.	Square	Sq. Root	No.	Square	Sq. Root	No.	Square	Sq. Root
251	6 30 01	15.843	**301**	9 06 01	17.349	**351**	12 32 01	18.735
252	6 35 04	15.875	**302**	9 12 04	17.378	**352**	12 39 04	18.762
253	6 40 09	15.906	**303**	9 18 09	17.407	**353**	12 46 09	18.788
254	6 45 16	15.937	**304**	9 24 16	17.436	**354**	12 53 16	18.815
255	6 50 25	15.969	**305**	9 30 25	17.464	**355**	12 60 25	18.841
256	6 55 36	16.000	**306**	9 36 36	17.493	**356**	12 67 36	18.868
257	6 60 49	16.031	**307**	9 42 49	17.521	**357**	12 74 49	18.894
258	6 65 64	16.062	**308**	9 48 64	17.550	**358**	12 81 64	18.921
259	6 70 81	16.093	**309**	9 54 81	17.578	**359**	12 88 81	18.947
260	6 76 00	16.125	**310**	9 61 00	17.607	**360**	12 96 00	18.974
261	6 81 21	16.155	**311**	9 67 21	17.635	**361**	13 03 21	19.000
262	6 86 44	16.186	**312**	9 73 44	17.664	**362**	13 10 44	19.026
263	6 91 69	16.217	**313**	9 79 69	17.692	**363**	13 17 69	19.053
264	6 96 96	16.248	**314**	9 85 96	17.720	**364**	13 24 96	19.079
265	7 02 25	16.279	**315**	9 92 25	17.748	**365**	13 32 25	19.105
266	7 07 56	16.310	**316**	9 98 56	17.776	**366**	13 39 56	19.131
267	7 12 89	16.340	**317**	10 04 89	17.804	**367**	13 46 89	19.157
268	7 18 24	16.371	**318**	10 11 24	17.833	**368**	13 54 24	19.183
269	7 23 61	16.401	**319**	10 17 61	17.861	**369**	13 61 61	19.209
270	7 29 00	16.432	**320**	10 24 00	17.889	**370**	13 69 00	19.235
271	7 34 41	16.462	**321**	10 30 41	17.916	**371**	13 76 41	19.261
272	7 39 84	16.492	**322**	10 36 84	17.944	**372**	13 83 84	19.287
273	7 45 29	16.523	**323**	10 43 29	17.972	**373**	13 91 29	19.313
274	7 50 76	16.553	**324**	10 49 76	18.000	**374**	13 98 76	19.339
275	7 56 25	16.583	**325**	10 56 25	18.028	**375**	14 06 25	19.365
276	7 61 76	16.613	**326**	10 62 76	18.055	**376**	14 13 76	19.391
277	7 67 29	16.643	**327**	10 69 29	18.083	**377**	14 21 29	19.416
278	7 72 84	16.673	**328**	10 75 84	18.111	**378**	14 28 84	19.442
279	7 78 41	16.703	**329**	10 82 41	18.138	**379**	14 36 41	19.468
280	7 84 00	16.733	**330**	10 89 00	18.166	**380**	14 44 00	19.494
281	7 89 61	16.763	**331**	10 95 61	18.193	**381**	14 51 61	19.519
282	7 95 24	16.793	**332**	11 02 24	18.221	**382**	14 59 24	19.545
283	8 00 89	16.823	**333**	11 08 89	18.248	**383**	14 66 89	19.570
284	8 06 56	16.852	**334**	11 15 56	18.276	**384**	14 74 56	19.596
285	8 12 25	16.882	**335**	11 22 25	18.303	**385**	14 82 25	19.621
286	8 17 96	16.912	**336**	11 28 96	18.330	**386**	14 89 96	19.647
287	8 23 69	16.941	**337**	11 35 69	18.358	**387**	14 97 69	19.672
288	8 29 44	16.971	**338**	11 42 44	18.385	**388**	15 05 44	19.698
289	8 35 21	17.000	**339**	11 49 21	18.412	**389**	15 13 21	19.723
290	8 41 00	17.029	**340**	11 56 00	18.439	**390**	15 21 00	19.748
291	8 46 81	17.059	**341**	11 62 81	18.466	**391**	15 28 81	19.774
292	8 52 64	17.088	**342**	11 69 64	18.493	**392**	15 36 64	19.799
293	8 58 49	17.117	**343**	11 76 49	18.520	**393**	15 44 49	19.824
294	8 64 36	17.146	**344**	11 83 36	18.547	**394**	15 52 36	19.849
295	8 70 25	17.176	**345**	11 90 25	18.574	**395**	15 60 25	19.875
296	8 76 16	17.205	**346**	11 97 16	18.601	**396**	15 68 16	19.900
297	8 82 09	17.234	**347**	12 04 09	18.628	**397**	15 76 09	19.925
298	8 88 04	17.263	**348**	12 11 04	18.655	**398**	15 84 04	19.950
299	8 94 01	17.292	**349**	12 18 01	18.682	**399**	15 92 01	19.975
300	9 00 00	17.321	**350**	12 25 00	18.708	**400**	16 00 00	20.000

Squares and Square Roots

No.	Square	Sq.Root	No.	Square	Sq.Root	No.	Square	Sq.Root
401	16 08 01	20.025	451	20 34 01	21.237	501	25 10 01	22.383
402	16 16 04	20.050	452	20 43 04	21.260	502	25 20 04	22.405
403	16 24 09	20.075	453	20 52 09	21.284	503	25 30 09	22.428
404	16 32 16	20.100	454	20 61 16	21.307	504	25 40 16	22.450
405	16 40 25	20.125	455	20 70 25	21.331	505	25 50 25	22.472
406	16 48 36	20.149	456	20 79 36	21.354	506	25 60 36	22.494
407	16 56 49	20.174	457	20 88 49	21.378	507	25 70 49	22.517
408	16 64 64	20.199	458	20 97 64	21.401	508	25 80 64	22.539
409	16 72 81	20.224	459	21 06 81	21.424	509	25 90 81	22.561
410	16 81 00	20.248	460	21 16 00	21.448	510	26 01 00	22.583
411	16 89 21	20.273	461	21 25 21	21.471	511	26 11 21	22.605
412	16 97 44	20.298	462	21 34 44	21.494	512	26 21 44	22.627
413	17 05 69	20.322	463	21 43 69	21.517	513	26 31 69	22.650
414	17 13 96	20.347	464	21 52 96	21.541	514	26 41 96	22.672
415	17 22 25	20.372	465	21 62 25	21.564	515	26 52 25	22.694
416	17 30 56	20.396	466	21 71 56	21.587	516	26 62 56	22.716
417	17 38 89	20.421	467	21 80 89	21.610	517	26 72 89	22.738
418	17 47 24	20.445	468	21 90 24	21.633	518	26 83 24	22.760
419	17 55 61	20.469	469	21 99 61	21.656	519	26 93 61	22.782
420	17 64 00	20.494	470	22 09 00	21.679	520	27 04 00	22.804
421	17 72 41	20.518	471	22 18 41	21.703	521	27 14 41	22.825
422	17 80 84	20.543	472	22 27 84	21.726	522	27 24 84	22.847
423	17 89 29	20.567	473	22 37 29	21.749	523	27 35 29	22.869
424	17 97 76	20.591	474	22 46 76	21.772	524	27 45 76	22.891
425	18 06 25	20.616	475	22 56 25	21.794	525	27 56 25	22.913
426	18 14 76	20.640	476	22 65 76	21.817	526	27 66 76	22.935
427	18 23 29	20.664	477	22 75 29	21.840	527	27 77 29	22.956
428	18 31 84	20.688	478	22 84 84	21.863	528	27 87 84	22.978
429	18 40 41	20.712	479	22 94 41	21.886	529	27 98 41	23.000
430	18 49 00	20.736	480	23 04 00	21.909	530	28 09 00	23.022
431	18 57 61	20.761	481	23 13 61	21.932	531	28 19 61	23.043
432	18 66 24	20.785	482	23 23 24	21.954	532	28 30 24	23.065
433	18 74 89	20.809	483	23 32 89	21.977	533	28 40 89	23.087
434	18 83 56	20.833	484	23 42 56	22.000	534	28 51 56	23.108
435	18 92 25	20.857	485	23 52 25	22.023	535	28 62 25	23.130
436	19 00 96	20.881	486	23 61 96	22.045	536	28 72 96	23.152
437	19 09 69	20.905	487	23 71 69	22.068	537	28 83 69	23.173
438	19 18 44	20.928	488	23 81 44	22.091	538	28 94 44	23.195
439	19 27 21	20.952	489	23 91 21	22.113	539	29 05 21	23.216
440	19 36 00	20.976	490	24 01 00	22.136	540	29 16 00	23.238
441	19 44 81	21.000	491	24 10 81	22.159	541	29 26 81	23.259
442	19 53 64	21.024	492	24 20 64	22.181	542	29 37 64	23.281
443	19 62 49	21.048	493	24 30 49	22.204	543	29 48 49	23.302
444	19 71 36	21.071	494	24 40 36	22.226	544	29 59 36	23.324
445	19 80 25	21.095	495	24 50 25	22.249	545	29 70 25	23.345
446	19 89 16	21.119	496	24 60 16	22.271	546	29 81 16	23.367
447	19 98 09	21.142	497	24 70 09	22.293	547	29 92 09	23.388
448	20 07 04	21.166	498	24 80 04	22.316	548	30 03 04	23.409
449	20 16 01	21.190	499	24 90 01	22.338	549	30 14 01	23.431
450	20 25 00	21.213	500	25 00 00	22.361	550	30 25 00	23.452

Squares and Square Roots

No.	Square	Sq. Root	No.	Square	Sq. Root	No.	Square	Sq. Root
551	30 36 01	23.473	601	36 12 01	24.515	651	42 38 01	25.515
552	30 47 04	23.495	602	36 24 04	24.536	652	42 51 04	25.534
553	30 58 09	23.516	603	36 36 09	24.556	653	42 64 09	25.554
554	30 69 16	23.537	604	36 48 16	24.576	654	42 77 16	25.573
555	30 80 25	23.558	605	36 60 25	24.597	655	42 90 25	25.593
556	30 91 36	23.580	606	36 72 36	24.617	656	43 03 36	25.612
557	31 02 49	23.601	607	36 84 49	24.637	657	43 16 49	25.632
558	31 13 64	23.622	608	36 96 64	24.658	658	43 29 64	25.652
559	31 24 81	23.643	609	37 08 81	24.678	659	43 42 81	25.671
560	31 36 00	23.664	610	37 21 00	24.698	660	43 56 00	25.690
561	31 47 21	23.685	611	37 33 21	24.718	661	43 69 21	25.710
562	31 58 44	23.707	612	37 45 44	24.739	662	43 82 44	25.729
563	31 69 69	23.728	613	37 57 69	24.759	663	43 95 69	25.749
564	31 80 96	23.749	614	37 69 96	24.779	664	44 08 96	25.768
565	31 92 25	23.770	615	37 82 25	24.799	665	44 22 25	25.788
566	32 03 56	23.791	616	37 94 56	24.819	666	44 35 56	25.807
567	32 14 89	23.812	617	38 06 89	24.839	667	44 48 89	25.826
568	32 26 24	23.833	618	38 19 24	24.860	668	44 62 24	25.846
569	32 37 61	23.854	619	38 31 61	24.880	669	44 75 61	25.865
570	32 49 00	23.875	620	38 44 00	24.900	670	44 89 00	25.884
571	32 60 41	23.896	621	38 56 41	24.920	671	45 02 41	25.904
572	32 71 84	23.917	622	38 68 84	24.940	672	45 15 84	25.923
573	32 83 29	23.937	623	38 81 29	24.960	673	45 29 29	25.942
574	32 94 76	23.958	624	38 93 76	24.980	674	45 42 76	25.962
575	33 06 25	23.979	625	39 06 25	25.000	675	45 56 25	25.981
576	33 17 76	24.000	626	39 18 76	25.020	676	45 69 76	26.000
577	33 29 29	24.021	627	39 31 29	25.040	677	45 83 29	26.019
578	33 40 84	24.042	628	39 43 84	25.060	678	45 96 84	26.038
579	33 52 41	24.062	629	39 56 41	25.080	679	46 10 41	26.058
580	33 64 00	24.083	630	39 69 00	25.100	680	46 24 00	26.077
581	33 75 61	24.104	631	39 81 61	25.120	681	46 37 61	26.096
582	33 87 24	24.125	632	39 94 24	25.139	682	46 51 24	26.115
583	33 98 89	24.145	633	40 06 89	25.159	683	46 64 89	26.134
584	34 10 56	24.166	634	40 19 56	25.179	684	46 78 56	26.153
585	34 22 25	24.187	635	40 32 25	25.199	685	46 92 25	26.173
586	34 33 96	24.207	636	40 44 96	25.219	686	47 05 96	26.192
587	34 45 69	24.228	637	40 57 69	25.239	687	47 19 69	26.211
588	34 57 44	24.249	638	40 70 44	25.259	688	47 33 44	26.230
589	34 69 21	24.269	639	40 83 21	25.278	689	47 47 21	26.249
590	34 81 00	24.290	640	40 96 00	25.298	690	47 61 00	26.268
591	34 92 81	24.310	641	41 08 81	25.318	691	47 74 81	26.287
592	35 04 64	24.331	642	41 21 64	25.338	692	47 88 64	26.306
593	35 16 49	24.352	643	41 34 49	25.357	693	48 02 49	26.325
594	35 28 36	24.372	644	41 47 36	25.377	694	48 16 36	26.344
595	35 40 25	24.393	645	41 60 25	25.397	695	48 30 25	26.363
596	35 52 16	24.413	646	41 73 16	25.417	696	48 44 16	26.382
597	35 64 09	24.434	647	41 86 09	25.436	697	48 58 09	26.401
598	35 76 04	24.454	648	41 99 04	25.456	698	48 72 04	26.420
599	35 88 01	24.474	649	42 12 01	25.475	699	48 86 01	26.439
600	36 00 00	24.495	650	42 25 00	25.495	700	49 00 00	26.458

No.	Square	Sq. Root	No.	Square	Sq. Root	No.	Square	Sq. Root
701	49 14 01	26.476	751	56 40 01	27.404	801	64 16 01	28.302
702	49 28 04	26.495	752	56 55 04	27.423	802	64 32 04	28.320
703	49 42 09	26.514	753	56 70 09	27.441	803	64 48 09	28.337
704	49 56 16	26.533	754	56 85 16	27.459	804	64 64 16	28.355
705	49 70 25	26.552	755	57 00 25	25.477	805	64 80 25	28.373
706	49 84 36	26.571	756	57 15 36	27.495	806	64 96 36	28.390
707	49 98 49	26.589	757	57 30 49	27.514	807	65 12 49	28.408
708	50 12 64	26.608	758	57 45 64	27.532	808	65 28 64	28.425
709	50 26 81	26.627	759	57 60 81	27.550	809	65 44 81	28.443
710	50 41 00	26.646	760	57 76 00	27.568	810	65 61 00	28.460
711	50 55 21	26.665	761	57 91 21	27.586	811	65 77 21	28.478
712	50 69 44	26.683	762	58 06 44	27.604	812	65 93 44	28.496
713	50 83 69	26.702	763	58 21 69	27.622	813	66 09 69	28.513
714	50 97 96	26.721	764	58 36 96	27.641	814	66 25 96	28.531
715	51 12 25	26.739	765	58 52 25	27.659	815	66 42 25	28.548
716	51 26 56	26.758	766	58 67 56	27.677	816	66 58 56	28.566
717	51 40 89	26.777	767	58 82 89	27.695	817	66 74 89	28.583
718	51 55 24	26.796	768	58 98 24	27.713	818	66 91 24	28.601
719	51 69 61	26.814	769	59 13 61	27.731	819	67 07 61	28.618
720	51 84 00	26.833	770	59 29 00	27.749	820	67 24 00	28.636
721	51 98 41	26.851	771	59 44 41	27.767	821	67 40 41	28.653
722	52 12 84	26.870	772	59 59 84	27.785	822	67 56 84	28.671
723	52 27 29	26.889	773	59 75 29	27.803	823	67 73 29	28.688
724	52 41 76	26.907	774	59 90 76	27.821	824	67 89 76	28.705
725	52 56 25	26.926	775	60 06 25	27.839	825	68 06 25	28.723
726	52 70 76	26.944	776	60 21 76	27.857	826	68 22 76	28.740
727	52 85 29	26.963	777	60 37 29	27.875	827	68 39 29	28.758
728	52 99 84	26.981	778	60 52 84	27.893	828	68 55 84	28.775
729	53 14 41	27.000	779	60 68 41	27.911	829	68 72 41	28.792
730	53 29 00	27.019	780	60 84 00	27.928	830	68 89 00	28.810
731	53 43 61	27.037	781	60 99 61	27.946	831	69 05 61	28.827
732	53 58 24	27.055	782	61 15 24	27.964	832	69 22 24	28.844
733	53 72 89	27.074	783	61 30 89	27.982	833	69 38 89	28.862
734	53 87 56	27.092	784	61 46 56	28.000	834	69 55 56	28.879
735	54 02 25	27.111	785	61 62 25	28.018	835	69 72 25	28.896
736	54 16 96	27.129	786	61 77 96	28.036	836	69 88 96	28.914
737	54 31 69	27.148	787	61 93 69	28.054	837	70 05 69	28.931
738	54 46 44	27.166	788	62 09 44	28.071	838	70 22 44	28.948
739	54 61 21	27.185	789	62 25 21	28.089	839	70 39 21	28.965
740	54 76 00	27.203	790	62 41 00	28.107	840	70 56 00	28.983
741	54 90 81	27.221	791	62 56 81	28.125	841	70 72 81	29.000
742	55 05 64	27.240	792	62 72 64	28.142	842	70 89 64	29.017
743	55 20 49	27.258	793	62 88 49	28.160	843	71 06 49	29.034
744	55 35 36	27.276	794	63 04 36	28.178	844	71 23 36	29.052
745	55 50 25	27.295	795	63 20 25	28.196	845	71 40 25	29.069
746	55 65 16	27.313	796	63 36 16	28.213	846	71 57 16	29.086
747	55 80 09	27.331	797	63 52 09	28.231	847	71 74 09	29.103
748	55 95 04	27.350	798	63 68 04	28.249	848	71 91 04	29.120
749	56 10 01	27.368	799	63 84 01	28.267	849	72 08 01	29.138
750	56 25 00	27.386	800	64 00 00	28.284	850	72 25 00	29.155

Squares and Square Roots

No.	Square	Sq. Root	No.	Square	Sq. Root	No.	Square	Sq. Root
851	72 42 01	29.172	**901**	81 18 01	30.017	**951**	90 44 01	30.838
852	72 59 04	29.189	**902**	81 36 04	30.033	**952**	90 63 04	30.854
853	72 76 09	29.206	**903**	81 54 09	30.050	**953**	90 82 09	30.871
854	72 93 16	29.223	**904**	81 72 16	30.067	**954**	91 01 16	30.887
855	73 10 25	29.240	**905**	81 90 25	30.083	**955**	91 20 25	30.903
856	73 27 36	29.257	**906**	82 08 36	30.100	**956**	91 39 36	30.919
857	73 44 49	29.275	**907**	82 26 49	30.116	**957**	91 58 49	30.935
858	73 61 64	29.292	**908**	82 44 64	30.133	**958**	91 77 64	30.952
859	73 78 81	29.309	**909**	82 62 81	30.150	**959**	91 96 81	30.968
860	73 96 00	29.326	**910**	82 81 00	30.166	**960**	92 16 00	30.984
861	74 13 21	29.343	**911**	82 99 21	30.183	**961**	92 35 21	31.000
862	74 30 44	29.360	**912**	83 17 44	30.199	**962**	92 54 44	31.016
863	74 47 69	29.377	**913**	83 35 69	30.216	**963**	92 73 69	31.032
864	74 64 96	29.394	**914**	83 53 96	30.232	**964**	92 92 96	31.048
865	74 82 25	29.411	**915**	83 72 25	30.249	**965**	93 12 25	31.064
866	74 99 56	29.428	**916**	83 90 56	30.265	**966**	93 31 56	31.081
867	75 16 89	29.445	**917**	84 08 89	30.282	**967**	93 50 89	31.097
868	75 34 24	29.462	**918**	84 27 24	30.299	**968**	93 70 24	31.113
869	75 51 61	29.479	**919**	84 45 61	30.315	**969**	93 89 61	31.129
870	75 69 00	29.496	**920**	84 64 00	30.332	**970**	94 09 00	31.145
871	75 86 41	29.513	**921**	84 82 41	30.348	**971**	94 28 41	31.161
872	76 03 84	29.530	**922**	85 00 84	30.364	**972**	94 47 84	31.177
873	76 21 29	29.547	**923**	85 19 29	30.381	**973**	94 67 29	31.193
874	76 38 76	29.563	**924**	85 37 76	30.397	**974**	94 86 76	31.209
875	76 56 25	29.580	**925**	85 56 25	30.414	**975**	95 06 25	31.225
876	76 73 76	29.597	**926**	85 74 76	30.430	**976**	95 25 76	31.241
877	76 91 29	29.614	**927**	85 93 29	30.447	**977**	95 45 29	31.257
878	77 08 84	29.631	**928**	86 11 84	30.463	**978**	95 64 84	31.273
879	77 26 41	29.648	**929**	86 30 41	30.480	**979**	95 84 41	31.289
880	77 44 00	29.665	**930**	86 49 00	30.496	**980**	96 04 00	31.305
881	77 61 61	29.682	**931**	86 67 61	30.512	**981**	96 23 61	31.321
882	77 79 24	29.698	**932**	86 86 24	30.529	**982**	96 43 24	31.337
883	77 96 89	29.715	**933**	87 04 89	30.545	**983**	96 62 89	31.353
884	78 14 56	29.732	**934**	87 23 56	30.561	**984**	96 82 56	31.369
885	78 32 25	29.749	**935**	87 42 25	30.578	**985**	97 02 25	31.385
886	78 49 96	29.766	**936**	87 60 96	30.594	**986**	97 21 96	31.401
887	78 67 69	29.783	**937**	87 79 69	30.610	**987**	97 41 69	31.417
888	78 85 44	29.799	**938**	87 98 44	30.627	**988**	97 61 44	31.432
889	79 03 21	29.816	**939**	88 17 21	30.643	**989**	97 81 21	31.448
890	79 21 00	29.833	**940**	88 36 00	30.659	**990**	98 01 00	31.464
891	79 38 81	29.850	**941**	88 54 81	30.676	**991**	98 20 81	31.480
892	79 56 64	29.866	**942**	88 73 64	30.692	**992**	98 40 64	31.496
893	79 74 49	29.883	**943**	88 92 49	30.708	**993**	98 60 49	31.512
894	79 92 36	29.900	**944**	89 11 36	30.725	**994**	98 80 36	31.528
895	80 10 25	29.916	**945**	89 30 25	30.741	**995**	99 00 25	31.544
896	80 28 16	29.933	**946**	89 49 16	30.757	**996**	99 20 16	31.559
897	80 46 09	29.950	**947**	89 68 09	30.773	**997**	99 40 09	31.575
898	80 64 04	29.967	**948**	89 87 04	30.790	**998**	99 60 04	31.591
899	80 82 01	29.983	**949**	90 06 01	30.806	**999**	99 80 01	31.607
900	81 00 00	30.000	**950**	90 25 00	30.822	**1000**	100 00 00	31.623

Logarithms of Numbers

N	0	1	2	3	4	5	6	7	8	9	1	2	3	4	5	6	7	8	9
10	0000	0043	0086	0128	0170	0212	0253	0294	0334	0374	4	8	12	17	21	25	29	33	37
11	0414	0453	0492	0531	0569	0607	0645	0682	0719	0755	4	8	11	15	19	23	26	30	34
12	0792	0828	0864	0899	0934	0969	1004	1038	1072	1106	3	7	10	14	17	21	24	28	31
13	1139	1173	1206	1239	1271	1303	1335	1367	1399	1430	3	6	10	13	16	19	23	26	29
14	1461	1492	1523	1553	1584	1614	1644	1673	1703	1732	3	6	9	12	15	18	21	24	27
15	1761	1790	1818	1847	1875	1903	1931	1959	1987	2014	3	6	8	11	14	17	20	22	25
16	2041	2068	2095	2122	2148	2175	2201	2227	2253	2279	3	5	8	11	13	16	18	21	24
17	2304	2330	2355	2380	2405	2430	2455	2480	2504	2529	2	5	7	10	12	15	17	20	22
18	2553	2577	2601	2625	2648	2672	2695	2718	2742	2765	2	5	7	9	12	14	16	19	21
19	2788	2810	2833	2856	2878	2900	2923	2945	2967	2989	2	4	7	9	11	13	16	18	20
20	3010	3032	3054	3075	3096	3118	3139	3160	3181	3201	2	4	6	8	11	13	15	17	19
21	3222	3243	3263	3284	3304	3324	3345	3365	3385	3404	2	4	6	8	10	12	14	16	18
22	3424	3444	3464	3483	3502	3522	3541	3560	3579	3598	2	4	6	8	10	12	14	15	17
23	3617	3636	3655	3674	3692	3711	3729	3747	3766	3784	2	4	6	7	9	11	13	15	17
24	3802	3820	3838	3856	3874	3892	3909	3927	3945	3962	2	4	5	7	9	11	12	14	16
25	3979	3997	4014	4031	4048	4065	4082	4099	4116	4133	2	3	5	7	9	10	12	14	15
26	4150	4166	4183	4200	4216	4232	4249	4265	4281	4298	2	3	5	7	8	10	11	13	15
27	4314	4330	4346	4362	4378	4393	4409	4425	4440	4456	2	3	5	6	8	9	11	13	14
28	4472	4487	4502	4518	4533	4548	4564	4579	4594	4609	2	3	5	6	8	9	11	12	14
29	4624	4639	4654	4669	4683	4698	4713	4728	4742	4757	1	3	4	6	7	9	10	12	13
30	4771	4786	4800	4814	4829	4843	4857	4871	4886	4900	1	3	4	6	7	9	10	11	13
31	4914	4928	4942	4955	4969	4983	4997	5011	5024	5038	1	3	4	6	7	8	10	11	12
32	5051	5065	5079	5092	5105	5119	5132	5145	5159	5172	1	3	4	5	7	8	9	11	12
33	5185	5198	5211	5224	5237	5250	5263	5276	5289	5302	1	3	4	5	6	8	9	10	12
34	5315	5328	5340	5353	5366	5378	5391	5403	5416	5428	1	3	4	5	6	8	9	10	11
35	5441	5453	5465	5478	5490	5502	5514	5527	5539	5551	1	2	4	5	6	7	9	10	11
36	5563	5575	5587	5599	5611	5623	5635	5647	5658	5670	1	2	4	5	6	7	8	10	11
37	5682	5694	5705	5717	5729	5740	5752	5763	5775	5786	1	2	3	5	6	7	8	9	10
38	5798	5809	5821	5832	5843	5855	5866	5877	5888	5899	1	2	3	5	6	7	8	9	10
39	5911	5922	5933	5944	5955	5966	5977	5988	5999	6010	1	2	3	4	5	7	8	9	10
40	6021	6031	6042	6053	6064	6075	6085	6096	6107	6117	1	2	3	4	5	6	8	9	10
41	6128	6138	6149	6160	6170	6180	6191	6201	6212	6222	1	2	3	4	5	6	7	8	9
42	6232	6243	6253	6263	6274	6284	6294	6304	6314	6325	1	2	3	4	5	6	7	8	9
43	6335	6345	6355	6365	6375	6385	6395	6405	6415	6425	1	2	3	4	5	6	7	8	9
44	6435	6444	6454	6464	6474	6484	6493	6503	6513	6522	1	2	3	4	5	6	7	8	9
45	6532	6542	6551	6561	6571	6580	6590	6599	6609	6618	1	2	3	4	5	6	7	8	9
46	6628	6637	6646	6656	6665	6675	6684	6693	6702	6712	1	2	3	4	5	6	7	7	8
47	6721	6730	6739	6749	6758	6767	6776	6785	6794	6803	1	2	3	4	5	5	6	7	8
48	6812	6821	6830	6839	6848	6857	6866	6875	6884	6893	1	2	3	4	4	5	6	7	8
49	6902	6911	6920	6928	6937	6946	6955	6964	6972	6981	1	2	3	4	4	5	6	7	8
50	6990	6998	7007	7016	7024	7033	7042	7050	7059	7067	1	2	3	3	4	5	6	7	8
51	7076	7084	7093	7101	7110	7118	7126	7135	7143	7152	1	2	3	3	4	5	6	7	8
52	7160	7168	7177	7185	7193	7202	7210	7218	7226	7235	1	2	2	3	4	5	6	7	7
53	7243	7251	7259	7267	7275	7284	7292	7300	7308	7316	1	2	2	3	4	5	6	6	7
54	7324	7332	7340	7348	7356	7364	7372	7380	7388	7396	1	2	2	3	4	5	6	6	7
N	0	1	2	3	4	5	6	7	8	9	1	2	3	4	5	6	7	8	9

Logarithms of Numbers

N	0	1	2	3	4	5	6	7	8	9	1	2	3	4	5	6	7	8	9
55	7404	7412	7419	7427	7435	7443	7451	7459	7466	7474	1	2	2	3	4	5	5	6	7
56	7482	7490	7497	7505	7513	7520	7528	7536	7543	7551	1	2	2	3	4	5	5	6	7
57	7559	7566	7574	7582	7589	7597	7604	7612	7619	7627	1	2	2	3	4	5	5	6	7
58	7634	7642	7649	7657	7664	7672	7679	7686	7694	7701	1	1	2	3	4	4	5	6	7
59	7709	7716	7723	7731	7738	7745	7752	7760	7767	7774	1	1	2	3	4	4	5	6	7
60	7782	7789	7796	7803	7810	7818	7825	7832	7839	7846	1	1	2	3	4	4	5	6	6
61	7853	7860	7868	7875	7882	7889	7896	7903	7910	7917	1	1	2	3	4	4	5	6	6
62	7924	7931	7938	7945	7952	7959	7966	7973	7980	7987	1	1	2	3	3	4	5	6	6
63	7993	8000	8007	8014	8021	8028	8035	8041	8048	8055	1	1	2	3	3	4	5	5	6
64	8062	8069	8075	8082	8089	8096	8102	8109	8116	8122	1	1	2	3	3	4	5	5	6
65	8129	8136	8142	8149	8156	8162	8169	8176	8182	8189	1	1	2	3	3	4	5	5	6
66	8195	8202	8209	8215	8222	8228	8235	8241	8248	8254	1	1	2	3	3	4	5	5	6
67	8261	8267	8274	8280	8287	8293	8299	8306	8312	8319	1	1	2	3	3	4	5	5	6
68	8325	8331	8338	8344	8351	8357	8363	8370	8376	8382	1	1	2	3	3	4	4	5	6
69	8388	8395	8401	8407	8414	8420	8426	8432	8439	8445	1	1	2	2	3	4	4	5	6
70	8451	8457	8463	8470	8476	8482	8488	8494	8500	8506	1	1	2	2	3	4	4	5	6
71	8513	8519	8525	8531	8537	8543	8549	8555	8561	8567	1	1	2	2	3	4	4	5	5
72	8573	8579	8585	8591	8597	8603	8609	8615	8621	8627	1	1	2	2	3	4	4	5	5
73	8633	8639	8645	8651	8657	8663	8669	8675	8681	8686	1	1	2	2	3	4	4	5	5
74	8692	8698	8704	8710	8716	8722	8727	8733	8739	8745	1	1	2	2	3	4	4	5	5
75	8751	8756	8762	8768	8774	8779	8785	8791	8797	8802	1	1	2	2	3	3	4	5	5
76	8808	8814	8820	8825	8831	8837	8842	8848	8854	8859	1	1	2	2	3	3	4	5	5
77	8865	8871	8876	8882	8887	8893	8899	8904	8910	8915	1	1	2	2	3	3	4	4	5
78	8921	8927	8932	8938	8943	8949	8954	8960	8965	8971	1	1	2	2	3	3	4	4	5
79	8976	8982	8987	8993	8998	9004	9009	9015	9020	9025	1	1	2	2	3	3	4	4	5
80	9031	9036	9042	9047	9053	9058	9063	9069	9074	9079	1	1	2	2	3	3	4	4	5
81	9085	9090	9096	9101	9106	9112	9117	9122	9128	9133	1	1	2	2	3	3	4	4	5
82	9138	9143	9149	9154	9159	9165	9170	9175	9180	9186	1	1	2	2	3	3	4	4	5
83	9191	9196	9201	9206	9212	9217	9222	9227	9232	9238	1	1	2	2	3	3	4	4	5
84	9243	9248	9253	9258	9263	9269	9274	9279	9284	9289	1	1	2	2	3	3	4	4	5
85	9294	9299	9304	9309	9315	9320	9325	9330	9335	9340	1	1	2	2	3	3	4	4	5
86	9345	9350	9355	9360	9365	9370	9375	9380	9385	9390	1	1	2	2	3	3	4	4	5
87	9395	9400	9405	9410	9415	9420	9425	9430	9435	9440	0	1	1	2	2	3	3	4	4
88	9445	9450	9455	9460	9465	9469	9474	9479	9484	9489	0	1	1	2	2	3	3	4	4
89	9494	9499	9504	9509	9513	9518	9523	9528	9533	9538	0	1	1	2	2	3	3	4	4
90	9542	9547	9552	9557	9562	9566	9571	9576	9581	9586	0	1	1	2	2	3	3	4	4
91	9590	9595	9600	9605	9609	9614	9619	9624	9628	9633	0	1	1	2	2	3	3	4	4
92	9638	9643	9647	9652	9657	9661	9666	9671	9675	9680	0	1	1	2	2	3	3	4	4
93	9685	9689	9694	9699	9703	9708	9713	9717	9722	9727	0	1	1	2	2	3	3	4	4
94	9731	9736	9741	9745	9750	9754	9759	9763	9768	9773	0	1	1	2	2	3	3	4	4
95	9777	9782	9786	9791	9795	9800	9805	9809	9814	9818	0	1	1	2	2	3	3	4	4
96	9823	9827	9832	9836	9841	9845	9850	9854	9859	9863	0	1	1	2	2	3	3	4	4
97	9868	9872	9877	9881	9886	9890	9894	9899	9903	9908	0	1	1	2	2	3	3	4	4
98	9912	9917	9921	9926	9930	9934	9939	9943	9948	9952	0	1	1	2	2	3	3	4	4
99	9956	9961	9965	9969	9974	9978	9983	9987	9991	9996	0	1	1	2	2	3	3	3	4
N	0	1	2	3	4	5	6	7	8	9	1	2	3	4	5	6	7	8	9

Logarithms of $\sqrt{1-r^2}$

TABLE C

Values of $\dfrac{.6745}{\sqrt{N}}$

TABLE D

r	Log.	r	Log.	N		N	
.00	00000	.50	93753			50	.0954
.01	99998	.51	93459	1	.6745	51	.0944
.02	99991	.52	93154	2	.4769	52	.0935
.03	99980	.53	92839	3	.3894	53	.0926
.04	99965	.54	92514	4	.3372	54	.0918
.05	99946	.55	92177	5	.3016	55	.0909
.06	99922	.56	91829	6	.2754	56	.0901
.07	99893	.57	91468	7	.2549	57	.0893
.08	99861	.58	91095	8	.2385	58	.0886
.09	99823	.59	90709	9	.2248	59	.0878
.10	99782	.60	90309	10	.2133	60	.0871
.11	99736	.61	89895	11	.2034	61	.0864
.12	99685	.62	89465	12	.1947	62	.0857
.13	99630	.63	89019	13	.1871	63	.0850
.14	99570	.64	88557	14	.1803	64	.0843
.15	99506	.65	88078	15	.1742	65	.0837
.16	99437	.66	87579	16	.1686	66	.0830
.17	99363	.67	87062	17	.1636	67	.0824
.18	99285	.68	86523	18	.1590	68	.0818
.19	99202	.69	85962	19	.1547	69	.0812
.20	99114	.70	85379	20	.1508	70	.0806
.21	99021	.71	84770	21	.1472	71	.0800
.22	98923	.72	84134	22	.1438	72	.0795
.23	98820	.73	83470	23	.1406	73	.0789
.24	98712	.74	82776	24	.1377	74	.0784
.25	98599	.75	82049	25	.1349	75	.0779
.26	98480	.76	81286	26	.1323	76	.0774
.27	98356	.77	80485	27	.1298	77	.0769
.28	98227	.78	79642	28	.1275	78	.0764
.29	98092	.79	78754	29	.1252	79	.0759
.30	97952	.80	77815	30	.1231	80	.0754
.31	97806	.81	76822	31	.1211	81	.0749
.32	97654	.82	75767	32	.1192	82	.0745
.33	97496	.83	74645	33	.1174	83	.0740
.34	97332	.84	73447	34	.1157	84	.0736
.35	97162	.85	72163	35	.1140	85	.0732
.36	96986	.86	70782	36	.1124	86	.0727
.37	96803	.87	69289	37	.1109	87	.0723
.38	96614	.88	67667	38	.1094	88	.0719
.39	96417	.89	65893	39	.1080	89	.0715
.40	96214	.90	63938	40	.1066	90	.0711
.41	96004	.91	61764	41	.1053	91	.0707
.42	95786	.92	59320	42	.1041	92	.0703
.43	95561	.93	56533	43	.1029	93	.0699
.44	95328	.94	53298	44	.1017	94	.0696
.45	95087	.95	49450	45	.1005	95	.0692
.46	94837	.96	44716	46	.0994	96	.0688
.47	94580	.97	38579	47	.0984	97	.0685
.48	94313	.98	29885	48	.0974	98	.0681
.49	94038	.99	14943	49	.0964	99	.0678

All mantissae above except the first have characteristic − 1. The first has zero characteristic.

The Normal Probability Curve   TABLE E
(N = 1)

Areas and Ordinates Corresponding to Sigma Distances from the Mean						Areas Corresponding to P.E. Distances from the Mean			
σ	% Area	Ordinate	σ	% Area	Ordinate	P. E.	% Area	P. E.	% Area
.00	0.00	.3989	2.00	47.72	.0540	.00	0.00	2.00	41.13
.05	1.99	.3984	2.05	47.98	.0488	.05	1.35	2.05	41.66
.10	3.98	.3970	2.10	48.21	.0440	.10	2.69	2.10	42.17
.15	5.96	.3945	2.15	48.42	.0395	.15	4.03	2.15	42.65
.20	7.93	.3910	2.20	48.61	.0355	.20	5.36	2.20	43.11
.25	9.87	.3867	2.25	48.78	.0317	.25	6.70	2.25	43.54
.30	11.79	.3814	2.30	48.93	.0283	.30	8.02	2.30	43.96
.35	13.68	.3752	2.35	49.06	.0252	.35	9.33	2.35	44.35
.40	15.54	.3683	2.40	49.18	.0224	.40	10.63	2.40	44.72
.45	17.36	.3605	2.45	49.29	.0198	.45	11.93	2.45	45.08
.50	19.15	.3521	2.50	49.38	.0175	.50	13.21	2.50	45.41
.55	20.88	.3429	2.55	49.46	.0154	.55	14.47	2.55	45.73
.60	22.57	.3332	2.60	49.53	.0136	.60	15.71	2.60	46.02
.65	24.22	.3230	2.65	49.60	.0119	.65	16.95	2.65	46.31
.70	25.80	.3123	2.70	49.65	.0104	.70	18.16	2.70	46.57
.75	27.34	.3011	2.75	49.70	.0091	.75	19.35	2.75	46.82
.80	28.81	.2897	2.80	49.74	.0079	.80	20.53	2.80	47.05
.85	30.23	.2780	2.85	49.78	.0069	.85	21.68	2.85	47.27
.90	31.59	.2661	2.90	49.81	.0060	.90	22.81	2.90	47.48
.95	32.89	.2541	2.95	49.84	.0051	.95	23.92	2.95	47.67
1.00	34.13	.2420	3.00	49.87	.0044	1.00	25.00	3.00	47.85
1.05	35.31	.2299	3.05	49.89	.0038	1.05	26.06	3.05	48.02
1.10	36.43	.2179	3.10	49.90	.0033	1.10	27.09	3.10	48.17
1.15	37.49	.2059	3.15	49.92	.0028	1.15	28.10	3.15	48.31
1.20	38.49	.1942	3.20	49.93	.0024	1.20	29.08	3.20	48.45
1.25	39.44	.1826	3.25	49.94	.0020	1.25	30.04	3.25	48.58
1.30	40.32	.1714	3.30	49.95	.0017	1.30	30.97	3.30	48.70
1.35	41.15	.1604	3.35	49.96	.0015	1.35	31.88	3.35	48.81
1.40	41.92	.1497	3.40	49.97	.0012	1.40	32.75	3.40	48.91
1.45	42.65	.1394	3.45	49.97	.0010	1.45	33.60	3.50	49.09
1.50	43.32	.1295	3.50	49.98	.0009	1.50	34.41	3.60	49.24
1.55	43.94	.1200	3.55	49.98	.0007	1.55	35.21	3.70	49.37
1.60	44.52	.1109	3.60	49.98	.0006	1.60	35.97	3.80	49.48
1.65	45.05	.1023	3.65	49.99	.0005	1.65	36.71	3.90	49.57
1.70	45.54	.0940	3.70	49.99	.0004	1.70	37.42	4.00	49.65
1.75	45.99	.0863	3.75	49.99	.0004	1.75	38.11	4.10	49.71
1.80	46.41	.0790	3.80	49.99	.0003	1.80	38.76	4.20	49.77
1.85	46.78	.0721	3.85	49.99	.0002	1.85	39.39	4.30	49.81
1.90	47.13	.0656	3.90	50.00	.0002	1.90	40.00	4.40	49.85
1.95	47.44	.0596	3.95	50.00	.0002	1.95	40.57	4.50	49.88

Values of $\sqrt{pq}$, where $p + q = 1$

TABLE F

p or q		p or q	
.00	.0000	.25	.4330
.01	.0995	.26	.4386
.02	.1400	.27	.4440
.03	.1706	.28	.4490
.04	.1960	.29	.4538
.05	.2179	.30	.4583
.06	.2375	.31	.4625
.07	.2551	.32	.4665
.08	.2713	.33	.4702
.09	.2862	.34	.4737
.10	.3000	.35	.4770
.11	.3129	.36	.4800
.12	.3250	.37	.4828
.13	.3363	.38	.4854
.14	.3470	.39	.4877
.15	.3571	.40	.4899
.16	.3666	.41	.4918
.17	.3756	.42	.4936
.18	.3842	.43	.4951
.19	.3923	.44	.4964
.20	.4000	.45	.4975
.21	.4073	.46	.4984
.22	.4142	.47	.4991
.23	.4208	.48	.4996
.24	.4271	.49	.4999

BIBLIOGRAPHY

Garrett, Henry E. *Statistics in Psychology and Education.* (2nd Ed.) Longmans, Green & Co., Inc., New York, 1937.

Holzinger, Karl J. *Statistical Methods for Students in Education.* Ginn & Co., Boston, 1928.

Li, Chen-Nan. "Summation Method of Fitting Parabolic Curves and Calculating Linear and Curvilinear Correlation Coefficients on a Scatter-Diagram." In *Journal of the American Statistical Association,* Vol. 29, pp. 405-409 (Dec., 1934).

Lindquist, E. F. *First Course in Statistics.* Houghton Mifflin Co., Boston, 1938.

Mudgett, Bruce D. *Statistical Tables and Graphs.* Houghton Mifflin Co., Boston, 1930.

Peters, C. C., and Van Voorhis, W. R. *Statistical Procedures and Their Mathematical Bases.* School of Education, The Pennsylvania State College, State College, Pennsylvania, 1935.

Sorenson, Herbert, *Statistics for Students of Psychology and Education.* McGraw-Hill Book Co., Inc., New York, 1936.

Thurstone, L. L. *The Fundamentals of Statistics.* The Macmillan Co., New York, 1928.

Walker, Helen M. *Mathematics Essential for Elementary Statistics.* Henry Holt & Co., Inc., New York, 1934.

Walker, Helen M. *Studies in the History of Statistical Method.* The Williams & Wilkins Co., Baltimore, 1929.

ANSWERS TO EXERCISES AND PROBLEMS

3. Rank of boys: 7, 3.5, 10, 9, 7, 2, 1, 5, 3.5, 7.
Rank of girls: 10, 6, 1.5, 3, 6, 8, 1.5, 4, 6, 9.

4.

Contestants:	A	B	C	D	E	F	G
Composite Rank....	5	1.5	6	4	1.5	7	3
Awards............		$40		$10	$40		$20

5.

Contestants:			A	B	C
Composite Rank would have been......			1	2	3

6.

Class Intervals	*f*
17	2
16	2
15	4
14	7
13	6
12	3
11	1
	25

7. (a)

Class Intervals	*f*
8½	1
8	2
7½	4
7	7
6½	6
6	4
5½	3
	27

(b) 6½.   (c) 7.

8. (a)

Class Intervals	*f*
60–64	2
55–59	3
50–54	4
45–49	4
40–44	7
35–39	12
30–34	9
25–29	6
20–24	3
	50

(b) 37.   (c) 39.5.

9.

Class Intervals	*f*
A	5
B	8
C	7
D	4
F	2
	26

10. (a)

Class Intervals	f
10	2
9	4
8	8
7	6
6	1
	21

(b) 8.5.   (c) 8 − 8.99+.

11. (a)

Class Intervals	f
60.0–64.9	2
55.0–59.9	3
50.0–54.9	4
45.0–49.9	6
40.0–44.9	5
35.0–39.9	2
	22

(b) 50.   (c) 47.45.

(d) 44.95.   (e) 49.95.

12. (a)

Class Intervals	f
55–59	2
50–54	4
45–49	6
40–44	5
35–39	3
30–34	1
	21

(b) 47.

13.

Class Intervals	Percentage Math.	Frequencies H.E.
A	16.9	28.4
B	25.9	34.2
C	30.0	30.0
D	16.9	7.4
F	10.3	0.0

14.

Class Intervals	f	Cum. f (Top)	Cum. f (Midpoint)
60–64	2	50	49
55–59	3	48	46½
50–54	4	45	43
45–49	4	41	39
40–44	7	37	33½
35–39	12	30	24
30–34	9	18	13½
25–29	6	9	6
20–24	3	3	1½
	50		

15. Revised Class Intervals	Distri- bution f	(Approxi- mated) $\% f$	
18	30	.5	
17½	140	2.3	
17	220	3.6	
16½	380	6.2	O.A. 61.3%
16	480	7.9	
15½	680	11.1	
15	810	13.3	
14½	1000	16.4	
14	850	13.9	
13½	750	12.3	N.A. 34.1%
13	480	7.9	
12½	250	4.1	U.A 4.6%
12	30	.5	
	6100		

CHAPTER 2

1. (a) 29.125.   (b) 29.125.   (c) 29.063.   (d) 28.938.

2. (a), (b), and (c) 56.82.

3. 98.72.

4. 65.45.

5. (a) 12.59.   (b) 13.34.

6. (a) Half the size of an interval.   (b) 2.

7. Would increase the mean by 10.

8. 44.30.

9. 2.69.

10. (a) Systematic error.   (b) .5.   (c) Too high.

11. (a) 45.57.   (b) Yes.

12. 16.37.

13. 2.23.

14. .2.

Chapter 3

1. 31.

2. (a) 45–49 and 25–29.   (b) 40–44 and 30–34.   (c) 35–39.

3. 61.69.

4. 73.75.

5. $624.50.

6. 28.79.

7. 33.32.

8. (a) 11.63.   (b) 12.13.

9. Solution impossible.   **10.** 1.3175 or 1.32.

11. ab-g, 19.05%.   at-g, 44.05%.   b-g, 36.90%.

12. (a) 1.028.   (b) 4319.   **13.** (a) 1.86.   (b) 32.26.

14. (a) None.   (b) Yes.   (c) Yes, both will affect the mean.

Chapter 4

4. (a) $Q_3 = 61.58$ (b) $P_{90} = 79.25$ $P_{40} = 43.90$
         Md. $= 48.88$ $P_{80} = 65.50$ $P_{30} = 39.80$
         $Q_1 = 37.56$ $P_{70} = 58.50$ $P_{20} = 35.28$
         $P_{12.5} = 31.11$ $P_{60} = 53.50$ $P_{10} = 29.64$
                                              $P_{50} = 48.88$

5. (a) 29.27.   (b) 35.37.   (c) 34.15.   (d) 64.63.

6. Raw   %ile
   Score Equiv.

79 = 100	69 = 94	59 = 72	49 = 34	39 = 9
78 = 99	68 = 92	58 = 69	48 = 31	38 = 8
77 = 99	67 = 91	57 = 66	47 = 28	37 = 6
76 = 99	66 = 89	56 = 63	46 = 25	36 = 5
75 = 98	65 = 88	55 = 60	45 = 22	35 = 4
74 = 98	64 = 86	54 = 56	44 = 19	34 = 3
73 = 97	63 = 83	53 = 52	43 = 17	33 = 2
72 = 96	62 = 80	52 = 47	42 = 15	32 = 1
71 = 95	61 = 78	51 = 42	41 = 13	31 = 1
70 = 95	60 = 75	50 = 38	40 = 11	30 = 0

7. P.R.$_A$ = 55.56.   P.R.$_B$ = 57.14.

8. Ab. Rank: 5, 8, 1.5, 9, 5, 7, 1.5, 5, 12, 3, 10.5, 10.5.
P.R: 63, 38, 92, 29, 63, 46, 92, 63, 4, 79, 17, 17.

9. Average P.R.$_A$ = 71.1.   Average P.R.$_B$ = 63.6.

CHAPTER 5

1. (a) Same absolute range.   (b) Q$_A$ = 3.5.   Q$_B$ = 6.5.

2. 1.34.

3. 5.5.

4. 9.17.

5. (a) 42.   (b) 6.63.   (c) 6.03.   (d) 2.64.   (e) 2.41.

6. (a) or (b) 1.24.

7. (a) 7.27.   (b) A.D. is longer.   (c) 1.10.

8. (a), (b), or (c) 1.85.

9. M = 41.50.   S.D. = 8.88.   (b) 4.50.   (c) 1.29.
(d) Dif. = .11.

10. (a) 2.33.   (b) 1.06.

11. M = 51.69.   S.D. = 9.68.

12. M = 52.26.   S.D. = 10.08.

13. 44 and 24.

14. More variable in A.R. (27 and 16).

CHAPTER 6

2. 2000.

3. Approximately 39, 16, 37, 68, 82.

4. (b) 34.13, 45.99, 37.21, 24.17, 18.65, .13, .62.   (c) 1.35.
(d) .85.   (e) −.55.   (f) 68.26.   (g) 24.17.

5. (a) .102.   (b) No.

6. (a) No.   (b) ½.

7. (a) Yes.   (b) 46/1000.

8. (a) No.   (b) Less than 1/1000.   (c) Superior class, superior teacher, class coached on test, etc.

9. .04.

10. 100.

11. (a) .80.   (b) 62.62 to 64.22.

12. Yes, critical ratio = 3.16.

13. (a) No.   (b) About 74/100.

14. (a) .057.   (b) .062.   (c) .14.   (d) .084.   (e) 1.67.

15. S.E.$_\sigma$(Robert) = .089.   S.E.$_\sigma$(Seniors) = .017.   S.E.$_{\text{Dif.}_\sigma}$ = .091.   Dif.$_\sigma$ = .29. $\dfrac{\text{Dif.}}{\text{S.E. }_{\text{Dif.}}}$ = 3.2, highly significant.

16. P.E.$_{p_1}$ = .010213.   P.E.$_{p_2}$ = .013314.   P.E.$_{\text{Dif.}}$ = .0168. $p_1 - p_2$ = .10.   Ratio of Dif. to P.E.$_{\text{Dif.}}$ = 5.95, significant.

17. No. P.E.$_{.p}$ of .5 = .0276, whereas girls exceeded proportion of .05 by only .02.

18. Yes. P.E.$_{.pb}$ = .010451.   P.E.$_{.pg}$ = .010558.   Dif.$_p$ = .05. P.E.$_{\text{Dif.}}$ = .015.   Ratio = 3.33.

19. 30,240   **20.** 1/624.

21. P.E.$_{.\text{C.V.A.R.}}$ = 2.03.   P.E.$_{.\text{C.V.A.C.}}$ = 1.16.   Dif.$_{\text{C.V.}}$ = 11. P.E.$_{.\text{Dif.}}$ = 2.34.   Ratio = 4.70, significant.

22. (a) Zero.   (b) About ¼.   (P.E. of mean number right = 3.54, which is convertible to a score of + 7.08.)

23. About 73.

Chapter 7

1. Mark	f	%f
A	2	6.67
B	7	23.33
C	12	40.00
D	7	23.33
F	2	6.67
	30	100.00

2. 88.32, 52.34, 80.61.

3. 120.

4. 6, 12, 44, 70.

5. (b)

Raw Score	T-Score Equiv.
60	80
59	78
58	77
Etc.	to
10	20

6. M = 44.68. S.D. = 14.52.
49 = T-S 53.   31 = T-S 41.
41 = T-S 47.   Etc.

7. 78.81.

8. −.38, +.51, +1.31.

9. 55, 40, 63, 31, 84.

10. 82, 75, 70, 67, 63, ... 25, 18.

CHAPTER 8

1. +.74 ± .09.

2. +.98.

3. $r = +.76$, $P.E._r = .06$.

4. +.50.

5. +.86.

6. (a) +.93.   (b) .01.   (c) $M_x = 53.82$. $\sigma_x = 5.96$.
(d) $M_y = 28.48$. $\sigma_y = 3.37$.

7. +.93.

8. −.91.

9. (a) +.85.   (b) Yes.

CHAPTER 9

1. $P.E._{MG_1} = 1.16$. $P.E._{MG_2} = 1.24$. $Dif._M = 2.2$. $P.E._{Dif. M} = 1.1$.   Ratio = 2.

2. Yes. $\dfrac{Dif.}{P.E._{Dif.}} = 3.87$.

3. $P.E._{Dif. M} = 1.77$. $Dif._M = 1$.   Ratio = .57.   Chance Prob. = 60/100.

4. No. $E.P._F = 16$. $E.P._{S\sigma} = 26$.

6. $r_4 = .898$. $r_5 = .914$. $r_6 = .922$. $r_7 = .925$.

7. $+.84$.

8. 120.

9. (a) $\overline{Y} = .0241X - .15$. (b) 2.79.
(c) $\overline{X} = 18.0840Y + 59.13$. (d) 127.

10. 104.4, 92.4, 68.4, 52.4, 32.4.

11. (a) .37. (b) 10.13.

12. (a) $\overline{Y} = .956X + 2.212$. (b) 2.47.

13. $m_{xy} = -.071$. Therefore, for 1 day .071, for 5 days .355, and for 10 days .71.

14. $\overline{X} = 1.41$. P.E. $= .39$.

15. .67.

16. Yes. $V.C._{T(4\cdot6\cdot9)} = .942$. $V.C._{T(4\cdot6\cdot8)} = .895$.

CHAPTER 10

1. (a) $.87 \pm .02$. (b) $.37 \pm .05$. (c) .62. (d) .0533. (e) 11.63. (f) No. (aa) $.54 \pm .04$. (cc) .1547. (dd) .0389. (ee) 3.98. (ff) No.

2. (a) $C = .095$. Corrected $C = .116$. (b) .06. (c) No.

3. .058.

4. (a) .37. (b) .07. (c) The probability is $\frac{1}{2}$ that $r_{bis.}$ of the parent population is within .07 of .37.

5. (a) $+.28$. (b) $+.32$. (c) $+.20$.

6. (a) $+.96$. Yes. 4.55 P.E.'s above r_{13}. (b) $+.90$.

7. (a) $X_1 = .0089X_2 + .0607X_3 - 4.7948$. (b) 2.42. (c) .41.

INDEX